Framework 9

MATHS C

TEACHER'S BOOK

David Capewell	Formerly Westfield School, Sheffield
Marguerite Comyns	Queen Mary's High School, Walsall
Gillian Flinton	All Saints Catholic High School, Sheffield
Paul Flinton	Chaucer School, Sheffield
Geoff Fowler	Maths Strategy Manager, Birmingham
Derek Huby	Mathematics Consultant
Peter Johnson	Waitakere College, Auckland, N.Z.
Jayne Kranat	Langley Park School for Girls, Bromley
Ian Molyneux	St. Bedes RC High School, Ormskirk
Peter Mullarkey	Netherhall School, Maryport, Cumbria
Nina Patel	Ifield Community College, West Sussex
Claire Turpin	Sidney Stringer Community Technology College, Coventry

OXFORD
UNIVERSITY PRESS

OXFORD
UNIVERSITY PRESS

Great Clarendon Street, Oxford OX2 6DP

Oxford University Press is a department of the University of Oxford.
It furthers the University's objective of excellence in research,
scholarship, and education by publishing worldwide in

Oxford New York

Auckland Bangkok Buenos Aires Cape Town Chennai
Dar es Salaam Delhi Hong Kong Istanbul Karachi Kolkata
Kuala Lumpur Madrid Melbourne Mexico City Mumbai Nairobi
São Paulo Shanghai Taipei Tokyo Toronto

Oxford is a registered trade mark of Oxford University Press
in the UK and in certain other countries

British Library Cataloguing in Publication Data

Data available

ISBN 0 19 914857 0

10 9 8 7 6 5 4 3 2 1

Typeset by Mathematical Composition Setters Ltd.

Printed at Bell & Bain, UK.

Acknowledgements

The photograph on the cover is reproduced courtesy of Pictor.

The Publisher would like to thank the following for permission to reproduce
photographs:

Alamy/Alan Copson City Pictures: p 51; Corbis/Richard Klune: p 184 (bottom);
Corbis/James Noble: p 184 (top); Corel Professional Photos: pp 203, 231;
Empics/Nigel French: p 137; Iconotec Royalty Free: p 147; National Statistics
website: www.statistics.gov.uk: p 71, 132; Oxford University Press: pp 44 (all),
45 (top); Press Association/Toby Melville: p 1.

Figurative artwork is by Paul Daviz

Data on p 190 courtesy of www.vcacarfueldata.org.uk

About this book

This book has been written specifically for Year 9 of the Framework for Teaching Mathematics. It is aimed at students who are following the Year 9 teaching programme from the Framework and leads to the 5–7 tier of entry in the NC tests. To make the most of the material contained in this book it is strongly recommended that your students use the corresponding Student Book as shown on the back cover.

The authors are experienced teachers and maths consultants who have been incorporating the Framework approaches into their teaching for many years and so are well qualified to help you successfully introduce the Framework objectives in your classroom.

The book is made up of units based on the sample medium term plans that complement the Framework document, thus maintaining the required pitch, pace and progression.

The units are:

The last five units in this book are designed to consolidate KS3 work and bridge to KS4 work.

Each unit comprises double page spreads that should take a lesson to teach. These are shown on the full contents list.

References are made to resource material available on CD-ROM. There is more information about the *Coursemaster* CD-ROM on the back cover of this book.

How to use this book

This book is organised into double page spreads that correspond to a 50–60 minute lesson. Each page shows the corresponding Student Book page so that the book is self-contained. The page numbers in the two books correspond, making it very easy to use.

The left-hand page gives suggestions for an engaging three-part lesson.

The **mental starter** is designed to be inclusive, that is all students should be able to participate most of the time. It usually provides a lead in to the concepts of the main lesson or revises key concepts.

An overview of the **teaching objectives** covered in each unit is provided on the first page of a unit so you can include references in your scheme of work.

Useful resources are listed here including CD-ROM references. These are also listed at the beginning of each unit so you can be fully prepared in advance.

The **introductory activity** will help you bring the associated student book to life as it provides engaging questions that will help students discuss the mathematical ideas.

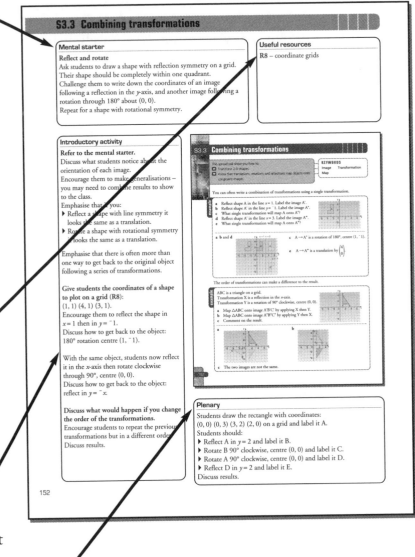

The **plenary** is a vital part of the three-part lesson, suggesting a way of rounding up the learning and helping to overcome any difficulties students may have faced.

The right-hand page of each spread corresponds to the Student Book exercise and will help you to make the most of the material provided.

Further activities are suggested that extend the questions provided, meaning you are unlikely to run out of work for students to do.
ICT resources are highlighted here.

The exercises contain three levels of **differentiation**: lead-in, focus and challenge. These three levels are highlighted to make it easier for you to differentiate within ability groups and to manage the learning environment effectively.

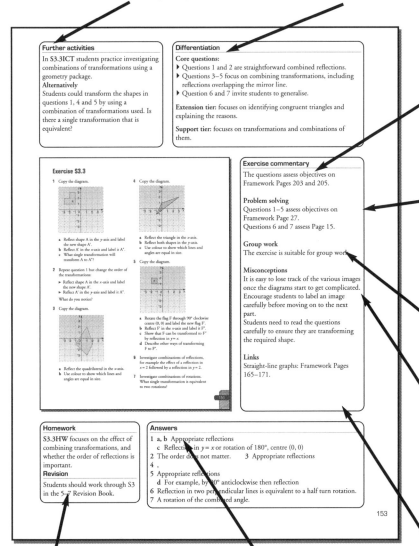

The **exercise commentary** shows the Framework coverage and there is an overview on the first page of each unit.

Problem solving is integrated throughout and the opportunities in each exercise are clearly highlighted here so you can make the most of them.

Opportunities for **group work** are highlighted so that you can vary the ways students learn.

Common **misconceptions** are highlighted and there are suggestions for helping students overcome difficulties. This is designed to avoid longer-term problems arising.

Links to other topics are clearly highlighted to help you design your own scheme of work. Helping students make links with other subject areas can contribute to a whole-school numeracy policy.

Homework sheets from the CD-ROM or homework books are described so you can choose which ones to use.
References to **Revision Books** are highlighted in later units, giving access to a fully structured revision plan.

The **answers** to the exercises are given so that you have all the information you need.

Contents

Mental starters

Objectives covered in this unit:
▸ Count on or back in steps.
▸ Know and use squares.
▸ Solve equations.
▸ Derive formulae.
▸ Order, add, subtract, multiply and divide integers.
▸ Recall multiplication and division facts to 10×10.
▸ Use factors to multiply and divide mentally.
▸ Multiply a two-digit number by a one-digit number.

Resources needed

* means class set needed
Useful:
A1.1OHP – sequence patterns
A1.2OHP – more sequence patterns
Counters
A1.3ICT* – quadratic sequences

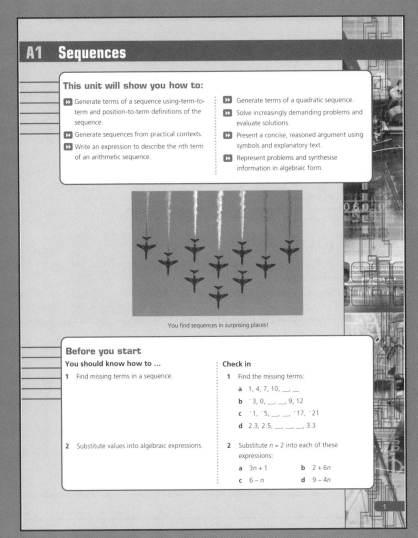

A1   Sequences

This unit will show you how to:

▸▸ Generate terms of a sequence using-term-to-term and position-to-term definitions of the sequence.

▸▸ Generate sequences from practical contexts.

▸▸ Write an expression to describe the *n*th term of an arithmetic sequence.

▸▸ Generate terms of a quadratic sequence.

▸▸ Solve increasingly demanding problems and evaluate solutions.

▸▸ Present a concise, reasoned argument using symbols and explanatory text.

▸▸ Represent problems and synthesise information in algebraic form.

You find sequences in surprising places!

Before you start

You should know how to ...

1 Find missing terms in a sequence.

2 Substitute values into algebraic expressions.

Check in

1 Find the missing terms:

  a 1, 4, 7, 10, __, __

  b ¯3, 0, __, __, 9, 12

  c ¯1, ¯5, __, __, ¯17, ¯21

  d 2.3, 2.5, __, __, __, 3.3

2 Substitute $n = 2$ into each of these expressions:

  a $3n + 1$ b $2 + 6n$

  c $6 - n$ d $9 - 4n$

Unit commentary

Aim of the unit

The unit aims to develop students' understanding of the general term of a sequence, finding $T(n)$ and describing sequence patterns.

The focus of the unit is on finding the general term by looking at differences, emphasising that a constant difference gives a linear sequence.

It develops to consider simple quadratic sequences by looking at second differences.

Introduction

Discuss sequences from students' own experiences or other subjects (population growth, tile patterns etc).

Emphasise that in each case there is a consistent rule that shows you how the sequence grows.

Framework references

This unit focuses on:
Teaching objectives pages:
149, 151, 153, 155, 157.
Problem solving pages:
7, 9, 27, 31.

Check in activity

Count on or back

▸ Ask students to count on or back in decimal steps, going round the class and varying the rule and direction:
  $+0.4, -0.6, +1.1, -0.8$ etc.

▸ Challenge them to count on or back using a more complex rule: always add two more than the person before you.

Differentiation

Support tier

Focuses on using term-to-term and position-to-term rules to describe sequences.

Extension tier

Focuses on quadratic sequences.

A1.1 Revising sequences

Mental starter

What's the value?

Write these four expressions on the board or on cards:
$3n + 2, 5n - 1, 8 - 3n, 2n + 5$.

Choose a card.

Ask for the value of the card when $n = 1, 2, 3$ and 4.

Explain that these are the first four terms of the sequence.

Ask for the value of the 10th term.

Repeat for other cards.

Useful resources

A1.1OHP – sequence patterns

Introductory activity

Refer to the mental starter.

Discuss the terminology of sequences.
Emphasise that:

▶ $n = 1$ gives the first term.

▶ You write T(1).

▶ The general term or rule is T(n).

Discuss how to find the next term in a sequence. Emphasise that you use:

▶ A term-to-term rule to find the next term from the previous term.

▶ A position-to-term rule when you use T(n).

Emphasise that the two different rules are linked.

Discuss the advantages of each rule:

▶ A term-to-term rule is usually easy to find.

▶ Refer back to the mental starter: a position-to-term rule makes it easy to find the 10th or any term.

Emphasise that diagrams can help students find a position-to-term rule.
Encourage students to draw diagrams to illustrate the sequence:
9, 12, 15, ...
Emphasise that it is $3 \times 3, 3 \times 4, 3 \times 5, ...$
so using rectangles of width 3 is sensible (shown on **A1.1OHP**).
Discuss how the pattern grows – by 3 each time.
Shade all but the first 3 of the first pattern – 6 squares.
Shade these 6 squares in every pattern.
Discuss how this makes the rule $3n + 6$.
Repeat with other sequences.

A1.1OHP shows the sequence pattern from the example in the Students' book.

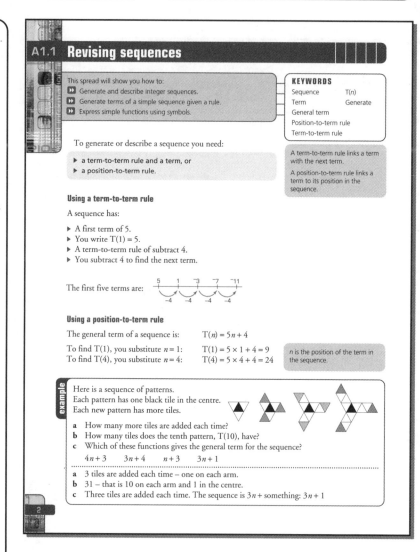

A1.1 Revising sequences

This spread will show you how to:
▶▶ Generate and describe integer sequences.
▶▶ Generate terms of a simple sequence given a rule.
▶▶ Express simple functions using symbols.

KEYWORDS
Sequence   T(n)
Term   Generate
General term
Position-to-term rule
Term-to-term rule

To generate or describe a sequence you need:

▶ a term-to-term rule and a term, or
▶ a position-to-term rule.

A term-to-term rule links a term with the next term.

A position-to-term rule links a term to its position in the sequence.

Using a term-to-term rule

A sequence has:

▶ A first term of 5.
▶ You write T(1) = 5.
▶ A term-to-term rule of subtract 4.
▶ You subtract 4 to find the next term.

The first five terms are:
$$5 \quad 1 \quad ^-3 \quad ^-7 \quad ^-11$$
$$-4 \quad -4 \quad -4 \quad -4$$

Using a position-to-term rule

The general term of a sequence is: T(n) = $5n + 4$

To find T(1), you substitute $n = 1$: T(1) = $5 \times 1 + 4 = 9$
To find T(4), you substitute $n = 4$: T(4) = $5 \times 4 + 4 = 24$

n is the position of the term in the sequence.

example

Here is a sequence of patterns.
Each pattern has one black tile in the centre.
Each new pattern has more tiles.

a How many more tiles are added each time?
b How many tiles does the tenth pattern, T(10), have?
c Which of these functions gives the general term for the sequence?
   $4n + 3$ $3n + 4$ $n + 3$ $3n + 1$

a 3 tiles are added each time – one on each arm.
b 31 – that is 10 on each arm and 1 in the centre.
c Three tiles are added each time. The sequence is $3n + $ something: $3n + 1$

Plenary

Encourage students to explain in words the different rules they find in question 3b.

Discuss question 7 as a class.

Ask students to work in pairs to explain the two different rules and share their explanations with the class.

Challenge them to make up a similar example.

Further activities

Challenge students to find the rules for the sequences in question 1.

Differentiation

Core questions:

▸ Questions 1 and 2 are straightforward examples of following rules.
▸ Questions 3–6 focus on explaining or deriving rules.
▸ Question 7 is a challenging question, focusing on explaining different rules for the same pattern.

Extension tier: focuses on linear and quadratic sequences.

Support tier: focuses on describing and generating sequences using term-to-term rules.

Exercise A1.1

1 Here is a rule to find the next term of a sequence: Add □.
Choose a first term for the sequence, T(1), and a number to go in the box so that your rule will generate all the terms of the sequence:
a multiples of 5   b even numbers
c odd numbers
d all numbers ending in the same digit.

2 Write down the first five terms of a sequence when the nth term or T(n) is:
a $3n - 2$ b $8n + 3$
c $18 - 4n$ d $2n - \frac{1}{2}$
e $0.5n + 1.5$ f $3.5 - 0.5n$

3 Here is a number chain:
$1 \rightarrow 3 \rightarrow 5 \rightarrow 7 \rightarrow 9 \rightarrow$
The rule is 'The first term is 1, add on 2 each time'.
a A different number chain is:
$1 \rightarrow 3 \rightarrow 9 \rightarrow 27 \rightarrow 81 \rightarrow 243 \rightarrow$
What is the rule?
b A chain starts like this:
$1 \rightarrow 5 \rightarrow \_ \rightarrow \_ \rightarrow \_ \rightarrow$
Show three different ways to continue this number chain.
For each chain, write down the next three numbers and the rule you are using.

4 For each sequence, write down the first five terms.

	1st Term	Term-to-term rule
a	7	add 6
b	4	subtract 3
c	6	subtract 4
d	⁻3	add 6

5 Match each of these general terms with a sequence from question 4.
$10 - 4n, 6n - 9, 7 - 3n, 6n + 1$

6 Charmaine is making a series of patterns with black and white tiles.

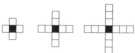

Charmaine says: 'The rule for finding the number of tiles in pattern number n is: number of tiles T(n) = $4n + 1$'.
a The '1' in Charmaine's rule represents the black tile.
What does the $4n$ represent?
b Charmaine wants to make pattern number 12.
How many black tiles and how many white tiles does she need?
c Charmaine use 61 tiles altogether to make a pattern.
What is the number of the pattern she makes?
d Charmaine has 100 black tiles and 100 white tiles.
What is the pattern number of the biggest pattern Charmaine can make?

7 Here are the 2nd and 3rd patterns in a series.

a Draw the first pattern in the series.
Jack says the rule for finding the number of lines on pattern number n is: $4n + 4$.
Jill says the rule is: $2n + 2$.
They each explain what they mean by their rule and the teacher marks both correct.
b Explain Jack's rule and Jill's rule so that they are both correct.

3

Exercise commentary

The questions assess objectives on Framework Page 149.

Problem solving

Questions 3 and 6 assess objectives on Framework Pages 7–9.
Question 7 assesses Page 31.

Group work

Questions 1 and 2 can be answered orally as a class. Questions 3 and 7 are useful group exercises where students can discuss rules.

Misconceptions

Students tend to find position-to-term rules difficult.
Emphasise the link with the term-to-term rule: if the sequence increases by 5, the rule will start $5n$; if it decreases by 3, the rule will start $⁻3n$.

Links

Substitution: Framework Page 139.

Homework

A1.1HW provides further practice in identifying and using position-to-term rules.

Answers

1 a 5, +5   b 2, +2   c 1, +2   d Any of 0 to 9, +10
2 a 1, 4, 7, 10, 13   b 11, 19, 27, 35, 43   c 14, 10, 6, 2, ⁻2
  d $1\frac{1}{2}, 3\frac{1}{2}, 5\frac{1}{2}, 7\frac{1}{2}, 9\frac{1}{2}$ e 2, 2.5, 3, 3.5, 4   f 3, 2.5, 2, 1.5, 1
3 a First term is 1, then multiply by 3 each time
  b 1, 5, 25, 125, 625; first term is 1, then multiply by 5. 1, 5, 9, 13, 17; first term is 1, then add 4. 1, 5, 13, 29, 61; first term is 1, then double and add 3
4 a 7, 13, 19, 25, 31   b 4, 1, ⁻2, ⁻5, ⁻8   c 6, 2, ⁻2, ⁻6, ⁻10   d ⁻3, 3, 9, 15, 21
5 c, d, b, a   6 a White tiles   b 1 black, 48 white   c 15   d 25   7 a pattern with one whole square.   b Jack: Start with 8 lines and add 4. Jill: Start with 4 L-shapes and add 2.

Mental starter

Reuse the four expressions on the board or on cards from **A1.1**.
$3n + 2$, $5n - 1$, $8 - 3n$, $2n + 5$.
Choose a card: $5n - 1$.
Give the value of the card and ask for the term:
▸ find n if $T(n) = 44$.
Discuss strategies.
Emphasise the use of the 5 times table for $5n$.
▸ $5 \times 9 = 45$ so $n = 9$.
Repeat for other cards and values.

Useful resources

A1.2OHP – sequence patterns from the Students' book

Introductory activity

Refer to the mental starter.
Ask questions to check that students understand the terminology of sequences:
▸ The general term or rule is $T(n)$.
Emphasise that the rule is linked to the difference between terms. If it:
▸ increases by 5 the rule starts $5n$
▸ decreases by 3 the rule starts ^-3n.

Draw this first term of a sequence on the board (or show **A1.2OHP**):

Discuss whether it is possible to describe a unique sequence given the first term.
Emphasise that you need another term or a rule.

Discuss how to draw $T(2) = 13$, then how to find $T(3)$.
Encourage students to explain what is happening each time.
Discuss how to find $T(5)$ and $T(10)$: it is easier if you find $T(n)$.

Emphasise that the pattern grows by 3 each time so $T(n)$ starts with $3n$.
There are $3 + 7$ circles in the first pattern so the sequence is $3n + 7$.

Discuss the sequences on **A1.2OHP**, emphasising the strategy of finding the increase and then the rest from the parts left over in the first term.

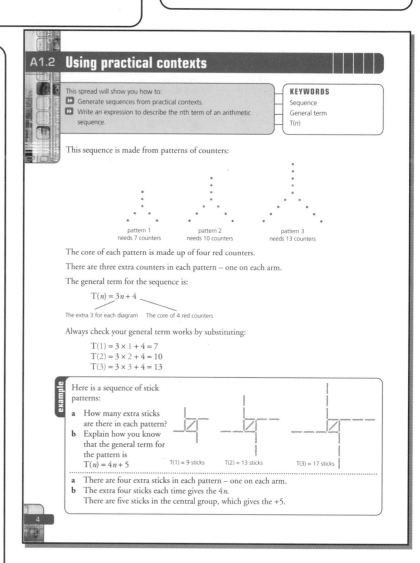

This spread will show you how to:
▸▸ Generate sequences from practical contexts.
▸▸ Write an expression to describe the nth term of an arithmetic sequence.

KEYWORDS
Sequence
General term
$T(n)$

This sequence is made from patterns of counters:

pattern 1
needs 7 counters

pattern 2
needs 10 counters

pattern 3
needs 13 counters

The core of each pattern is made up of four red counters.
There are three extra counters in each pattern – one on each arm.
The general term for the sequence is:

$T(n) = 3n + 4$

The extra 3 for each diagram   The core of 4 red counters

Always check your general term works by substituting:

$T(1) = 3 \times 1 + 4 = 7$
$T(2) = 3 \times 2 + 4 = 10$
$T(3) = 3 \times 3 + 4 = 13$

example

Here is a sequence of stick patterns:
a How many extra sticks are there in each pattern?
b Explain how you know that the general term for the pattern is $T(n) = 4n + 5$

$T(1) = 9$ sticks $T(2) = 13$ sticks $T(3) = 17$ sticks

a There are four extra sticks in each pattern – one on each arm.
b The extra four sticks each time gives the $4n$.
There are five sticks in the central group, which gives the $+5$.

4

Plenary

Discuss answers to question 2c:
▸ Why was the rule $T(n) = 4n + 1$?
▸ What would the other rules show?

Discuss students' simplifications in question 3b:
▸ Why does $n + 1 + 2n = 3n + 1$?
Develop this idea with other expressions.

Further activities

Challenge students to draw patterns for each of the sequences in question 2c.

Students can investigate other tiling patterns in question 3, for example, increasing the width and height by one hexagon each time.

Differentiation

Core questions:

▶ Question 1 focuses on matching patterns to rules.
▶ Question 2 is a worded question similar to those on Key Stage 3 test papers.
▶ Question 3 is more complex as the pattern numbers in the table are not grouped.

Extension tier: focuses on generalising, justifying and exploring more complex sequences.

Support tier: focuses on simple position-to-term rules.

Exercise A1.2

1 Counter pattern match
Match each counter pattern with its position-to-term rule and its general term T(n).

Pattern		Rule		T(n)	
a		i	T(1) = 7 T(2) = 9 T(5) = 15	**I**	T(n) = $4n + 3$
b		ii	T(1) = 7 T(2) = 11 T(5) = 23	**II**	T(n) = $2n + 5$
c		iii	T(1) = 8 T(2) = 11 T(5) = 20	**III**	T(n) = $3n + 5$

2 These huts have been made with matches.

T(1) = 6   T(2) = 11   T(3) = 16 matches

A rule to find how many matches are needed is T(n) = $5n + 1$.
  a Use this rule to find how many matches are needed for 12 huts.
  b I use 81 matches to make some huts. How many huts do I make?
  c Different huts are made with matches:

T(1) = 5   T(2) = 9   T(3) = 13

Which of these rules shows how many matches are needed?

T(n) = $n + 4$ T(n) = $5n + 4$
T(n) = $4n + 5$ T(n) = $4n + 1$
T(n) = $5n - 2$

Explain why you have chosen this rule.

3 Here is a sequence of tile patterns.

Pattern 1   Pattern 2   Pattern 3
T(1)   T(2)   T(3)

  a Look at the patterns carefully and complete the table. Check the pattern number carefully.

Pattern number	Number of blue tiles	Number of white tiles
T(1)		
T(3)	4	
T(5)		
T(16)		
T(n)		

  b Look at the numbers of blue and white tiles for the general term T(n) and write an expression to show the total number of tiles in the pattern. Simplify your expression.

Exercise commentary

The questions assess objectives on Framework Pages 155 and 157.

Problem solving

Question 2 assesses objectives on Framework Page 31.
Question 3 assesses Page 27.

Group work

Question 1 is suitable for paired work.

Misconceptions

In question 1 many students will fail to spot that the terms are not consecutive which will cause problems as the differences are not constant.
This is a useful discussion point – how many differences are there between T(2) and T(5)?
Similarly, in question 3 less able students may need to complete the table for T(1), T(2), T(3) etc., in order to find the pattern.
Many students will continue to find position-to-term rules difficult.
Emphasise that if the sequence increases by 5, the rule will start $5n$ and if it decreases by 3, the rule will start ^-3n.

Links

Simplifying: Framework Page 117.

Homework

A1.2HW investigates more sequences in practical contexts.

Answers

1 a i, II **b** iii, III **c** ii, I
2 a 61 **b** 16 **c** T(n) = $4n + 1$; There are 4 extra matches each time ($4n$). You start with 1 match before you add on 4 (+1).
3 a Blue tiles: 2, 4, 6, 17, $n + 1$; White tiles: 2, 6, 10, 32, $2n$
  b Total number of tiles = Blue + White tiles = $n + 1 + 2n = 3n + 1$

A1.3 Quadratic sequences

Mental starter

Find the rule

Recap finding the rule for a linear sequence.

Challenge students to find T(n) for 7, 15, 23, 31, ...

Discuss strategies.

Emphasise that the difference is always 8, so compare with $8n$.

The sequence is one less, so T(n) = $8n - 1$.

Repeat for other sequences:

15, 9, 3, ⁻3, ...   T(n) = ⁻$6n + 21$.

Useful resources

Counters may be useful for question 5

Introductory activity

Refer to the mental starter.

Emphasise that the strategy works when there is a constant difference.

Discuss what you call sequences that increase or decrease by the same amount each time.

Emphasise that the sequence is linear.

Encourage students to visualise the shape of the graph – the term number and pattern number increase or decrease at the same rate so it will be a straight line.

Challenge students to find the rule for this sequence:

▸ 1, 4, 9, 16, ...

Emphasise that there is not a constant difference.

The differences make a pattern – they are the odd numbers starting at 3.

Encourage students to explain the term-to-term rule clearly in words and then find the position-to-term rule.

Encourage students to recognise the numbers – they are square numbers.

Discuss other quadratic sequences:

▸ 2, 5, 10, 17, ... ($n^2 + 1$)

▸ 3, 6, 11, 18, ... ($n^2 + 2$)

▸ 0, 3, 8, 15, ... ($n^2 - 1$).

Emphasise that the differences all grow by the odd numbers starting at 3.

Discuss how to find the rule: compare with n^2.

Emphasise the terminology: an n^2 gives a quadratic sequence.

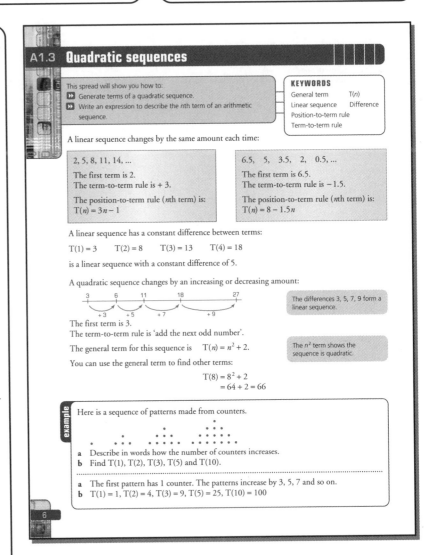

A1.3 Quadratic sequences

This spread will show you how to:
▸ Generate terms of a quadratic sequence.
▸ Write an expression to describe the nth term of an arithmetic sequence.

KEYWORDS
General term   T(n)
Linear sequence   Difference
Position-to-term rule
Term-to-term rule

A linear sequence changes by the same amount each time:

2, 5, 8, 11, 14, ...

The first term is 2.
The term-to-term rule is + 3.
The position-to-term rule (mth term) is:
T(n) = $3n - 1$

6.5, 5, 3.5, 2, 0.5, ...

The first term is 6.5.
The term-to-term rule is −1.5.
The position-to-term rule (mth term) is:
T(n) = $8 - 1.5n$

A linear sequence has a constant difference between terms:

T(1) = 3   T(2) = 8   T(3) = 13   T(4) = 18

is a linear sequence with a constant difference of 5.

A quadratic sequence changes by an increasing or decreasing amount:

3   6   11   18   27
  + 3 + 5 + 7 + 9

The differences 3, 5, 7, 9 form a linear sequence.

The first term is 3.
The term-to-term rule is 'add the next odd number'.
The general term for this sequence is   T(n) = $n^2 + 2$.

The n^2 term shows the sequence is quadratic.

You can use the general term to find other terms:

T(8) = $8^2 + 2$
    = 64 + 2 = 66

example

Here is a sequence of patterns made from counters.

a Describe in words how the number of counters increases.
b Find T(1), T(2), T(3), T(5) and T(10).

a The first pattern has 1 counter. The patterns increase by 3, 5, 7 and so on.
b T(1) = 1, T(2) = 4, T(3) = 9, T(5) = 25, T(10) = 100

6

Plenary

Write these five sequences on the board:

▸ 4, 6, 10, 16, 24
▸ 7, 11, 19, 31, 47
▸ 1, 4, 13, 34, 73
▸ 17, 23, 29, 35, 41
▸ 39, 37, 33, 27, 19.

Challenge students to discuss which are quadratic. Encourage students to describe the sequence of differences in words.

Further activities

In **A1.3ICT** students use a spreadsheet to investigate quadratic sequences.

Alternatively

Challenge able students to devise a rule for the sequence of second differences for quadratic sequences of the form:

▸ n^2 [add 2]
▸ $\frac{1}{2}n^2$ [add 1]
▸ $3n^2$ [add 6].

Differentiation

Core questions:

▸ Question 1 focuses on finding a rule from the first three terms and question 2 revises linear sequences.
▸ Questions 3–5 focus on finding terms and recognising quadratic sequences.
▸ Question 6 requires students to find the rule for a quadratic sequence.

Extension tier: focuses on the sequences of square and triangular numbers.

Support tier: focuses on how patterns from practical contexts grow.

Exercise A1.3

1 For each of these sequences, you are given the first three terms and the sixth term. Work out T(4) and T(5) and explain the sequence in words.
  a T(1) = 2, T(2) = 5, T(3) = 10, T(6) = 37
  b T(1) = 0, T(2) = 1, T(3) = 3, T(6) = 15
  c T(1) = 2, T(2) = 5, T(3) = 11, T(6) = 47
  d T(1) = 25, T(2) = 16, T(3) = 9, T(6) = 0

2 Write down the first five terms in each of these sequences.
  a The first term is 2 and the term-to-term differences increase by the even numbers 2, 4, 6, 8, ...
  b T(1) = 24 and the term-to-term differences decrease by the odd numbers 3, 5, 7, ...
  c T(n) = $n^2 + 7$
  d T(n) = $n(n + 1)$
  e T(n) = $2n^2 - 3$

3 This sequence pattern matches one of the five sequences in question 2.

Which one does it match?

4 Find the general term for each of these linear sequences:
  a 21, 27, 33, 39, 45, ...
  b 54, 62, 70, 78, 86, ...
  c 68, 61, 54, 47, 40, ...
  d 2.3, 2.5, 2.7, 2.9, 3.1, ...
  e $^-$5, $^-$14, $^-$23, $^-$32, $^-$41, ...

5 Here is a sequence of patterns made from counters.

pattern 1   pattern 2   pattern 3   pattern 4

  a Copy and complete the table.

Pattern	1	2	3	4	5	10
Number of counters		3				

  b Describe the term-to-term rule.
  c This sequence of numbers is known as the set of triangular numbers and T(n) = $\frac{1}{2}n(n + 1)$.
     Use this expression (formula) to find T(8) and T(15).

6 Here is a sequence of square patterns.

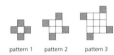

pattern 1   pattern 2   pattern 3

  a How many white tiles will be used in each of the first five patterns?
  b How many white tiles and how many red tiles will be used in pattern number 8?
  c How many white tiles and how many red tiles will be used in pattern number 12?
  d How many white tiles and how many red tiles will be used in pattern number n?
  e Write down an equation to show the total number of tiles used in T(n):
     T(n) =

Exercise commentary

The questions assess objectives on Framework Pages 151 and 153.

Problem solving

Questions 4–6 assess objectives on Framework Page 27.

Group work

Question 1 is suitable for paired work.

Misconceptions

Students often make mistakes in sequence work by assuming the terms are in sequence when they are not.
Question 1 encourages students to check their work as it gives T(6). Emphasise the need to always do so.
In question 2e, students may work out $(2n)^2$.
Emphasise that you work out n^2 first.
In question 6 students should be encouraged to see that the pattern of white squares makes the square numbers, then the four others are added.

Links

Squares: Framework Pages 57–59.

Homework

A1.3HW gives practice in identifying quadratic sequences and using the general term of a sequence to find values.

Answers

1 a 17, 26; Start at 2 and add 3, 5, 7, ... b 6, 10; Start at 0 and add 1, 2, 3, ...
  c 20, 32; Start at 2 and add 3, 6, 9, ... d 4, 1; Start at 25 and subtract 9, 7, 5, ...
2 a 2, 4, 8, 14, 22 b 24, 21, 16, 9, 0 c 8, 11, 16, 23, 32
  d 2, 6, 12, 20, 30 e $^-$1, 5, 15, 29, 47
3 d
4 a $6n + 15$ b $8n + 46$ c $75 - 7n$ d $0.2n + 2.1$ e $4 - 9n$
5 a 1, 3, 6, 10 b Start at 1, add 1 − term number. c 36, 120
6 a 1, 4, 9, 16, 25 b 64 white, 4 red c 144 white, 4 red d n^2 white, 4 red
  e $n^2 + 4$

Summary

The key objectives for this unit are:
▸ Generate terms of a sequence using term-to-term and position-to-term definitions of the sequence. (149–151)
▸ Write an expression to describe the nth term of an arithmetic sequence. (155–157)
▸ Present a concise and reasoned argument using symbols and explanatory text. (31)

Check out commentary

1 Reinforce that n represents the position of each term. Students should calculate the terms mentally, but could check their answers using a calculator.

2 All these sequences are linear. Students should state the first term and the constant difference, for each sequence. They should then use the difference pattern to derive the general rule.

3 For part **a** students should count the number of lines in each diagram and write these as a sequence.
To work out $T(10)$ and $T(25)$, students could use the term-to-term rule 'add 2', finding $T(10)$ and $T(25)$ by adding $(n-1) \times 2$ to the first term. In part **c** students need to describe their method clearly, including an explanation of the term-to-term rule or pattern of the sequence.
Students can use their answer to part **a** to work out the general term by looking at the differences.

Plenary activity

Discuss methods of finding the position-to-term formula for linear and quadratic sequences. Ask students to write one example of each type of sequence and give it to a partner to find the position-to-term formula.

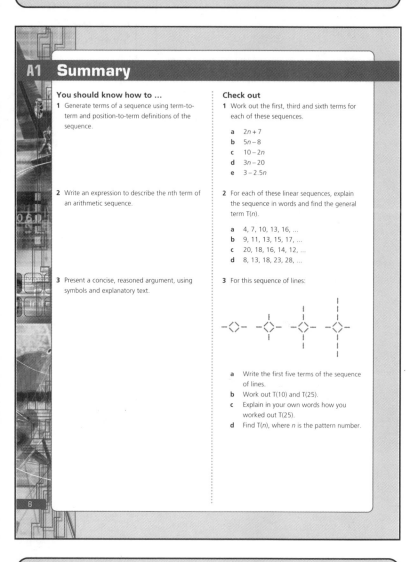

A1 Summary

You should know how to ...

1 Generate terms of a sequence using term-to-term and position-to-term definitions of the sequence.

2 Write an expression to describe the nth term of an arithmetic sequence.

3 Present a concise, reasoned argument, using symbols and explanatory text.

Check out

1 Work out the first, third and sixth terms for each of these sequences.

  a $2n + 7$
  b $5n - 8$
  c $10 - 2n$
  d $3n - 20$
  e $3 - 2.5n$

2 For each of these linear sequences, explain the sequence in words and find the general term $T(n)$.

  a $4, 7, 10, 13, 16, \ldots$
  b $9, 11, 13, 15, 17, \ldots$
  c $20, 18, 16, 14, 12, \ldots$
  d $8, 13, 18, 23, 28, \ldots$

3 For this sequence of lines:

  a Write the first five terms of the sequence of lines.
  b Work out $T(10)$ and $T(25)$.
  c Explain in your own words how you worked out $T(25)$.
  d Find $T(n)$, where n is the pattern number.

Development

This is the main unit on sequences in Year 9. Students will revise the key concepts in **A2.1** but it is important that they are confident with the themes of **A1.1** and **A1.2** before the Key Stage 3 tests.

Links

Students should be encouraged to develop their understanding of sequences in other subject areas such as Science and Geography.

Mental starters

Objectives covered in this unit:
▸ Solve equations.
▸ Derive formulae and change the subject.
▸ Use metric units and units of time for calculations.
▸ Use compound measures.
▸ Discuss and interpret graphs.
▸ Order, add, subtract, multiply and divide integers.
▸ Recall multiplication and division facts to 10×10.
▸ Apply mental skills to solve simple problems.

Resources needed

* means class set needed
Essential:
A2.2OHP – distance–time graph
A2.3OHP – real-life graph
Graph paper*

Useful:
R7 – function machines
Calculators*
A2.3ICT* – real-life graphs

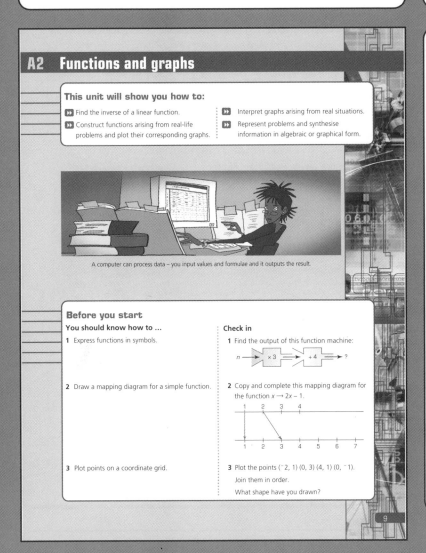

A2 Functions and graphs

This unit will show you how to:

▸▸ Find the inverse of a linear function.

▸▸ Construct functions arising from real-life problems and plot their corresponding graphs.

▸▸ Interpret graphs arising from real situations.

▸▸ Represent problems and synthesise information in algebraic or graphical form.

A computer can process data – you input values and formulae and it outputs the result.

Before you start

You should know how to ...

1 Express functions in symbols.

2 Draw a mapping diagram for a simple function.

3 Plot points on a coordinate grid.

Check in

1 Find the output of this function machine:

$n \longrightarrow \boxed{\times 3} \longrightarrow \boxed{+ 4} \longrightarrow ?$

2 Copy and complete this mapping diagram for the function $x \rightarrow 2x - 1$.

3 Plot the points $(^-2, 1)$ $(0, 3)$ $(4, 1)$ $(0, ^-1)$.
Join them in order.
What shape have you drawn?

Unit commentary

Aim of the unit

This unit focuses on drawing and interpreting real-life graphs, including distance-time graphs and curved graphs. Students start by revising functions and considering how to find the inverse function which builds to work on solving equations in A3.

The emphasis is firmly on understanding the graphs and the units used including compound measures.

Introduction

Discuss the different uses of computers. Emphasise that they perform routine work quickly and accurately, especially when using functions. They will also change between different forms of display readily and accurately.

Framework references

This unit focuses on:
Teaching objectives pages:
161, 173, 175.
Problem solving page: 27.

Check in activity

Think of a number

Tell students to think of a number, double it and add 1.
Challenge students to:
▸ Write this as a function. [$n \rightarrow 2n + 1$]
▸ Show the function in a function machine.
▸ Show the function on a mapping diagram – emphasise that the number you think of maps onto the outcome.
▸ Show pairs of values on a graph (plot input and output values).

Differentiation

Support tier

Focuses on linking sequences to functions and graphs, extending to real-life graphs.

Extension tier

Focuses on graphs of inverse functions, quadratic and cubic functions.

Mental starter

Think of a number

Ask questions similar to:

▶ I think of a number, double it, subtract 15 and the answer is 5. What was my number?

Develop to include algebra:

▶ I think of a number, *m*, multiply by 4, subtract 13 and the answer is 23. What is the value of *m*?

Discuss students' strategies.

Useful resources

R7 – function machines

Calculators for question 3

Introductory activity

Refer to the mental starter.

Discuss how to write the 'think of a number' questions.

Emphasise the form of equations:

$2n - 15 = 5$

$4m - 13 = 23$

Encourage the use of function machines (use **R7**):

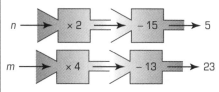

Discuss students' strategies for finding the numbers.

Emphasise the strategy of working backwards through the operations.

Discuss how to write this strategy down.

Encourage the use of function machines as an easy way to see the order of the operations (use **R7**).

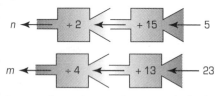

Discuss how the machines are linked.

Emphasise that they show the inverse functions.

Ensure that all students know the pairs of inverse operations.

Discuss how to write the inverse equation:

Inverse of $m \rightarrow 4m - 13$

is $\qquad m \rightarrow \dfrac{m + 13}{4}$

Encourage students to show the relationship on a mapping diagram.

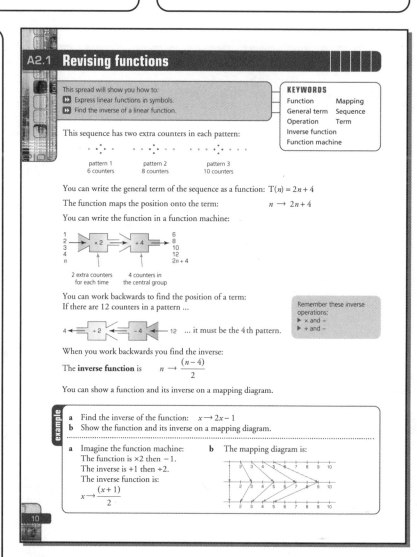

A2.1 Revising functions

This spread will show you how to:

▶▶ Express linear functions in symbols.

▶▶ Find the inverse of a linear function.

KEYWORDS

Function   Mapping
General term Sequence
Operation   Term
Inverse function
Function machine

This sequence has two extra counters in each pattern:

pattern 1   pattern 2   pattern 3
6 counters 8 counters 10 counters

You can write the general term of the sequence as a function: $T(n) = 2n + 4$

The function maps the position onto the term: $\qquad n \rightarrow 2n + 4$

You can write the function in a function machine:

2 extra counters   4 counters in
for each time   the central group

You can work backwards to find the position of a term:

If there are 12 counters in a pattern ...

... it must be the 4th pattern.

Remember these inverse operations:
▶ × and ÷
▶ + and −

When you work backwards you find the inverse:

The **inverse function** is $\qquad n \rightarrow \dfrac{(n - 4)}{2}$

You can show a function and its inverse on a mapping diagram.

example

a   Find the inverse of the function: $x \rightarrow 2x - 1$

b   Show the function and its inverse on a mapping diagram.

a   Imagine the function machine:
    The function is ×2 then −1.
    The inverse is +1 then ÷2.
    The inverse function is:
    $x \rightarrow \dfrac{(x + 1)}{2}$

b   The mapping diagram is:

10

Plenary

Discuss how to check whether the inverse functions are correct in question 4.

Emphasise the strategy of:

▶ substituting values for *n* into the function, then

▶ substituting the outputs into the inverse function.

Further activities

In question 5, challenge students to explain why the inverse function of $4 - x$ is $4 - x$. ($x \times {}^-1$ is the same as $x \div {}^-1$). Challenge them to find other functions with the same property.

Differentiation

Core questions:
▸ Questions 1 and 2 focus on using function machines to find inputs, outputs and the rule for a sequence.
▸ Questions 3 and 4 focus on using inverse functions.
▸ Question 5 focuses on understanding the operations of × and ÷ with negative numbers.

Extension tier: focuses on shapes of graphs and using the equation $y = mx + c$.

Support tier: focuses on functions and mappings.

Exercise commentary

The questions assess objectives on Framework Page 161.

Problem solving
Questions 4 and 5 assess objectives on Framework Page 27.

Group work
Question 2 is suitable for paired work for weaker students.

Misconceptions
Many students find the concept of inverse functions confusing and difficult. Encourage them to always start from first principles, and in particular to visualise the function machine. Emphasise that the mapping diagram provides a good check on working as you can see whether the inverse takes the output back to its original position.

Links
Deriving formulae and changing the subject: Framework Pages 139–143.

Exercise A2.1

1 Copy and complete these function machines.

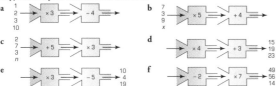

2 For each of these sequence patterns, copy and complete the function machine.

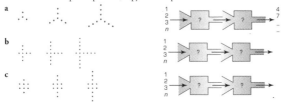

3 Use the inverse method to find the missing input values.

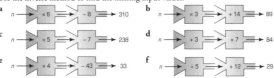

4 Find the inverse of these linear functions. The first one is done for you.

a $n \to 6n - 8$ inverse is $n \to \dfrac{(n + 8)}{6}$

b $n \to 3n + 14$ c $n \to 5n - 7$ d $n \to 7(n + 3)$ e $n \to \dfrac{n}{5} + 12$

5 **Challenge**
For the function $x \to 4 - x$:
a Copy and complete this function machine.

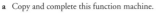 

b Find the inverse function.
c Simplify your answer. What do you notice?

Homework

A2.1HW provides more practice in identifying functions and their inverses.

Answers

1 a ${}^-1, 2, 5, 26$ b $39, 19, 49, 5x + 4$ c $21, 36, 24, 3(n + 5)$
 d $3, 4, 5$ e $5, 3, 8$ f $9, 10, 4$
2 a $\times 3, +1; 10, 13, 3n + 1$ b $\times 3, +5; 8, 11, 14, 3n + 5$
 c $\times 2, +6; 8, 10, 12, 2n + 6$
3 a 53 b 25 c 49 d 9 e 19 f 85
4 b $n \to \dfrac{(n - 14)}{3}$ c $n \to \dfrac{(n + 7)}{5}$ d $n \to \dfrac{n}{7} - 3$ e $n \to 5(n - 12)$
5 a $x \to \times {}^-1 \to +4$ b $x \to 4 - x$
 c The function and its inverse are the same.

11

Mental starter

Average speed

Write these formulae on the board:

$$\text{Speed} = \frac{\text{Distance}}{\text{Time}} \qquad \text{and} \qquad \text{Distance} = \text{Speed} \times \text{Time}$$

Give students time and speed and ask them for the distance.

Give distance and time and ask for speed.

Encourage them to state the units.

Useful resources

A2.2OHP – example graph from Students' book

Graph paper for question 3

Introductory activity

Refer to the mental starter.

Check by asking questions that students understand:

▸ Units of distance and time

▸ How the units relate to speed.

Discuss any strategies students have for remembering that:

$$\text{Speed} = \frac{\text{Distance}}{\text{Time}}$$

Emphasise that:

▸ mph means miles per hour, which means: $\dfrac{\text{miles}}{\text{hours}}$.

Discuss how to describe a journey: for any stage you need two of the three elements.

Discuss the distance–time graph from the Students' book (on A2.2OHP).

Emphasise the key elements of the graph:

▸ The horizontal axis shows time.

▸ The vertical axis shows distance.

▸ Each line represents a different stage of the journey.

▸ A horizontal line shows no movement.

▸ Sloping lines show the average speed for a particular stage.

Discuss how to find the average speed from the graph.

Discuss what a downwards sloping line represents. Emphasise that it means you are travelling back towards the starting location of the journey.

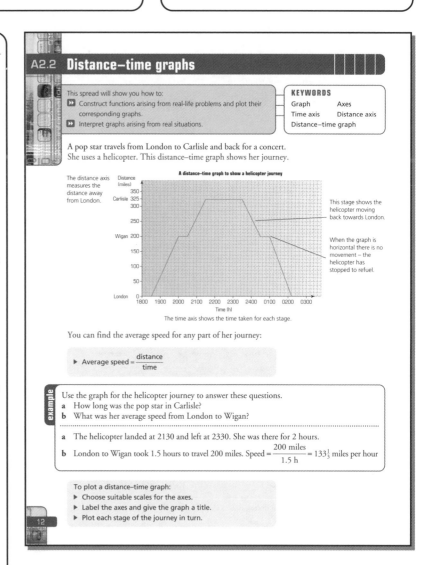

A2.2 Distance–time graphs

This spread will show you how to:
▸ Construct functions arising from real-life problems and plot their corresponding graphs.
▸ Interpret graphs arising from real situations.

KEYWORDS
Graph
Time axis
Distance–time graph
Axes
Distance axis

A pop star travels from London to Carlisle and back for a concert. She uses a helicopter. This distance–time graph shows her journey.

A distance–time graph to show a helicopter journey

The distance axis measures the distance away from London.

This stage shows the helicopter moving back towards London.

When the graph is horizontal there is no movement – the helicopter has stopped to refuel.

The time axis shows the time taken for each stage.

You can find the average speed for any part of her journey:

▸ Average speed = $\dfrac{\text{distance}}{\text{time}}$

example

Use the graph for the helicopter journey to answer these questions.
a How long was the pop star in Carlisle?
b What was her average speed from London to Wigan?

a The helicopter landed at 2130 and left at 2330. She was there for 2 hours.
b London to Wigan took 1.5 hours to travel 200 miles. Speed $= \dfrac{200\text{ miles}}{1.5\text{ h}} = 133\frac{1}{3}$ miles per hour

To plot a distance–time graph:
▸ Choose suitable scales for the axes.
▸ Label the axes and give the graph a title.
▸ Plot each stage of the journey in turn.

12

Plenary

Discuss how you know when two objects are the same distance away from a given point (as in questions 2c and 3c).

Emphasise that they are the same distance away at the same time and discuss how this is shown on the graph.

Discuss why this doesn't necessarily mean they will crash – they could be in different places or at different heights (for the planes).

Further activities

Students could work out the average speed for the two trains in question 3, for the London–Edinburgh journey as a whole and for the different legs of the journey.

Differentiation

Core questions:
▶ Question 1 is a straightforward problem on distance and time.
▶ Question 2 involves comparing two journeys.
▶ Question 3 involves drawing a distance–time graph.

Extension tier: focuses on inverse functions and their graphs.

Support tier: focuses on plotting coordinates and graphs of functions.

Exercise A2.2

1 Jon won a holiday travelling to New York by the QM2 and returning by jet.
   a How many nights did he spend on board the QM2?
   b The return journey from New York by jet (2490 miles) took five hours. What was the average speed?
   c Write a paragraph to describe Jon's travels.

2 This graph shows an aeroplane travelling from London to Majorca via Barcelona and one flying directly to Majorca.
   a What is the first aeroplane's average speed from London to Barcelona?
   b How can you tell from the graph that the aeroplane's average speed from London to Barcelona is greater than from Barcelona to Majorca?
   c At what time are the two planes the same distance from London?

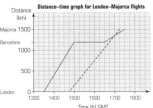

3 On squared paper, copy this grid.
   a Here is part of the London Express timetable:

depart Edinburgh	0600
arrive York	0800
depart York	0845
arrive London	1130

On your grid, show the train's journey from Edinburgh to London.
   b The 'Early Riser' train follows this timetable:

London	depart	0630
Peterborough	arrive	0730
	depart	0745
York	arrive	0945
	depart	1000
Newcastle	arrive	1100
	depart	1115
Edinburgh	arrive	1215

Show this journey on the same graph.
   c At what time are the two trains the same distance from Edinburgh? How far are the trains from Edinburgh at this time?
   d When is the London Express travelling fastest? What is its average speed for this part of the journey?

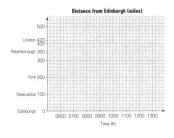

Exercise commentary

The questions assess objectives on Framework Pages 173 and 175.

Problem solving
The exercise assesses objectives on Framework Page 27.

Group work
Students could work in pairs on question 1c.

Misconceptions
Students will need to read the graphs very carefully to successfully read and draw distance–time graphs.
You may want to discuss the scale on the time axis before students attempt question 1 to help emphasise this.
It is important to emphasise that a downward sloping line shows a return journey rather than a vehicle moving backwards. You could discuss how to show the return journey in question 2.

Links
Measures: Framework Pages 229–231.

Homework

A2.2HW gives practice in interpreting a distance–time graph.

Answers

1 a 4   b 498 mph   c Jon left Southampton and travelled to Le Havre on Sunday. He left on the QM2 on Sunday night. He then took $3\frac{1}{2}$ days to sail to New York, before flying back to Southampton early on Saturday morning.
2 a 800 km/h   b Steeper slope from London to Barcelona   c 1700
3 a,b

c 0915, 280 miles
d Edinburgh to York, 100 mph

A2.3 Interpreting graphs

Mental starter

Show **A2.2OHP** from the previous spread.
Recap what each of the parts of the graph mean.
Discuss why there are no vertical parts – you would be travelling in no time at all.
Discuss what students did between 8 pm and 10 pm the previous evening. Discuss what you would put on the vertical axis if you wanted to illustrate their evening on a graph.

Useful resources

A2.3OHP – real-life graph for discussion
Graph paper

Introductory activity

Ask students how to cook frozen peas.
Emphasise that you:
▸ Put them in boiling water (100 °C).
▸ Bring the water back to the boil.
▸ Boil for a few minutes.

Discuss how to show this on a graph
(as in the Students' book).
Emphasise that the variables are time and temperature.
Encourage the use of a sensible scale.
Discuss whether straight lines or curves are appropriate and why.

Emphasise the important features when reading information from a graph:
▸ What does an upward slope show?
▸ What does a downward slope show?
▸ What does a horizontal line show?
▸ What does a vertical line show?

Refer to **A2.2** for the work on distance–time graphs where these aspects are also important.

A2.3OHP shows a graph that will help students realise the need for a detailed understanding.
The graph shows how the amount of petrol in a car varies during a week.
Discuss:
▸ When does the amount of fuel change and why?
▸ When does the amount of fuel remain the same and why?
▸ There is a vertical line on Wednesday – why? What happened?

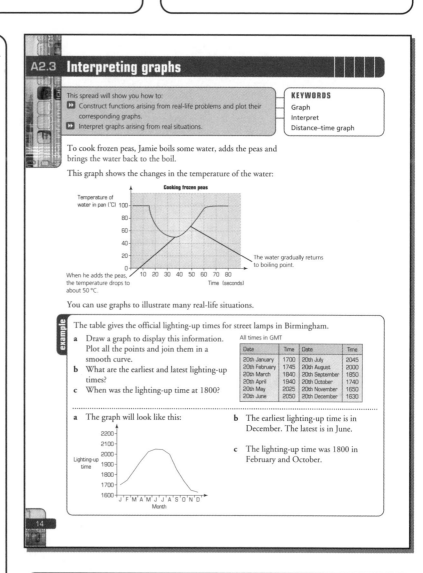

Plenary

Discuss question 3.
Encourage students to explain how the gradients reflect the filling up of the containers.

Challenge students to draw a container for this graph:

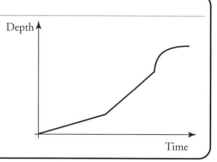

Further activities

In **A2.3ICT** students use a spreadsheet to plot and draw examples of real-life graphs.

Alternatively

Challenge able students to split the stopping distance into braking and thinking distances in question 4, and to plot these graphs on the same axes.

Differentiation

Core questions:
▸ Question 1 focuses on a straight-line graph.
▸ Questions 2 and 3 involve interpreting curved graphs.
▸ Question 4 involves drawing a curved graph.

Extension tier: focuses on graphs of cubic and quadratic functions.

Support tier: focuses on drawing and interpreting conversion and distance–time graphs.

Exercise A2.3

1 This is a simplified graph showing the depth of water in a bath.

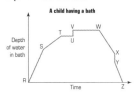

A child having a bath

Between R and T water fills the bath.
a What could have happened at point S?
b At what point did the child get into the bath?
c At what point did the child get out of the bath?
d In a short paragraph, describe the story of the child having a bath.

2 The graph shows the heights of two rockets during their flights at a firework display.

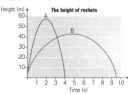

The height of rockets

a Rocket A flew for four seconds. What was the total flight time for rocket B?
b Estimate how much higher rocket A reached than rocket B.
c Estimate the time after the start when the two rockets were at the same height.
d Estimate how much longer rocket B was more than 30 m above the ground than rocket A.

3 Here are four containers.

Water is poured at a constant rate into the containers.
The graphs show the depth of water as the containers fill up.

a Which graph matches each container?
b A fifth container looks like this:
Sketch a graph to show the depth of water over time as the container fills up.

4 The highway code gives these minimum stopping distances for cars travelling at different speeds.

Speed	Stopping distance
10 mph	10 m
20 mph	12 m
30 mph	23 m
40 mph	36 m
50 mph	53 m
60 mph	73 m
70 mph	96 m

a Draw a graph to represent this data. Plot all the points and join them in a smooth curve.
b Estimate the stopping distance for a car travelling at 35 mph.

Exercise commentary

The questions assess objectives on Framework Pages 173 and 175.

Problem solving

The exercise assesses objectives on Framework Page 27.

Group work

Weaker students could work in pairs throughout the exercise.

Misconceptions

The main difficulty students have is in thinking that a steeper line or curve corresponds to a thicker vase in question 3 – in other words they will consider the amount of space in the vase rather than how long it takes to fill that vase. Emphasise that the thicker the vase the longer it takes to fill and so the slower the depth of liquid will increase.
Encourage students to share their thinking to help others understand.

Links

Measures: Framework Pages 229–231.

Homework

A2.3HW focuses on interpreting and drawing graphs of average height. Students will need graph paper.

Answers

1 a Flow from hot or cold tap reduced to adjust temperature. **b** U **c** X
  d Both taps are run, then one is turned off, then the second. The child gets into the bath. Some water is let out before the child gets out and lets out the rest.
2 a About $9\frac{1}{2}$ s **b** 13–16 m
  c About $3\frac{1}{4}$ s **d** About 3 s
3 a A2, B1, C4, D3 **b** Depth of water / Time (curve) **4 a** Stopping distance / Speed (curve) **b** 29 mph

Summary

The key objective for this unit is:
▶ Construct functions arising from real-life problems and plot their corresponding graphs. (173–175)
▶ Interpret graphs arising from real situations. (173–175)

Plenary activity

Sketch this graph on the board:

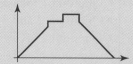

Encourage students to think of and describe situations this graph could represent. How should they label the axes?

Check out commentary

1 Students need to read the scales on the graph carefully in order to draw an accurate graph. They should represent the 'waits' at stations by horizontal lines.

2 Students should use a ruler to draw a line from the horizontal axis to the graph and then across to the vertical axis, for part **a**.
In part **b** they should read the distance from the vertical axis.
For part **c**, students should use the formula

$$\text{Speed} = \frac{\text{Distance}}{\text{Time}}$$

They need to read the time taken accurately from the graph, or refer back to the table in question 1.

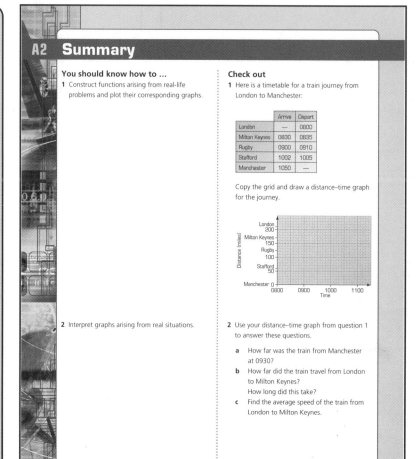

A2 Summary

You should know how to ...

1 Construct functions arising from real-life problems and plot their corresponding graphs.

2 Interpret graphs arising from real situations.

Check out

1 Here is a timetable for a train journey from London to Manchester:

	Arrive	Depart
London	—	0800
Milton Keynes	0830	0835
Rugby	0900	0910
Stafford	1002	1005
Manchester	1050	—

Copy the grid and draw a distance–time graph for the journey.

2 Use your distance–time graph from question 1 to answer these questions.

a How far was the train from Manchester at 0930?

b How far did the train travel from London to Milton Keynes?
How long did this take?

c Find the average speed of the train from London to Milton Keynes.

16

Development

This is the main unit for building the skills required to solve problems involving real-life graphs.
Students will revisit graphs in **A3** and **A4**, in particular focusing on the meaning of the gradient, and use the idea of inverse functions to solve equations in **A3**.

Links

Students should be encouraged to develop their understanding of real-life graphs in other subject areas such as Science and Geography.

Mental starters

The objectives covered are:

▶ Order, add, subtract, multiply and divide integers.
▶ Use squares, cubes, roots and index notation.
▶ Know prime numbers less than 30 and factor pairs.
▶ Convert between fractions, decimals and percentages.
▶ Find fractions and percentages of quantities.

▶ Add and subtract several small numbers or multiples of 10.
▶ Multiply and divide a two-digit number by a one-digit number.
▶ Use factors to multiply and divide mentally.
▶ Use approximations to estimate answers.
▶ Apply mental skills to solve simple problems.

N1 Proportional reasoning

This unit will show you how to:

▶▶ Round numbers.
▶▶ Use prime factor decomposition of a number.
▶▶ Use efficient methods to add, subtract, multiply and divide fractions, interpreting division as a multiplicative inverse.
▶▶ Cancel common factors before calculating.
▶▶ Recognise when fractions and percentages are needed to compare proportions.
▶▶ Solve problems involving percentage changes.
▶▶ Use proportional reasoning to solve a problem.
▶▶ Compare two ratios.
▶▶ Interpret and use ratio in a range of contexts.
▶▶ Understand the effects of multiplying and dividing by numbers between 0 and 1.

▶▶ Use the laws of arithmetic and inverse operations.
▶▶ Understand the order of precedence and effect of powers.
▶▶ Make and justify estimates and approximations of calculations.
▶▶ Use known facts to derive unknown facts.
▶▶ Extend mental methods of calculation.
▶▶ Solve increasingly demanding problems and evaluate solutions.
▶▶ Solve problems using a range of efficient methods.
▶▶ Present a concise, reasoned argument.
▶▶ Give solutions to an appropriate degree of accuracy.

Percentages are used in everyday life.

Before you start

You should know how to ...
1 Find the HCF and LCM of two numbers.

2 Find equivalent fractions.

3 Convert between fractions, decimals and percentages.

4 Simplify a ratio.

Check in
1 The factors of 12 can be written as: $2 \times 2 \times 3$
The factors of 40 can be written as: $2 \times 2 \times 2 \times 5$
Find the HCF and LCM of 12 and 40.

2 Which of these pairs of fractions are equivalent?
$\frac{1}{2}$ $\frac{24}{40}$ $\frac{3}{5}$ $\frac{15}{60}$ $\frac{1}{10}$ $\frac{3}{24}$ $\frac{3}{12}$ $\frac{24}{36}$

3 Express:
a 20% as a fraction   b 0.45 as a percentage
c $\frac{3}{20}$ as a decimal   d $\frac{11}{25}$ as a percentage

4 Simplify:
a 5:15   b 100:30   c 36:60   d 2 km:10 m

17

Check in activity

Write '40' in the middle of the board. Encourage students to write around it multiplications that give 40.
Discuss students' multiplications. Focus on those involving fractions and decimals (0.5×80, $\frac{1}{4}$ of 160) and strategies for working these out.

Resources needed

* means class set needed
Essential:
N1.3OHP – fraction and decimal cards
N1.7OHP – weights of fish
R6 – number lines
R30 – pairs cards
R31 – loop cards
R32 – algebraic pairs cards
R33 – two-operation loop cards
Ordinary dice
Useful:
N1.6OHP – percentage change
N1.2F – multiplication pyramids
N1.7F – comparing squares
N1.8F – graph investigation
N1.8ICT* – constant multipliers
Nutritional information (food packaging)
R18 – operation cards

Unit commentary

Aim of the unit
This unit develops understanding of proportion and extends to expressing properties as fractions, decimals and percentages and converting between them. Multiplicative methods are used to solve problems involving percentage change, ratio and proportionality.

Introduction
Discuss the language used to describe multiplication by a whole number (times) and by a fraction (of) and the effect of each.

Framework references
This unit focuses on:
Teaching objectives pages:
45, 55, 61, 65–69, 75, 77, 79, 81, 83, 85, 87, 89, 103.
Problem solving pages: 3–9, 29, 31.

Differentiation

Support tier
Focuses on fractions, decimals and percentages, and using these in problems involving ratio and direct proportion.

Extension tier
Focuses on algebraic fractions, compound percentages and the unitary method.

Mental starter

Pair chase

Challenge students to put these 10 numbers into pairs:

12, 14, 18, 20, 24, 27, 28, 30, 36, 45,

so that each pair has an (HCF; LCM) of:

(2; 210) (4; 180) (6; 72) (4; 84) (9; 135).

Students can work in teams to guess pairs.

Useful resources

R6 – number lines for exercise

Introductory activity

Check by asking questions that students can:

▶ **Find simple equivalent fractions:**
  ▶ Give $\frac{45}{63}$ in its simplest form.
▶ **Add and subtract simple fractions:**
  ▶ Find $\frac{7}{8} + \frac{5}{8} + \frac{13}{8}$.
  ▶ Find $\frac{2}{3} + \frac{5}{9}$.

Discuss methods used.

Give two fractions, $\frac{13}{18}$ and $\frac{17}{24}$.

Challenge students to work out:

▶ **The larger fraction**
▶ **The sum of the fractions.**

Discuss strategies students use.

Emphasise the steps:

▶ Use prime factors to find the LCM of the denominators:
  LCM of 18 and 24 is 72.
▶ Find equivalent fractions:
  $\frac{13}{18} = \frac{52}{72}$ $\frac{17}{24} = \frac{51}{72}$
▶ Add as they have the same denominator:
  $\frac{52}{72} + \frac{51}{72} = \frac{103}{72}$

Develop the idea that the steps are the same for all fractions, however different the denominators. [There is more information on finding the LCM in A4.1 and A4.2]

Challenge students to cancel $\frac{105}{180}$ to its simplest form.

Discuss methods:

▶ Use prime factors to find the HCF and divide:
  HCF = $3 \times 5 = 15$
▶ Divide each part by prime factors:
  $\frac{105}{180} = \frac{35}{60} = \frac{7}{12}$

Discuss how to see when a fraction is in its simplest form.

▶ Denominator cannot be divided.

Revise divisibility rules if necessary.

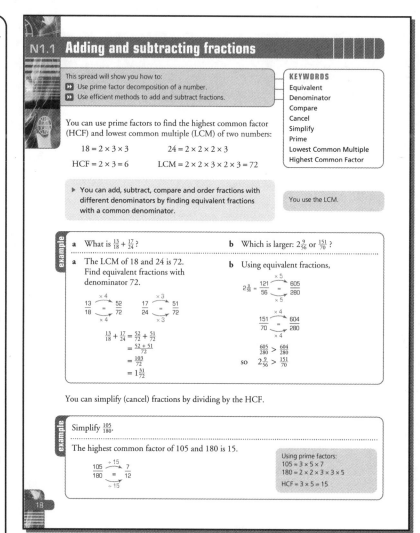

Plenary

Challenge students to solve this problem, similar to question 8a:

▶ $x + y = 1\frac{3}{35}$
▶ $x - y = \frac{18}{35}$.

Encourage students to explain how to start solving the problem [estimate then substitution].

Discuss what values to expect for x and y, and what strategies to use.

Discuss solutions. [$x = \frac{2}{7}$, $y = \frac{4}{5}$]

Further activities

Students could make up puzzles similar to questions 7 and 8 for a partner to solve.

Differentiation

Core questions:

▸ Questions 1–3 practise adding and subtracting fractions in a range of contexts.
▸ Questions 4–7 focus on fractions with larger denominators and mixed numbers.
▸ Question 8 extends to further problem solving, including explaining methods used.

Extension tier: focuses on numerical and algebraic fractions.
Support tier: focuses on adding and subtracting fractions.

Exercise N1.1

1 Work out these answers as mixed numbers where appropriate.

   a $\frac{3}{7} + \frac{5}{7}$ b $2\frac{3}{5} - \frac{6}{5}$
   c $\frac{2}{5} + \frac{3}{10}$ d $\frac{2}{3} - \frac{1}{5}$
   e $\frac{5}{8} + \frac{1}{2}$ f $\frac{7}{9} - \frac{2}{5}$
   g $\frac{7}{10} + 1\frac{1}{4}$ h $3\frac{2}{7} - \frac{5}{8}$

2 **Puzzle**
   Choose two fractions from the fraction box that have:

Fraction box			
$\frac{2}{3}$	$\frac{1}{2}$	$\frac{4}{5}$	$\frac{2}{6}$
$\frac{3}{4}$	$\frac{1}{3}$	$\frac{3}{5}$	$\frac{5}{6}$

   a a total of $\frac{5}{6}$
   b a total greater than 1
   c a difference of $\frac{1}{12}$
   d a sum of $\frac{17}{20}$
   e a total greater than $1\frac{1}{4}$ but less than $1\frac{1}{3}$.

3 **Investigation**
   a Use four different digits to make a fraction sum with a total of 1.

   $$\frac{\square}{\square} + \frac{\square}{\square} = 1$$

   b Investigate different possible pairs of fractions with a sum of 1 that use four different digits.

4 Work out these answers as mixed numbers where appropriate.

   a $\frac{3}{10} + \frac{3}{4}$ b $\frac{13}{15} - \frac{3}{5}$
   c $\frac{11}{12} + \frac{7}{9}$ d $\frac{17}{24} + \frac{11}{18}$
   e $\frac{17}{20} + \frac{-8}{15}$ f $1\frac{7}{12} + \frac{7}{10}$
   g $2\frac{7}{18} - 1\frac{11}{12}$ h $3\frac{7}{16} - \frac{-8}{15}$

5 For each pair of numbers, insert >, < or = in between them. Show your working out clearly for each question.

   a $\frac{11}{15}$ $\frac{7}{9}$ b $\frac{-7}{18}$ $\frac{-13}{30}$
   c $\frac{29}{12}$ $2\frac{2}{5}$ d $\frac{17}{24}$ $\frac{39}{56}$
   e $\frac{47}{64}$ $\frac{83}{112}$ f $\frac{19}{51}$ $\frac{47}{136}$

6 a Rukia mixed $2\frac{5}{18}$ litres of blue paint with $1\frac{5}{15}$ litres of white paint to make a 'sky-blue' paint.
     How many litres of 'sky-blue' paint did she make?
   b Joshua pours $3\frac{3}{11}$ pints from a container holding $7\frac{1}{4}$ pints.
     How much liquid is left in the container?
   c An envelope is $6\frac{7}{8}$ inches long and $4\frac{11}{15}$ inches wide.
     What is the perimeter of the envelope?

7 **Puzzle**
   In these pyramids, the brick that sits directly above two bricks is the sum of these two bricks.
   Copy and complete these pyramids:

   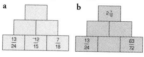

   a   b

8 **Puzzle**
   a The difference between two numbers is $\frac{47}{48}$.
     The sum of the two numbers is $\frac{19}{48}$.
     What are the two numbers?
     Explain clearly the method you have used to solve the problem.
   b The numbers x, $\frac{13}{18}$, y, z and $1\frac{2}{9}$ are in increasing order of size.
     The difference between each successive pair of numbers is the same.
     What are the values of x, y and z?
     Explain clearly the method you have used to solve the problem.

Exercise commentary

The questions assess objectives on Framework Pages 55, 65 and 67.

Problem solving

Questions 2, 3, 6 and 7 assess objectives on Framework Pages 5–9.
Question 8 assesses objectives on Page 31.

Group work

Questions 3 and 8 are suitable for working in pairs.

Misconceptions

Some students will forget to change a mixed number into an improper fraction, or subtract the smaller fraction from the larger:

$$2\frac{3}{5} - \frac{6}{5} = 2 + \frac{6}{5} - \frac{3}{5}$$

Encourage the use of a number line. Emphasise the need to change all mixed numbers to improper fractions.

Many students will use wrong place value for negative numbers:

$$\frac{-35}{90} < \frac{-39}{90}$$

Encourage use of a number line, emphasising the distance away from 0.

Links

Add algebraic fractions: Framework Page 119.

19

Homework

N1.1HW provides further practice at adding and subtracting fractions and mixed numbers. It includes an investigation into fraction series.

Answers

1 a $1\frac{1}{7}$ b $1\frac{2}{5}$ c $\frac{7}{10}$ d $\frac{7}{15}$ e $1\frac{1}{8}$ f $\frac{17}{45}$ g $1\frac{19}{20}$ h $2\frac{37}{56}$

2 a $\frac{1}{2}, \frac{1}{3}$ b Example: $\frac{2}{3}, \frac{1}{2}$ c $\frac{3}{4}, \frac{2}{3}$ d $\frac{1}{4}, \frac{3}{5}$ e $\frac{2}{3}, \frac{3}{5}$

3 a Example: $\frac{1}{2} + \frac{4}{8}$ b For example, $\frac{1}{3} + \frac{4}{6}$, $\frac{1}{4} + \frac{6}{8}$

4 a $1\frac{1}{20}$ b $\frac{4}{15}$ c $1\frac{25}{36}$ d $1\frac{23}{72}$ e $\frac{19}{60}$ f $2\frac{17}{60}$ g $\frac{17}{36}$ h $1\frac{233}{240}$

5 a < b > c > d > e < f >   6 a $3\frac{11}{18}$ litres b $3\frac{39}{44}$ pints
   c $23\frac{13}{60}$ inches   7 a $\frac{-241}{360}$; $\frac{-31}{120}$, $\frac{-37}{90}$ b $1\frac{1}{8}$, $1\frac{11}{24}$; $\frac{7}{12}$ 8 a $\frac{11}{16}$, $\frac{-7}{24}$ b $\frac{5}{9}$, $\frac{8}{9}$, $1\frac{1}{18}$

Mental starter

Use the cards from **R30**. The aim is to match pairs of cards showing fractions, decimals and percentages.

▶ Split the class into two teams.

▶ Team 1 turns over one card, then another. If the value matches, they get one point. If does not, the cards are turned back over and the turn passes to Team 2.

▶ The team with the most points after all the cards have been turned over wins.

Useful resources

R30 – pairs cards for the mental starter

R6 – number lines

N1.2F – multiplication pyramid puzzles

Introductory activity

Check by asking questions that students can:

▶ **Multiply a fraction by an integer:**
  ▶ $\frac{4}{7} \times 3$

▶ **Cancel fractions to their simplest form:**
  ▶ $\frac{18}{30}$ in its simplest form

▶ **Convert from mixed numbers to improper fractions and vice versa:**
  ▶ $\frac{43}{6}$ as a mixed number

Discuss methods used.

Use a number line (R6) marked in 15s to challenge students to work out $\frac{1}{5} \times \frac{1}{3}$.

Discuss strategies students use.

Discuss how to use the number line to show the answer. Show on the number line that $\frac{1}{5}$ of $\frac{1}{3}$ is $\frac{1}{15}$.

Emphasise that:

$\frac{1}{5} \times \frac{1}{3} = \frac{1}{5}$ of $\frac{1}{3} = \frac{1}{15}$.

Challenge students to work in pairs to solve $\frac{4}{5} \times \frac{2}{3}$, then encourage two pairs to explain their methods to the class.

Discuss responses and methods.

Emphasise that $\frac{4}{5} = \frac{1}{5} \times 4$ and $\frac{2}{3} = \frac{1}{3} \times 2$.

Use these unit fractions to break down the calculation into smaller steps:

$\frac{4}{5} \times \frac{2}{3} = \frac{1}{5} \times 4 \times \frac{1}{3} \times 2 = \frac{1}{15} \times 8 = \frac{8}{15}$

Discuss how to solve $\frac{18}{4}$ of $\frac{12}{15}$.

Remind students how to use unit fractions.

Demonstrate that:

$\frac{18}{4}$ of $\frac{12}{15} = \frac{18}{4} \times \frac{12}{15}$

$= \frac{1}{4} \times 18 \times \frac{1}{15} \times 12 = \frac{216}{60} = 3\frac{3}{5}$

Emphasise that the fraction can be cancelled down before or after multiplication:

$\frac{18}{4} \times \frac{12}{15} = \frac{\cancel{18}^6 \times \cancel{12}^3}{\cancel{4} \times \cancel{15}_5} = \frac{6 \times 3}{5 \times 1} = 3\frac{3}{5}$

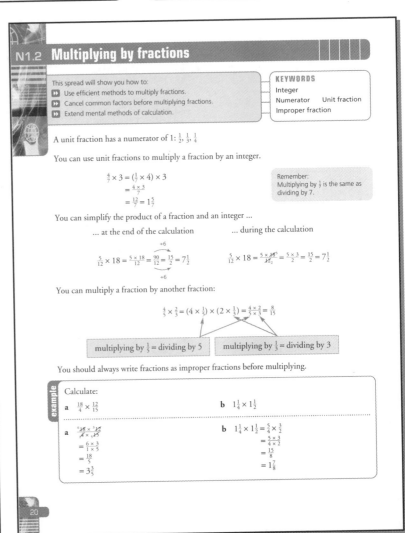

This spread will show you how to:
▶▶ Use efficient methods to multiply fractions.
▶▶ Cancel common factors before multiplying fractions.
▶▶ Extend mental methods of calculation.

KEYWORDS
Integer
Numerator   Unit fraction
Improper fraction

A unit fraction has a numerator of 1: $\frac{1}{2}, \frac{1}{3}, \frac{1}{4}$

You can use unit fractions to multiply a fraction by an integer.

$\frac{4}{7} \times 3 = (\frac{1}{7} \times 4) \times 3$
$= \frac{4 \times 3}{7}$
$= \frac{12}{7} = 1\frac{5}{7}$

Remember:
Multiplying by $\frac{1}{7}$ is the same as dividing by 7.

You can simplify the product of a fraction and an integer ...

... at the end of the calculation

$\frac{5}{12} \times 18 = \frac{5 \times 18}{12} = \frac{90}{12} = \frac{15}{2} = 7\frac{1}{2}$

... during the calculation

$\frac{5}{12} \times 18 = \frac{5 \times \cancel{18}^3}{\cancel{12}_2} = \frac{5 \times 3}{2} = \frac{15}{2} = 7\frac{1}{2}$

You can multiply a fraction by another fraction:

$\frac{4}{5} \times \frac{2}{3} = (4 \times \frac{1}{5}) \times (2 \times \frac{1}{3}) = \frac{4 \times 2}{5 \times 3} = \frac{8}{15}$

multiplying by $\frac{1}{5}$ = dividing by 5   multiplying by $\frac{1}{3}$ = dividing by 3

You should always write fractions as improper fractions before multiplying.

example

Calculate:

a $\frac{18}{4} \times \frac{12}{15}$

b $1\frac{1}{4} \times 1\frac{1}{2}$

a $\frac{\cancel{18} \times \cancel{12}}{\cancel{4} \times \cancel{15}}$
$= \frac{6 \times 3}{1 \times 5}$
$= \frac{18}{5}$
$= 3\frac{3}{5}$

b $1\frac{1}{4} \times 1\frac{1}{2} = \frac{5}{4} \times \frac{3}{2}$
$= \frac{5 \times 3}{4 \times 2}$
$= \frac{15}{8}$
$= 1\frac{7}{8}$

Plenary

Discuss two answers to $2\frac{2}{5} \times 3\frac{1}{3}$: Peter's answer: 8; Karen's answer: $6\frac{2}{15}$. Encourage students to decide which answer is correct, what mistake has been made in the other answer, and to demonstrate their methods. Emphasise the need to:

▶ Estimate first.

▶ Use improper fractions.

▶ Simplify by cancelling common factors.

Further activities

N1.2F contains multiplication pyramid puzzles for students to solve.
Students could investigate division calculations involving fractions with a given answer.
For example, $\frac{2}{5} \div \square = \frac{3}{4}$

Differentiation

Core questions:
▸ Questions 1 and 2 practise multiplying a fraction by an integer and finding fractions of an amount.
▸ Questions 3–7 focus on multiplying fractions in context.
▸ Questions 8 and 9 extend to division of fractions and simple series.

Extension tier: focuses on multiplying numerical and algebraic fractions.

Support tier: focuses on unitary fractions and simple multiplication and division.

Exercise N1.2

1 Calculate these, giving your answer as a mixed number where appropriate:
 a $10 \times \frac{5}{8}$ b $18 \times \frac{7}{12}$ c $\frac{5}{7} \times 28$
 d $\frac{3}{8} \times 12$ e $14 \times \frac{5}{6}$ f $35 \times \frac{13}{28}$
 g $\frac{4}{24} \times 18$ h $3\frac{2}{5} \times 10$ i $\frac{3}{10} \times 8$
 j $\frac{9}{100} \times 4$

2 Calculate these fractions of amounts using an appropriate method:
 a $\frac{2}{5}$ of 18 b $\frac{7}{8}$ of 184 cm
 c $\frac{5}{13} \times £78$ d $\frac{11}{2} \times 20$ kg
 e $\frac{3}{7}$ of 120 cm f $\frac{9}{4} \times 92$ inches
 g $2\frac{5}{9}$ of 234 cows h $1\frac{4}{9}$ of £25

3 Calculate each answer in its simplest form:
 a $\frac{2}{3} \times \frac{4}{5}$ b $\frac{5}{7} \times \frac{14}{8}$ c $\frac{12}{5} \times \frac{15}{4}$
 d $\frac{6}{8} \times \frac{4}{9}$ e $\frac{9}{16} \times \frac{12}{1}$ f $\frac{8}{15} \times \frac{10}{12}$
 g $24 \times \frac{7}{18}$ h $\frac{18}{14} \times \frac{35}{27}$

4 **Puzzle**
Choose two fractions from the fraction box that have:

Fraction box			
$\frac{4}{7}$	$\frac{15}{8}$	$\frac{21}{12}$	$\frac{28}{25}$
$\frac{16}{57}$	$\frac{19}{14}$	$\frac{63}{10}$	$\frac{18}{5}$

 a a product of exactly 1
 b a product of exactly $1\frac{73}{95}$
 c a product that is less than $\frac{1}{4}$
 d the largest product
 e a product greater than $1\frac{3}{4}$ but less than 2.

5 Calculate each answer in its simplest form:
 a $1\frac{1}{3} \times 1\frac{3}{5}$ b $2\frac{5}{7} \times 2\frac{5}{8}$
 c $1\frac{7}{9} \times \frac{27}{32}$ d $1\frac{1}{15} \times 2\frac{5}{8}$
 e $\frac{28}{9} \times 1\frac{5}{7}$ f $2\frac{3}{16} \times 1\frac{1}{15}$
 g $1\frac{1}{11} \times \frac{44}{45}$ h $4\frac{1}{2} \times 1\frac{13}{27}$
 i $(2\frac{1}{4})^2$ j $\frac{3}{4} \times (2\frac{1}{5} - \frac{19}{45})$

6 Work out these, leaving your answers as mixed numbers where appropriate:
 a An envelope is $6\frac{3}{7}$ inches long and $4\frac{1}{5}$ inches wide.
 What is the area of the envelope?
 b The body weight of Walter the walrus is $1\frac{4}{21}$ tonnes. His tusks weigh $\frac{7}{90}$ of his total body weight.
 How heavy are Walter's tusks?
 c A jug holds $3\frac{3}{5}$ litres of orange squash. Lucy pours out $\frac{11}{12}$ of the orange squash into 6 glasses. How much orange squash is left in the jug? How much orange squash is in each glass?

7 **Puzzle**
Joanne spends $\frac{2}{5}$ of each weekday at work. During her work she spends $\frac{15}{22}$ of her time dealing with customers. She spends $\frac{3}{4}$ of her remaining time at work answering the phone.
What fraction of Joanne's day is spent:
 a dealing with customers
 b answering the phone?

8 Find the missing fraction in each of these calculations:
 a $\frac{4}{11} \times \underline{\hspace{1cm}} = \frac{1}{2}$
 b $\frac{5}{12} \times \underline{\hspace{1cm}} = \frac{3}{4}$
 c $\frac{7}{8} \times \underline{\hspace{1cm}} = \frac{2}{5}$
Explain your method for finding each of the missing fractions.

9 **Investigation**
 a Investigate what happens when you multiply:
 $\frac{1}{2} \times \frac{3}{4}$ $\frac{1}{2} \times \frac{3}{4} \times \frac{5}{6}$ $\frac{1}{2} \times \frac{3}{4} \times \frac{5}{6} \times \frac{7}{8}$ ...
 b Investigate what happens when you multiply other fractions:
 For example $\frac{1}{2} \times \frac{2}{3} \times \frac{3}{4} \times \frac{4}{5} \times \ldots$
 $\frac{1}{2} \times \frac{1}{4} \times \frac{1}{8} \times \frac{1}{16} \times \ldots$

21

Exercise commentary

The questions assess objectives on Framework Pages 67, 69 and 89.

Problem solving
Questions 4, 6, 7 and 9 assess objectives on Framework Pages 5–9.
Question 8 assesses objectives on Page 31.

Group work
Questions 3, 7 and 9 are suitable for working in pairs.

Misconceptions
Some students will confuse multiplication with finding an equivalent fraction:
$10 \times \frac{5}{8} = \frac{50}{80}$
Encourage the use of a number line. Emphasise that $10 \times \frac{5}{8}$ is 10 steps of $\frac{5}{8}$ along the number line. Also emphasise that an equivalent fraction can be written in the same place as the fraction itself: $\frac{50}{80} = \frac{5}{8}$.
Many students will forget to change a mixed fraction to an improper fraction before multiplying. Encourage them to estimate the answer first and emphasise the need to use improper fractions.

Links
Multiplying algebraic fractions: Framework Page 119; Mutually exclusive events: Pages 279–281.

Homework

N1.2HW provides further practice at multiplying fractions by fractions, including mixed numbers and improper fractions. The final question is a puzzle, where students design a flag with given fractions shaded different colours.

Answers

1 a $6\frac{1}{4}$ b $10\frac{1}{2}$ c 20 d $4\frac{1}{2}$ e $11\frac{2}{3}$ f $16\frac{1}{4}$ g 3 h 34 i $2\frac{2}{5}$ j $\frac{9}{25}$

2 a $7\frac{1}{5}$ b 161 cm c £30 d $18\frac{1}{3}$ kg e $51\frac{3}{7}$ cm f 207 inches
 g 598 cows h £36.11

3 a $\frac{8}{15}$ b $1\frac{1}{4}$ c 9 d $\frac{1}{3}$ e $2\frac{1}{4}$ f $\frac{4}{9}$ g $9\frac{1}{3}$ h $1\frac{2}{3}$

4 a $\frac{4}{7}, \frac{21}{12}$ b $\frac{16}{57}, \frac{63}{10}$ c $\frac{4}{7}, \frac{16}{57}$ d $\frac{63}{10}, \frac{18}{5}$ e $\frac{21}{12}, \frac{28}{25}$ or $\frac{16}{57}, \frac{63}{10}$

5 a $2\frac{2}{3}$ b $7\frac{1}{8}$ c $1\frac{1}{2}$ d $2\frac{4}{5}$ e $5\frac{1}{3}$ f $4\frac{1}{12}$ g $1\frac{3}{5}$ h $6\frac{2}{3}$ i $5\frac{1}{16}$ j $1\frac{1}{3}$

6 a 27 in^2 b $\frac{5}{54}$ tonne c $\frac{3}{10}$ litre left, $\frac{11}{20}$ litre per glass

7 a $\frac{3}{11}$ b $\frac{21}{220}$ 8 a $\frac{11}{8}$ b $\frac{9}{5}$ c $\frac{16}{35}$ 9 a $\frac{3}{8}, \frac{5}{16}, \frac{35}{128}$, ... b Own investigation

N1.3 Dividing by fractions

Mental starter

Higher or lower?

Make a set of cards from **N1.3OHP**, and also show the cards on the OHP during the game. Ask all the students to stand up.

▸ Place six cards face down on a table. Turn over the first one.

▸ Challenge students to guess if the next card will be higher or lower.

▸ Turn over the next card. Students who are wrong have to sit down. Ask them to explain their guesses.

Useful resources

N1.3OHP – fraction and decimal cards for the mental starter

R6 – number lines

Introductory activity

Check by that students can:

▸ **Multiply two fractions together:**
  ▸ $\frac{2}{5} \times \frac{3}{7}$

▸ **Divide an integer by a unit fraction:**
  ▸ $5 \div \frac{1}{3}$

Discuss methods used.

Use a number line (R6) from 0 to 3 marked in quarters to challenge students to find $3 \div \frac{3}{4}$.

Encourage students to demonstrate answers and discuss methods.

Emphasise:

▸ Use of a number line to show answers.

▸ Use of unit fractions:
  How many quarters are there in a whole?
  $1 \div \frac{1}{4} = 4$, $3 \div \frac{1}{4} = 12$ so $3 \div \frac{3}{4} = 4$

Encourage use of the multiplicative inverse to simplify the calculation.

Discuss how many $\frac{3}{4}$s there are in 3:

▸ $3 \div \frac{3}{4} = 4$

Emphasise that students know what to multiply 3 by to make 4:

▸ $3 \times \frac{4}{3} = 4$

Emphasise that you can replace the division by the multiplicative inverse.

▸ Dividing by $\frac{3}{4}$ is the same as multiplying by $\frac{4}{3}$.

Challenge students to find:

$4 \div \frac{3}{4}$, $5 \div \frac{3}{4}$, $6 \div \frac{3}{4}$, etc.

Encourage students to explain methods.

Extend the division to include one fraction divided by another:

$\frac{2}{5} \div \frac{3}{4}$, $\frac{3}{5} \div \frac{3}{4}$

Discuss strategies and extend the method to dividing by any fraction.

Discuss how to check answers.

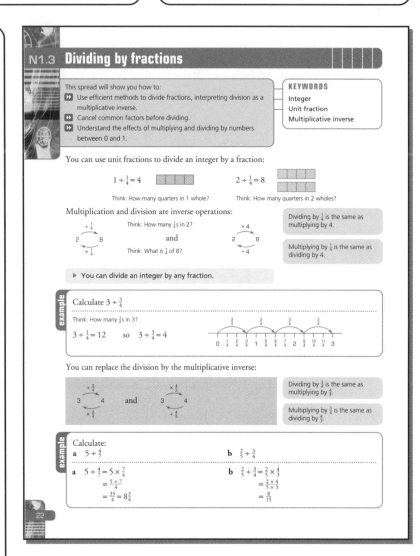

Plenary

Discuss question 8. Use these three types of calculations:

▸ Integer ÷ integer: $4 \div 6$

▸ Integer ÷ fraction: $5 \div \frac{15}{2}$

▸ Fraction ÷ fraction: $\frac{2}{5} \div \frac{3}{5}$.

Discuss students' answers and encourage them to check if each others' calculations are correct.

Discuss how to check answers by changing all fractions to decimals or by using a calculator.

Further activities

Students could make their own set of fraction multiplication and division dominoes, and play the game with a partner.

Differentiation

Core questions:
▶ Questions 1–4 practise dividing an integer by a fraction and use of the multiplicative inverse.
▶ Questions 5–7 focus on dividing fractions by fractions in different contexts.
▶ Questions 8 and 9 extend the relationship between multiplication and division by investigation.

Extension tier: focuses on dividing and simplifying numerical and algebraic fractions.

Support tier: focuses on dividing by non-unitary fractions.

Exercise N1.3

1 Copy and complete these fraction division patterns:

a $1 \div \frac{1}{10} = 10$
$2 \div \frac{1}{10} = 20$
$3 \div \frac{1}{10} =$
$4 \div \frac{1}{10} =$
$5 \div \frac{1}{10} =$

b $1 \div \frac{1}{5} = 5$
$2 \div \frac{1}{5} = 10$
$3 \div \frac{1}{5} =$
$4 \div \frac{1}{5} =$
$5 \div \frac{1}{5} =$

c $1 \div \frac{1}{8} = 8$
$2 \div \frac{1}{8} =$
$3 \div \frac{1}{8} =$

2 Use number lines to calculate:
a $4 \div \frac{1}{3}$ b $2 \div \frac{2}{5}$ c $10 \div \frac{5}{6}$

3 Copy and complete:

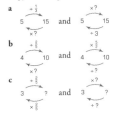

a

b

c

4 Calculate, giving your answer as a mixed number where appropriate:
a $8 \div \frac{3}{4}$ b $12 \div \frac{2}{5}$ c $21 \div \frac{3}{7}$
d $15 \div \frac{2}{5}$ e $2 \div \frac{5}{8}$ f $2 \div \frac{11}{12}$
g $4 \div \frac{3}{5}$ h $6 \div \frac{2}{7}$ i $6 \div \frac{3}{10}$

5 a Lynton is a long-distance runner. He can run every kilometre in $\frac{2}{15}$ of an hour. If he runs for 2 hours, how many kilometres has he covered?
b Dave makes 4 kg of bread dough. He uses $\frac{2}{3}$ kg of bread dough to make a large loaf. How many loaves of bread can he make?

6 **Puzzle**
Michael and Sean are working out the calculation: $\frac{1}{2} \div \frac{1}{6} = ?$
Michael thinks the answer is $\frac{1}{12}$.
Sean disagrees.
Write why you think Sean disagrees with Michael's answer. Use diagrams and number lines to support your explanation.

7 Calculate, giving your answer in its simplest form:
a $\frac{1}{2} \div \frac{1}{5}$ b $\frac{1}{5} \div \frac{1}{4}$ c $\frac{2}{3} \div \frac{3}{4}$
d $\frac{3}{4} \div \frac{1}{2}$ e $\frac{4}{5} \div \frac{3}{7}$ f $\frac{7}{10} \div \frac{2}{5}$
g $\frac{4}{3} \div \frac{5}{8}$ h $\frac{5}{3} \div \frac{4}{9}$ i $1\frac{1}{4} \div \frac{3}{5}$
j $2\frac{1}{6} \div \frac{2}{3}$ k $6\frac{1}{2} \div \frac{7}{10}$ l $4\frac{2}{3} \div \frac{7}{8}$

8 **Investigation**
Write three division calculations involving fractions with an answer of $\frac{2}{3}$.
For example: $\frac{7}{12} \div \frac{7}{8} = \frac{2}{3}$
Explain how you worked out your calculations.
Use your results to solve this problem:
$\frac{4}{5} \div ? = \frac{2}{3}$

9 **Puzzle**
John has a set of operations:

He applies each operation to the number 12, e.g. $12 \times \frac{1}{2} = 6$
He says he can predict if an operation will give an answer bigger or smaller than 12 without doing any calculating.
a Without calculating, identify which operations will give an answer bigger than 12. Explain and justify your answer.
b Check by calculating the answers.

Exercise commentary

The questions assess objectives on Framework Pages 69 and 83.

Problem solving
Question 5 assesses objectives on Framework Page 5.
Questions 6 and 9 assess objectives on Page 31.

Group work
Questions 8 and 9 are suitable for working in pairs.

Misconceptions
Some students will look for the multiplicative equivalent operation rather than the multiplicative inverse:
$5 \div \frac{1}{3} = 15$ so $15 \times 3 = 5$
Encourage students to use a set of whole numbers and show the operation and its inverse:
$4 \times 2 = 8$ and $8 \div 2 = 4$
Then ask for an equivalent calculation to $\times 2$, e.g. $\div \frac{1}{2}$ and demonstrate using a number line (**R6**). Finally ask for an equivalent calculation to $\div 2$, e.g. $\times \frac{1}{2}$ and demonstrate by finding the fraction of the amount.

Links
Ratio and proportion: Framework Pages 79–81.

Homework

N1.3HW provides further practice at dividing integers and fractions by fractions. It extends to finding calculations with the answer $\frac{3}{7}$.

Answers

1 a $30, 40, 50$ b $15, 20, 25$ c $16, 24$ 2 a 12 b 5 c 12
3 a $\times \frac{1}{3}; \times 3$ b $\times \frac{2}{5}; \div \frac{5}{2}$ c $7\frac{1}{2}; \times \frac{5}{2}, 7\frac{1}{2}, \div \frac{5}{2}$
4 a $10\frac{2}{3}$ b $14\frac{2}{5}$ c 49 d $37\frac{1}{2}$ e $3\frac{1}{5}$ f $2\frac{2}{11}$ g $6\frac{2}{3}$ h 21 i 20
5 a 15 km b 6 loaves 6 Answer is 3; there are three sixths in a half.
7 a $2\frac{1}{2}$ b $\frac{4}{5}$ c $\frac{8}{9}$ d $1\frac{1}{2}$ e $1\frac{13}{15}$ f $1\frac{3}{4}$ g $2\frac{2}{15}$ h $5\frac{5}{8}$ i $2\frac{1}{12}$ j $3\frac{1}{4}$
k $9\frac{2}{7}$ l $5\frac{1}{3}$ 8 Example: $\frac{4}{5} \div \frac{6}{5}, \frac{4}{5} \div \frac{6}{7}, \frac{4}{5} \div \frac{6}{5}$
9 a $\div \frac{1}{2}, \times 2, \times \frac{4}{3}, \div \frac{3}{4}$; Dividing by a number less than 1 or multiplying by a number greater than 1 will result in an answer bigger than 12.
b Answers in order: $6, 24, 24, 6, 9, 9, 16, 16$.

N1.4 Proportions of amounts

Mental starter

Estimating

Write up this problem: ___% of ___ = ___ on the board.

Divide students into two teams or pairs.

▶ One student picks a percentage from: 14%, 56%, 77%, 35%, 81%, 96% for the first box, and a number from: 245, 3870, 47, 667, 542, 7295 for the second box.

▶ The other student must estimate the answer.

▶ The difference between the approximate answer and the exact answer is the score for the first student.

Useful resources

R6 – number lines

Introductory activity

Refer to the mental starter, and link to previous work in **N1.3** on multiplying fractions.

Check by asking questions that students can:

▶ **Find simple percentages of amounts:**
  ▶ 60% of £3.50

▶ **Find simple fractions of amounts:**
  ▶ $\frac{3}{5}$ of 23.5

▶ **Multiply simple fractions by integers:**
  ▶ $\frac{3}{5} \times 20$

Discuss methods used.

Challenge students to work out a 9% increase from 275 cm. Encourage them to discuss strategies and write their answers around the calculation in a spider diagram.

Emphasise different methods used, and the links between the methods:

Mental methods:

▶ 9% of 275 = 10% of 275 − 1% of 275

Written methods:

▶ Equivalent calculation: 9% of 275
= $\frac{9}{100} \times 275 = 0.09 \times 275 = 24.75$

▶ Unitary method: 9% of 275
= $\frac{1}{100} \times 9 \times 275 = \frac{1}{100}$
$\times 2475 = 2475 \div 100 = 24.75$

Extend to methods that find the increase in a single calculation. Use a number line (**R6**) from 0% to 100% to show:

▶ If something is decreased by 9% then it is 91% (100% − 9%) of its original size.

▶ If something is increased by 9%, then it is 109% (100% + 9%) of its original size.
109% of 275 = 1.09 × 275 = 299.75 cm

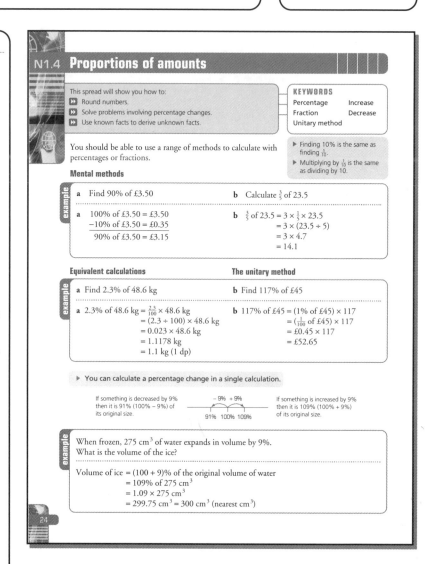

Plenary

Challenge students to find:

112% of 235 cm, 1.12 × 235 cm, $1\frac{12}{100}$ of 235 cm,

88% of 235 cm, 0.88 × 235 cm, $\frac{88}{100} \times 235$ cm.

Discuss the operations in each calculation, and what operation is always performed (multiplication).

Emphasise that a percentage or fractional change is the same as multiplying by a scale factor – less than 1 in the case of a decrease.

If students have access to a spreadsheet package they could investigate how to use a spreadsheet to increase/decrease a set of prices by a given percentage.

Differentiation

Core questions:

▶ Question 1 practises previous work on finding fractions and percentages of amounts.
▶ Questions 2–5 focus on calculating percentages and percentage increase/decrease in a single calculation.
▶ Question 6 extends to successive percentage increases/decreases.

Extension tier: focuses on percentage change.

Support tier: focuses on mental methods for calculating simple percentages.

Exercise N1.4

1 Use an appropriate method to calculate:
   a 10% of £380   b $\frac{2}{5}$ of 230 m
   c 65% of 48 kg   d $1\frac{1}{5}$ of 65 DVDs
   e 12% of 160 cm f $\frac{7}{20} \times 260$ glasses
   g 99% of 450 kg h 125% of 3.8 km

2 a Ian used $\frac{1}{5}$ of a 480 g bag of rice to make a risotto. Clyde used $\frac{2}{3}$ of the rice that remained to make a rice pudding. How many grams of rice were left in the bag?
   b Avril has £4500 to spend on a holiday. She uses 34% of the money to pay for the airfares. She spends 54% of the remaining money on luxury accommodation. How much spending money does she have left?

3 Calculate, giving your answer as a fraction or as a decimal to 1 dp where appropriate:
   a 28% of 72 kg   b 123% of 35 km
   c $\frac{3}{8}$ of 7.8 cm   d 2.5% of 64 mm
   e $2\frac{2}{5} \times 85$ litres   f 7.6% of 40 mm
   g 17.5% of £81   h $\frac{9}{25}$ of 34 hectares
   i 171% of 7.5 m

4 **Puzzle**
   a Lucy can buy a washing machine for one cash payment of £329, or pay using the '36-plan' option. With the '36-plan' she pays a deposit of 36% and then six equal monthly payments of £36. How much extra does she pay by the '36-plan' option?
   b Which is the better buy: a 50 g packet of crisps at 42p, or a packet of crisps with 50 g + 30% extra at 54p?
   c In a survey of 140 pupils, $\frac{2}{7}$ liked football best, $\frac{1}{5}$ liked cricket, and $\frac{3}{10}$ liked athletics. The rest liked cycling. How many liked cycling?

5 Calculate, giving your answers to 2 dp as appropriate:
   a A pair of designer jeans cost £62 in GIP Clothing shop. In a sale, all prices in the shop are reduced by 15%. What is the new price of the jeans?
   b A digital TV costs £345 plus a charge of 17.5% VAT. What is the total cost of the digital TV?
   c A joint of meat weighs 2.5 kg when frozen. It loses 7% of its weight when it is thawed. What is the weight of the meat when it is thawed?
   d If you invest more than £2000 in a Bigsaver account you will receive 3.9% interest a year. Roger invests £3400 in the Bigsaver account. How much interest will he receive after 1 year?
   e A metal bar is 4.6 m long. When heated it expands in length by 1.2%. What is the length of the bar after it has expanded?
   f When using his weighing scales, Ernie knows that his instruments have an error of up to 1.5%. If he weighs 3 kg of carrots using his scales, what is the:
      i Greatest possible weight the carrots could be
      ii Least possible weight the carrots could be?

6 **Puzzle**
   Bill Eatalot goes to a restaurant. At the end of the meal the waiter adds VAT at 17.5% and then a service charge of 8%. Bill tells the waiter that he should have added the service charge first and then added the VAT.
   Whose method was cheaper? Explain and justify your answer.

25

Exercise commentary

The questions assess objectives on Framework Pages 45, 77 and 89.

Problem solving

Question 3 and 6 assess objectives on Framework Page 319. Questions 2, 4 and 5 assess Pages 3–9.

Group work

Question 6 is suitable for work in pairs.

Misconceptions

Some students will have difficulty calculating a percentage decrease in a single calculation. They may fail to subtract the reduction from the original amount:

15% reduction from £62 = 15% of £62 = £9.30.

Encourage students to represent all stages of the calculation on a number line (R6). Encourage them to build up percentages mentally by addition or subtraction:

85% = 50% + (3 × 10%) + 5%
85% = 100% − 10% − 5%

Links

Enlargement and scale: Framework Pages 213; Area and volume: Pages 229–231.

Homework

N1.4HW provides practice at calculating proportions of amounts in context, including multiple calculations and an extended question on interest on a bank account.

Answers

1 a £38   b 92 m   c 31.2 kg   d 78 DVDs   e 19.2 cm   f 91 glasses
   g 445.5 kg   h 4.75 km   2 a 128 g   b £1366.20
3 a 20.2 kg   b 43.1 km   c 2.9 cm   d 1.6 mm   e $230\frac{5}{7}$ litres
   f 3.0 mm   g £14.18   h $12\frac{6}{25}$ ha   i 12.8 m
4 a £5.44   b 54 g + 30% extra   c 30 pupils
5 a £52.70   b £405.38   c 2.33 kg   d £132.60   e 4.66 m
   f i 3.05 kg   ii 2.96 kg
6 Order does not matter, due to the commutative nature of multiplication.

Mental starter

Complete the loop

Use the loop cards on **R31**.

▶ Give each student one card with an answer and a question.

▶ Start with one student reading out their question. Then ask the student who has the answer on their card to read it out.

▶ Encourage them to continue by reading out the question on their own card. Continue until every card has been read.

▶ Time how long it takes to 'complete the loop'.

Useful resources

R31 – loop cards for the mental starter.
Food packaging showing nutritional information, for Further activities.

Introductory activity

Check by asking questions that students:

▶ **Know that fractions and decimals are used to compare proportions.**
Encourage students to give examples to illustrate the uses of fraction and percentages as proportions.

▶ **Know how to change between fractions, decimals and percentages:**
  ▶ $\frac{13}{7}$ as a percentage/decimal

Discuss methods used.

Ask students to compare these two statements:

▶ In Treehorserace, 33.3% of people voted Labour.

▶ 41 out of every 124 people voted Conservative.

Discuss responses. Emphasise:

▶ A greater proportion of people voted Labour.

▶ To compare two proportions they need to be in the same form.

▶ The interchangeability of the words fractions, percentage and proportion.

Discuss the second example in the Students' book.

Emphasise the phrases:
new price, original price, reduction in price and percentage reduction.

Challenge the students to solve this similar problem:

▶ A camera is reduced in price from £280 to £220. Calculate the percentage reduction in price.

Discuss strategies.

Generalise to finding a percentage increase or reduction.

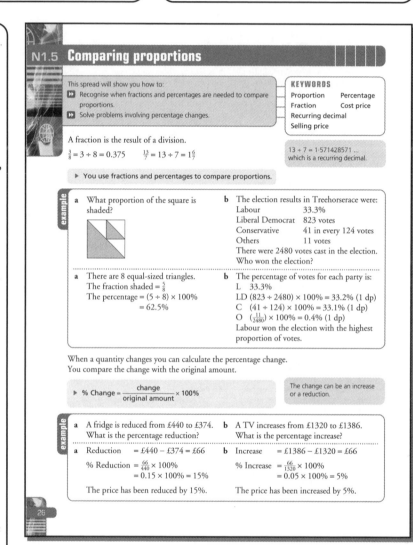

N1.5 Comparing proportions

This spread will show you how to:
▶ Recognise when fractions and percentages are needed to compare proportions.
▶ Solve problems involving percentage changes.

KEYWORDS
Proportion   Percentage
Fraction   Cost price
Recurring decimal
Selling price

A fraction is the result of a division.
$\frac{3}{8} = 3 \div 8 = 0.375$ $\frac{13}{7} = 13 \div 7 = 1\frac{6}{7}$

$13 \div 7 = 1.571428571 \ldots$ which is a recurring decimal.

▶ You use fractions and percentages to compare proportions.

example

a What proportion of the square is shaded?

b The election results in Treehorserace were:
Labour   33.3%
Liberal Democrat   823 votes
Conservative   41 in every 124 votes
Others   11 votes
There were 2480 votes cast in the election. Who won the election?

a There are 8 equal-sized triangles.
The fraction shaded = $\frac{5}{8}$
The percentage = $(5 \div 8) \times 100\%$
                       $= 62.5\%$

b The percentage of votes for each party is:
L   33.3%
LD $(823 \div 2480) \times 100\% = 33.2\%$ (1 dp)
C $(41 \div 124) \times 100\% = 33.1\%$ (1 dp)
O $(\frac{11}{2480}) \times 100\% = 0.4\%$ (1 dp)
Labour won the election with the highest proportion of votes.

When a quantity changes you can calculate the percentage change. You compare the change with the original amount.

▶ % Change = $\frac{\text{change}}{\text{original amount}} \times 100\%$

The change can be an increase or a reduction.

example

a A fridge is reduced from £440 to £374. What is the percentage reduction?

b A TV increases from £1320 to £1386. What is the percentage increase?

a Reduction   = £440 − £374 = £66
% Reduction = $\frac{66}{440} \times 100\%$
                    $= 0.15 \times 100\% = 15\%$
The price has been reduced by 15%.

b Increase   = £1386 − £1320 = £66
% Increase = $\frac{66}{1320} \times 100\%$
                  $= 0.05 \times 100\% = 5\%$
The price has been increased by 5%.

26

Plenary

Challenge students with this problem:
Johnny and Richard sell cars.
Johnny says, 'I'll knock £1000 off the price of any car!'
Richard says, 'I sometimes give a better deal than Johnny – I'll knock 10% off the price of any car!'

▶ When does each person give the better deal?

▶ How does Johnny's percentage reduction vary?

▶ What happens for cars that cost less than £1000?

Further activities

Students could repeat question 2 for the nutritional information from different food packets.

Differentiation

Core questions:

▶ Question 1 practises previous work on expressing quantities as fractions.
▶ Questions 2 and 3 focus on comparing proportions and calculating percentages.
▶ Question 4 extends to calculating percentage change.

Extension tier: focuses on using percentage to compare proportions.

Support tier: focuses on comparing simple proportions.

Exercise N1.5

1 What fraction of:
   a 120 is 35   b 4 days is 8 hours   c 5 kg is 2400 g   d £110 is £12
   e 240 paper clips is 7 paper clips?
     i Write your answers as fractions expressed in their simplest form.
     ii Write your answers as percentages (to 1 dp where appropriate).

2 This is the nutritional information for a 750 g packet of breakfast cereal.
   a Calculate the proportion of protein, carbohydrate, fat and fibre in the packet (give your answers to 1 dp where appropriate).
   b How much fibre would you expect to find in a 30 g serving?

Nutritional information	
Composition	750 g provides
Energy	2482 kcal
Protein	76.5g
Carbohydrate	503.3g
Fat	18g
Fibre	105.8g

3 Here are the heights of all the students in Year 9 from two schools:

South Park High School

Height (cm)	Less than 140	140 ≤ h < 150	150 ≤ h < 160	160 ≤ h < 170	170 ≤ h < 180	180 ≤ h < 190
Frequency	3	7	40	15	6	4

Greendale Sports College

Height (cm)	Less than 140	140 ≤ h < 150	150 ≤ h < 160	160 ≤ h < 170	170 ≤ h < 180	180 ≤ h < 190
Frequency	7	16	59	21	7	5

   a Which school has the highest proportion of students between 150 cm and 160 cm in height?
   b Work out the percentage of students in each height range for both schools.
   c Which school has the taller Year 9 students? Explain and justify your answer.

4 Calculate, giving your answers to 1 dp where appropriate:
   a The cost price of a car radio is £245. Its selling price is £196. What is the percentage reduction?
   b A piece of elastic is 64 cm long. It is stretched to a length of 73.6 cm. Find the percentage change in its length.
   c At Bigschool Technology College, the number of boys who obtained a level 5 or better in their KS3 tests increased from 124 (in 2002) to 146 (in 2003). By what percentage has the number of boys obtaining a level 5 or better increased?
   d DOTCOM2 shares cost 24p each in 2001. Three years later they rose in price to 32p. By what percentage has the cost of the shares risen?
   e A pair of RUNFAST trainers are reduced in price from £49 to £28. By what percentage has the price of the trainers been reduced?

27

Exercise commentary

The questions assess objectives on Framework Pages 61, 65, 75 and 77.

Problem solving
This exercise assesses objectives on Framework Pages 3–9.

Group work
Question 3 is suitable for work in pairs.

Misconceptions
Some students may express an increase/decrease as a fraction of the larger amount. For example,
▶ Change in length = 73.6 − 64 = 9.6 cm
▶ Percentage change = $\frac{9.6}{73.6}$ = 13.04%.
Encourage students to highlight the original amount. Emphasise that the change is compared with what you start with, not where you end up – you always use the original amount for a percentage change.
Encourage students to check their answers by working backwards

Links
Data interpretation: Framework Page 273; Enlargement and scale: Page 213.

Homework

N1.5HW provides practice at finding fractions and percentages of amounts in context, including comparing percentage increases.

Answers

1 a i $\frac{7}{24}$ ii 29.2% b i $\frac{1}{12}$ ii 8.3% c i $\frac{12}{25}$ ii 48%
  d i $\frac{6}{55}$ ii 10.9% e i $\frac{7}{240}$ ii 2.9%
2 a 10.2%, 67.1%, 2.4%, 14.1% b 4.2 g
3 a South Park
  b 4%, 9.3%, 53.3%, 20%, 8%, 5.3%; 6.1%, 13.9%, 51.3%, 18.3%, 6.1%, 4.3% c South Park
4 a 20% b 15% c 17.7% d 33.3% e 42.9%

Mental starter

Percentage cricket

▸ Divide students into two teams. Roll two dice. Multiply the first dice by 15 to give a percentage and the second dice by 20 to give an amount.

▸ A player from Team 1 finds the percentage. If correct, they may have another turn. A player may decide at any time to 'stick', end their turn and save their score.

▸ If a six is rolled, or if a player miscalculates, they lose their points and play moves on to the next team.

▸ Each team has five turns. The team with the highest total wins.

Useful resources

Two ordinary dice for the mental starter

N1.6OHP – reduced prices of items

R6 – number lines

Introductory activity

Refer to the mental starter.

Check by asking questions that students:

▸ **Can find simple percentages of amounts:**
  ▸ 75% of £240; 17% of £240

▸ **Can multiply simple fractions by integers:**
  ▸ $\frac{3}{4}$ of 60; $\frac{17}{100} \times 240$

▸ **Can find a percentage increase/decrease:**
  ▸ Increase £240 by 17%

Discuss methods used.

Challenge students to work out the original prices of these items (shown on N1.6OHP):

A shopkeeper reduces his prices by 35%. These are the new prices:

Coat – £45.50; TV – £325; DVD player – £162.50.

Discuss methods used, and encourage students to demonstrate their strategies. Use a number line (**R6**) to emphasise that reducing a quantity by 35% gives you 65% of the original amount.

Recap the unitary method for calculating the original percentage:

65% of original price = £45.50

1% of original price = £0.70

100% of original price = £70.00

Challenge students to solve the problem in one step as a single operation.

Emphasise:

▸ Multiplication and division as inverse operations.

▸ Multiplicative inverse.

▸ The connection between unitary method and use of the multiplicative inverse (same operations).

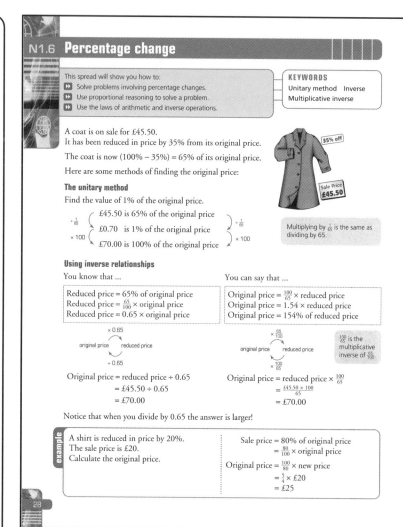

Plenary

Challenge students to decide if these statements are true:

▸ To find 20% of something you find 10% and double it.

▸ If something has been increased in price by 20%, you take off 20% to find the original price.

▸ Finding a percentage (such as 2%) of something is like multiplying by a decimal (0.2).

▸ An increase of 10% each year for two years is the same as a 20% increase.

Further activities

Students can work in pairs to investigate interest rates.

For different interest rates (4%, 6%, 8%, 10%) calculate how long it will take for an initial amount (£50, £100, £1000) to double.

Differentiation

Core questions:

▶ Question 1 practises calculating fractions and percentages of amounts.

▶ Questions 2–4 focus on calculating reverse percentages.

▶ Questions 5 and 6 extend into a problem-solving context.

Extension tier: focuses on calculating original amounts for a given increase/decrease.

Support tier: focuses on percentage increase and decrease.

Exercise N1.6

1 Calculate:
   a 15% of 64 kg
   b 8% of £1750
   c 5% of 27 m
   d 41% of 23.5 litres
   e $\frac{4}{7}$ of 336 gallons
   f 1% of 12.6 hectares.

2 **Investigation**
   a Mr Brown increases all the prices in his shop by 10%.
      Copy and complete this price list

Item	Original price	New price
Bread	80p	88p
Milk (1 litre)	60p	
Bran Flakes	£1.80	
Eggs (doz)	£1.30	

   b The new price of a 2 kg packet of frozen peas is £2.75.
      What was the original price?
   c Investigate how to find the original price of different items after a 10% increase.

3 In a sale, all prices are reduced by 20%. The sale price is 80% of the original price.

   a Use this information to copy and complete this conversion table:

Original price	Sale price
£10.00	
£16.99	
	£20.00
	£6.00

   b Explain your method for changing the sale price into the original price.

4 a A pair of trainers are on sale for £45 which is 75% of the original price. What was the original price of the trainers?
   b About 41 600 people visited the mini-golf course in 2003. This was an increase of 30% on 1998. How many visitors to the mini-golf course were there in 1998?
   c Emma sells her house for £92 400, making a profit of 65% on the amount she paid for it. What was the price she paid for the house?
   d A banner on a packet of biscuits says that it is 43% bigger. It contains 40 biscuits. How many biscuits are there in the normal packet?
   e Gareth follows a diet for 3 months. At the end of the 3 months he weighs 88 kg, which is 8% less than his weight before the diet. What did Gareth weigh before his diet?

5 **Puzzle**
   a Ivor bought a game-box video game console and 4 games in a sale and saved £48. The label said that it was a 15% reduction. What was the original price of the game-box and 4 games?
   b Karen's salary rises by 2.5%. This means that she earns an extra £450 each year. What is Karen's new annual salary after the pay rise?

6 **Puzzle**
   After a TV advertising campaign costing £50 000, Cars-R-Us car dealers found that their profits had risen by 12% to £488 000. From a financial point of view, was the advertising worthwhile? Justify your answer.

29

Exercise commentary

The questions assess objectives on Framework Pages 75, 77 and 85.

Problem solving

Questions 2–5 assess Framework Page 3 and Question 6 assesses Page 31.

Group work

Questions 2 and 3 are suitable for work in pairs.

Misconceptions

Some students may not understand a reverse percentage and find the standard percentage instead:

75% of £45 = £33.75 instead of $\frac{£45}{0.75}$ = £60.

Encourage students to read the questions carefully. Ask: What are you trying to find out? Will the answer be bigger or smaller than the amount given?

Encourage students to:

▶ Highlight the key words.

▶ Draw an arrow diagram.

▶ Check answers by working the problem backwards.

Links

Enlargement and scale: Framework Page 213.

Homework

N1.6HW provides further examples of percentage change in context, extending to an investigation involving percentage change and 'value for money'.

Answers

1 a 9.6 kg   b £140   c 1.35 m   d 9.64 litres   e 192 gallons
   f 0.126 hectares

2 a 66p, £1.98, £1.43   b £2.50   c ÷ 1.1, × $\frac{10}{11}$

3 a £8, £13.59, £25, £7.50   b ÷ 0.8, × $\frac{10}{8}$

4 a £60   b 32 000   c £56 000   d 28   e 95.7 kg

5 a £320   b £18 000

6 Yes, the increase in profit was £2286 more than the advertising cost.

Mental starter

Ask students to count off in twelves along the top of a counting stick, and in eights along the bottom.

Extend beyond the stick, asking for multiples of twelve and eight. Challenge students:

▶ What number is on the bottom if 144 is on the top?
▶ What number is on the top if 136 is on the bottom?

Encourage students to comment on the relationship between the top and bottom number. Repeat for different pairs of multiples.

Useful resources

Counting stick for the mental starter
N1.7OHP – weights of fish
N1.7F – comparing squares

Introductory activity

Refer to the mental starter, and link to previous work on ratios in Year 8.

Check by asking questions students understand that:

▶ **Ratios can be simplified:**
  ▶ Simplify 150 : 200.
▶ **A ratio is a way of comparing the sizes of two numbers:**
  ▶ Jeff is 150 cm tall, Jack is 200 cm tall. What is the ratio of their heights?

Discuss what a ratio tells you about the numbers you are comparing.

Ask students to work out the ratio of Bob's weight (1.5 kg) to Flipper's weight (4 kg) in its simplest form. (Use N1.7OHP.)

Discuss strategies, including how to change the ratio to whole numbers.

Emphasise that the ratio simplifies to 3 : 8.

Ask students to devise statements about the ratio or proportion of the weights of the fish, as in the Students' book example, e.g. Flipper's weight is $\frac{8}{3}$ times Bob's weight.

Discuss the statements. **Emphasise the connections between ratios, fractions, decimals and percentages.**

Collect the statements in a diagram as multipliers between the different fish. There is an example on **N1.7OHP.**

Challenge the students to solve:

▶ Compost is made in the ratio $3\frac{1}{4}$ parts peat to 2 parts sand. How much peat needs to be mixed with 16 kg of sand?

Encourage students to demonstrate their answers. **Emphasise the range of methods and link to calculating fractions and percentages of amounts.**

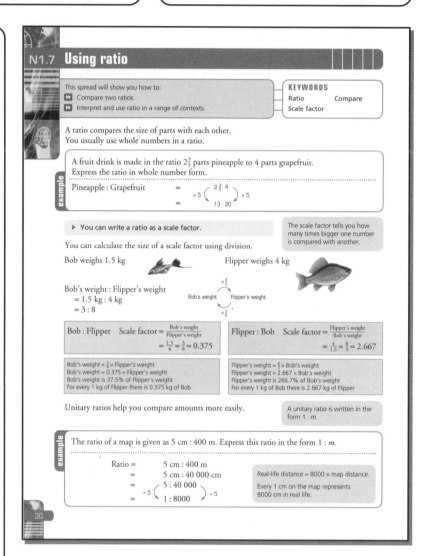

Plenary

Challenge students to solve this problem:

▶ The ratio of Sammy Shark's to Billy Whale's weight is 2 : 3.
  Billy Whale is 120% of Albert Seal's weight.
  Albert Seal is 120 kg heavier than Sammy Shark.
  What is the weight of each animal?

Ask students to work in pairs to explain and justify their answers.

Discuss answers, emphasising different ways of using ratio.

Differentiation

Core questions:

▶ Questions 1 and 2 practise simplifying ratios and ratios in context.
▶ Questions 3–6 focus on simplifying ratios in decimal form, unitary ratios and ratios as a scale factor.
▶ Questions 7 and 8 extend into a problem-solving context.

Extension tier: focuses on using ratio to solve problems, including scales.

Support tier: focuses on simplifying ratios and simple problems.

Exercise N1.7

1 Simplify these ratios.
   a 12 : 50   b 15 : 18 : 24
   c 3 m : 50 cm   d 800 g : 3 kg
   e 150 cm : 500 mm

2 a In a triangle, the ratio of the angles is 2 : 5 : 11. Calculate the angles.
   b Axel and Morrissey shared some milk in the ratio 2 : 5. Axel received 300 ml of milk.
   How much milk was there altogether?
   c To make orange paint, you mix 7 litres of yellow with 3 litres of red paint. How many litres of each colour do you need to make 120 litres of orange paint?

3 Express these as ratios in their simplest form.
   a 0.5 : 3   b $2\frac{1}{2}$: 4
   c 5.2 kg : 6.5 kg   d $3\frac{1}{4}$ m : 2 m
   e $4\frac{2}{5}$ kg : 3 kg

4 Express these ratios in the form 1 : m or m : 1.
   a 7 : 56   b 15 : 3
   c 25 cm : 12 cm   d 4 cm : 50 m
   e 3.5 cm : 84 cm

5 a Granny's biscuits are made from flour and butter in the ratio 7 : 4. How much butter will be needed to make 495 g of biscuits?
   b A type of plaster is made in the ratio $1\frac{3}{4}$ parts cement to 3 parts sand. How much cement needs to be mixed with 24 kg of sand to make the plaster?
   c An alloy is made from iron, copper and aluminium in the ratio 5 : 3 : 4. How much iron is needed to mix with 108 kg of aluminium?

6 One day, Mike did a survey of the birds on his walk round Shibden Hall. He saw 6 finches, 12 sparrows, 15 crows and 27 pigeons.
   a Write the ratio of finches : sparrows : crows : pigeons in its simplest form.
   b What percentage of the birds seen by Mike were pigeons?
   c A week later, Mike did the same survey. This time the number of finches had decreased by a $\frac{1}{3}$, the number of sparrows had increased by $\frac{5}{6}$, the number of crows had increased by 20% and the number of pigeons had decreased by $\frac{2}{9}$. Write the new ratio of finches : sparrows : crows : pigeons in its simplest form.

7 **Puzzle**
   On 24th October 1970 Peter is 120 cm tall. Ten years later his height has increased by 45%.
   What is the ratio of Peter's height in 1970 compared with his height in 1980?

8 a 3 parts of blue paint are mixed with 4 parts of yellow paint to make green paint.
   What is the maximum amount of green paint that can be made from 60 ml of blue and 72 ml of yellow paint?
   b At a circus, the cost of an adult ticket is $1\frac{3}{5}$ the cost of a child's ticket. If the total cost of one adult and one child ticket is £6.40, how much does an adult ticket cost?

Exercise commentary

The questions assess objectives on Framework Page 81.

Problem solving
Questions 2, 5, 6, 7 and 8 assess objectives on Framework Pages 3–5.

Group work
Question 7 is suitable for work in pairs, if students are asked to create similar problems of their own.

Misconceptions
Students may confuse ratio (comparing two quantities with each other) and proportion (comparing a quantity with the whole).
Encourage students to read the questions carefully and distinguish between ratio and proportion.
Encourage students to check answers by working the problem backwards.

Links
Enlargement and scale: Framework Page 213.

Homework

N1.7HW gives practice at using ratios in practical contexts, extending to a simple investigation into the ratios of the sides of right-angled triangles.

Answers

1 a 6 : 25   b 5 : 6 : 8   c 6 : 1   d 4 : 15   e 3 : 1
2 a 20°, 50°, 110°   b 1050 ml   c 84 litres of yellow and 36 litres of red
3 a 1 : 6   b 5 : 8   c 4 : 5   d 13 : 8   e 22 : 15
4 a 1 : 8   b 5 : 1   c $2\frac{1}{12}$: 1   d 1 : 1250   e 1 : 24
5 a 180 g   b 14 kg   c 135 kg
6 a 2 : 4 : 5 : 9   b 45%   c 4 : 22 : 18 : 21
7 20 : 29   8 a 126 ml   b £4

Matching pairs

Split students into two teams.

Place 14 cards (from **R32**) face down.

A player from Team 1 picks two cards.

If the ratios or fractions match, then they score a point and remove the cards. If they don't match, then turn them over and Team 2 has a turn.

Useful resources

R32 – algebraic pairs cards for the mental starter

N1.8F – graph investigation

Introductory activity

Check by asking questions that students:

▸ **Can compare two quantities using a ratio expressed in its simplest form:**
  ▸ 40 pounds : 70 euros
▸ **Can calculate a scale factor from a ratio:**
  ▸ $7 : 4 \rightarrow 1.75$
▸ **Understand when two sets of numbers are proportional.**
  ▸ Give two sets of numbers that are proportional.

Discuss what the word 'proportional' means.

Challenge students to work in pairs to solve the problem given in the second example in the Students' Book. Aim to make: 200 g; 350 g; 454 g of jam.

Discuss strategies.

Emphasise:

▸ The amount of sugar is proportional to the amount of jam made.
▸ The way different methods work:
  ▸ Unitary
  ▸ Scaling
  ▸ Use of ratio as a scale factor.

Extend to discussing what amount of jam can be made with:

70 g; 200 g; 454 g of sugar.

Ask students to decide which methods are best for solving each of the problems.

Discuss:

▸ Does each method work for all the problems?
▸ What operations do you use for each method?
▸ Are the methods the same?

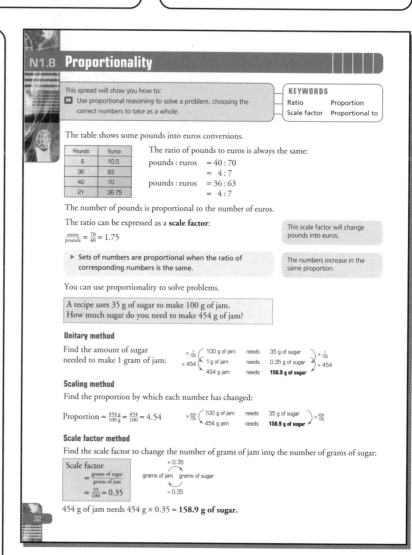

N1.8 Proportionality

This spread will show you how to:

▸▸ Use proportional reasoning to solve a problem, choosing the correct numbers to take as a whole.

KEYWORDS
Ratio   Proportion
Scale factor   Proportional to

The table shows some pounds into euros conversions.

Pounds	Euros
6	10.5
36	63
40	70
21	36.75

The ratio of pounds to euros is always the same:

pounds : euros $= 40 : 70$
                 $= 4 : 7$
pounds : euros $= 36 : 63$
                 $= 4 : 7$

The number of pounds is proportional to the number of euros.

The ratio can be expressed as a **scale factor**:

$\frac{euros}{pounds} = \frac{70}{40} = 1.75$

This scale factor will change pounds into euros.

▸ Sets of numbers are proportional when the ratio of corresponding numbers is the same.

The numbers increase in the same proportion.

You can use proportionality to solve problems.

A recipe uses 35 g of sugar to make 100 g of jam.
How much sugar do you need to make 454 g of jam?

Unitary method

Find the amount of sugar needed to make 1 gram of jam:

$\times \frac{1}{100}$ (100 g of jam needs 35 g of sugar) $\times \frac{1}{100}$
$\times 454$ (1 g of jam needs 0.35 g of sugar) $\times 454$
454 g jam needs **158.9 g of sugar**

Scaling method

Find the proportion by which each number has changed:

Proportion $= \frac{454 \text{ g}}{100 \text{ g}} = \frac{454}{100} = 4.54$

$\times \frac{454}{100}$ (100 g of jam needs 35 g of sugar) $\times \frac{454}{100}$
454 g jam needs **158.9 g of sugar**

Scale factor method

Find the scale factor to change the number of grams of jam into the number of grams of sugar:

Scale factor $= \frac{\text{grams of sugar}}{\text{grams of jam}}$
$= \frac{35}{100} = 0.35$

$\times 0.35$
grams of jam   grams of sugar
$\div 0.35$

454 g of jam needs 454 g $\times 0.35 = $ **158.9 g of sugar.**

32

Plenary

Review the main points:

▸ Proportional sets have a constant ratio.
▸ Use proportional reasoning to solve a problem.

Challenge students to write down a statement about proportionality. They must include a definition and an example problem and solution.

Encourage students to explain their problems on the board.

Further activities

In **N1.8ICT** students investigate proportional reasoning using a constant multiplier in a spreadsheet.
Alternatively
N1.8F is an investigation of a straight-line graph.

Differentiation

Core questions:
▸ Question 1 practises previous work on direct proportion.
▸ Questions 2–5 focus on problems involving proportionality in context.
▸ Questions 6 and 7 extend into intuitive problem-solving contexts: currency and speed.

Extension tier: focuses on using proportion to solve problems.

Support tier: focuses on using the unitary method to solve direct proportion problems.

Exercise N1.8

1 Work out each of these using a mental or written method:
 a 4 bars of chocolate cost 80p. How much would 3 bars of chocolate cost?
 b 5 miles is approximately equal to 8 kilometres. Roughly how many kilometres are equal to 35 miles? How many miles are equal to 112 km?
 c 7 pizzas cost £20.65. What is the cost of 14 pizzas? What is the cost of 5 pizzas?

2 A 5 kg bag of apples is about the same as an 11 pound bag of apples.

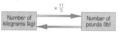

 a Use this information to copy and complete this conversion table:

Kilograms	Pounds
30	
1	
	187
	14

 b What is the scale factor for changing pounds into kilograms?

3 Solve these, clearly showing your method.
 a A recipe for jam uses 45 g of fruit for every 100 g of jam. Jack wants to make five 454 g jars of jam. How much fruit does he need?
 b A recipe for fruit squash requires 840 ml of water for 7 people. How much water would you need to make fruit squash for 11 people?
 c A pair of trainers are on sale for £33.60 which is 80% of the original price. What was the original price of the trainers?

4 The cost of a take-away meal for two is £7.60. The pie chart shows how the total cost of the meal is made up.

The cost of a fish is represented by a sector angle of 99° on the pie chart. What is the cost of a fish?

5 **Puzzle**
 a If £1 = 1.64 euros, how many euros would you get for £3.50? How many euros would you get for 85p?
 b If £1 = 10.4 rand, how many pounds would you get for 52 rand? How many pounds would you get for 4 rand?

6 a A train is travelling at a constant speed. After 3 hours it has travelled 255 km. How far had it travelled after 2 hours? How far had it travelled after 48 minutes?
 b A car is travelling at an average speed of 45 mph. How far does it travel in 4 hours? How far does it travel in $2\frac{1}{3}$ hours? How long will it take the car to travel 144 miles?

7 **Puzzle**
Here are some currency rates for different countries:

.	UK	France	India
UK		£1 = 1.64 euros	£1 = 71.2 rupees
France	1 euro =		1 euro =
India	1 rupee =	1 rupee =	

Work out the missing entries.

Exercise commentary

The questions assess objectives on Framework Pages 79 and 83.
Problem solving
This exercise assesses objectives on Framework Page 3–5.
Group work
Questions 2, 5 and 7 are suitable for work in pairs or groups.
Misconceptions
Students may use the unitary method to solve all proportionality problems.
840 ÷ 7 = 120 ml so 120 × 11 = 1320 ml
In some problems, not all the information needed is clearly stated, for example, the need to use 100% in percentage problems or 360° in pie charts. Encourage students to write down all the information in the problem and work out what they need. Encourage students to set out proportional problems as four piece of information, to prepare for future use in algebraic methods.
Links
Algebraic method for direct proportion (A3.4): Framework Page 137; Enlargement and scale: Page 213.

Homework

N1.8HW gives practice at using proportional reasoning in practical contexts.

Answers

1 a 60p b 56 km c £41.30, £14.75
2 a 66 lb, 2.2 lb, 85 kg, 6.4 kg b $\frac{5}{11}$
3 a 1021.5 g b 1320 ml c £42
4 £2.09
5 a 5.74 euros, 1.39 euros b £5, £0.38
6 a 170 km, 68 km b 180 miles, 105 miles, 3 h 12 min
7 1 euro = £0.61 = 43.4 rupees, 1 rupee = £0.014 = 0.023 euro

Mental starter

Use the loop cards on **R33**.

▸ Give each student one card with an answer and a question. They are all calculations with more than one operation.

▸ Start with one student reading out their question. Then ask the student who has the answer on their card to read it out.

▸ Encourage them to continue by reading out the question on their own card. Continue until every card has been read.

▸ Time how long it takes to 'complete the loop'.

Useful resources

R33 – two-operation loop cards for the mental starter

R18 – operation cards

Introductory activity

Check by asking questions that students:

▸ **Know the order of operations:**
  ▸ $12 + 3 \times 5 - (14 - 9)$ [22]

▸ **Know the square and cube of simple whole numbers:**
  ▸ 3^3 [27]

Write up six numbers on the board:
4, 5, 8, 15, 20, 40

and a three-digit target number. Challenge students to use the numbers on the board once only, with operations, to get as close as possible to the target number. They can use more than one expression.

R18 (operation cards) may be useful.

For example, target number = 632
$15 \times 40 = 600 \quad 4 \times (8 - 5) = 12$
$600 + 12 + 20 = 632$

Discuss strategies. Encourage students to write their answers using the correct order of operations.

Emphasise the order of operations: BIDMAS.

Challenge students to work through the expression in the Students' Book example, making sure they use the correct order of operations.

Discuss methods used.

Emphasise the order of operations, using a calculator where appropriate.

Challenge students in pairs to invent five operations of their own to give an answer of 20. Discuss strategies.

Emphasise the role of negatives and fractions in the calculations, especially the difference between:

▸ $^-7^2$ and $(^-7)^2$ ▸ $\frac{3^3}{4}$ and $\left(\frac{3}{4}\right)^3$.

Emphasise that adjacent brackets should be multiplied.

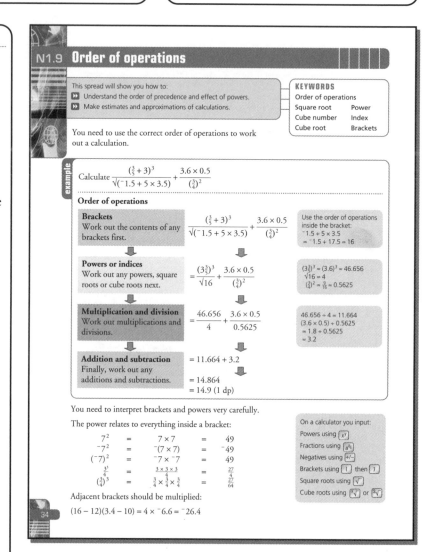

Plenary

Discuss question 4d.

Discuss strategies for evaluating each part of the calculation.

Ask questions to emphasise the order of operations:

▸ Which part of the calculation should you do first?

▸ What happens when there are brackets next to each other?

Extend the idea of the order of operations into substituting into complex formulae.

Differentiation

Core questions:
▸ Question 1 practises previous work on order of operations.
▸ Questions 2–5 provide more practice at problems involving order of operations, focusing on brackets.
▸ Question 6 extends into an algebraic context.

Extension tier: focuses on significant figures.

Support tier: focuses on the order of operations.

Exercise N1.9

1. Calculate these, using a mental, written or calculator method, giving your answer to 2 dp where appropriate:
   a $15 + 8 \times 19$ b $(3^2 + 5^2)^2$
   c $80 \div 10 \div 2$
   d $4.2 - (2.6 + 4.2) + (7 + 2.6)$
   e $\frac{17 - 3}{15 - 4}$ f $\frac{3.7 + 2.8}{2.6}$
   g $\frac{35}{8 \times 19}$ h $160 \div \{24 - (5^2 - 9)\}$

2. **Investigation**
   Peter says that 'Adding two numbers and then squaring them is always the same as squaring each number and then adding'. Kyle says that 'Adding two numbers and then squaring them is never the same as squaring each number and then adding'. Who do you think is correct? Explain and justify your answer.

3. Solve each of these calculations. You will need to decide whether to use a mental, written or calculator method. Where appropriate, give your answer to 2 dp.
   a $^-6^2 + 11$
   b $(11 - 17)(13 + 4)$
   c $(\frac{4}{3})^2$
   d $\frac{(16 - 12)^2(^-6 + ^-3)^2}{72}$
   e $\frac{(8 \times 5)^2}{\sqrt{(2 \times 8)}} + 14$
   f $\frac{(^-7)^2 - 31}{(3 \times 3)^2}$
   g $\frac{(17 - 6)^2(17 - 2)}{(3^2 - 4)}$
   h $^-(302 \times 4 + 256) + 4 \times 299 - (5 - 304)$
   i $15 \div [3 - 4(1 - 4)]$
   j $\sqrt{(21^2 - 14^2)}$
   k $\frac{(17 - 8)^2(18 - 15)^2}{3(14 - 8)^3}$

4. a Write down an approximate answer for each of these questions, clearly showing your method of approximation.
   i $\frac{44.63 \times 72.8}{2.1 \times (5.4 - 2.9)}$
   ii $3.7 + (5.5 - (12.3 \times 6.4))$
   iii $\{(2.3)^2 + (6.2 - 1.38)\}^2$
   iv $\frac{4 \times \sqrt{(3.7^2 + 3^2)}}{1.7}$
   b Use your calculator to work out the exact answer, where appropriate giving your answer to 2 dp.

5. **Puzzle**
   Copy these calculations, inserting the correct operations and brackets to make them correct.
   a $\frac{1}{2} \_\_ 4 \_\_ 3 \_\_ 8 = 28$
   b $20 \_\_ 4^2 \_\_ 6 \_\_ = 2$
   c $\sqrt{[2^2 \_\_ 3 \_\_ 11 \_\_ 5 \_\_ 8]} = 8$

6. Kyle uses this formula to work out the area of a special shape:

   $$\text{Area} = \tfrac{1}{2}ab + \frac{(a^2 + b^2)}{4}$$

   a For his first shape, Kyle uses $a = 3.5$ and $b = 5$ and substitutes them into his formula. Work out the value of:
   $$\tfrac{1}{2} \times 3.5 \times 5 + \frac{(3.5^2 + 5^2)}{4}$$
   b Work out the area of a shape when $a = 2.4$ and $b = 1.3$.

Exercise commentary

The questions assess objectives on Framework Pages 87 and 103.

Problem solving

Questions 1 and 3 assess objectives on Framework Page 29.
Question 2 assesses Page 31. Question 5 assesses Page 7.

Group work

Questions 2 and 5 are suitable for work in pairs or groups.

Misconceptions

Students may have difficulty with a negative number outside a bracket:
$^-(302 \times 4) = ^-302 \times ^-4$
Encourage students to work out the contents of a bracket first:
$^-(30 \times 4) = ^-(1208)$
Encourage students to see the negative sign as multiplication by $^-1$:
$^-(1208) = ^-1 \times 1208 = ^-1208$

Links

Substituting numbers into algebraic expressions: Framework Page 139;
Algebraic formulae: Pages 141–143.

Homework

N1.9HW provides a 'Countdown' style puzzle, using given numbers and different operations to make a target number.

Answers

1 a 167   b 1156   c 4   d 7   e 1.27   f 2.5   g 0.23   h 20
2 Kyle is correct (for non-zero numbers): $(x + y)^2 = x^2 + 2xy + y^2$
3 a $^-25$ b $^-102$ c $1\frac{7}{9}$ d 18   e 414   f 0.22   g 363
   h 31   i 1   j 15.65   k 1.13
4 a i $(40 \times 70) \div 5 = 560$ ii $4 + (6 - 12 \times 6) = ^-62$ iii $(5 + 5)^2 = 100$
   iv $4 \times \sqrt{(16 + 9)} \div 2 = 10$ b i 618.87   ii $^-69.52$ iii 102.21   iv 11.21
5 a $\frac{1}{2} \times (4 + 3) \times 8$ b $20 \div (4^2 - 6)$ c $\sqrt{(2^2 - 3 + 11 \times 5 + 8)}$
6 a 18.1   b 3.4

Summary

The key objectives for this unit are:

▸ Add, subtract, multiply and divide fractions. (65–69)
▸ Use proportional reasoning to solve a problem, choosing the correct numbers to take as a whole. (79)
▸ Make and justify estimates and approximations. (103)
▸ Solve problems using a range of efficient methods. (29)
▸ Present a concise, reasoned argument. (31)

Check out commentary

1 In part **a** students should find the LCM of 8 and 12, and write their answers in their simplest form. For part **d**, they should use their answer to part **c**. Emphasise the link between this more intuitive method and the formal multiplicative method.

2 Students may find the numbers difficult if using the unitary method.
They should consider alternative strategies, such as finding the grams of mushrooms in 25g of pie, or using the scale factor (new pie is $\frac{350}{225} = \frac{14}{9}$ times bigger than the recipe).

3 Students commonly think of multiplication as increasing size and division as decreasing size.
Emphasise the effect of $\div 0.1 = \times \frac{1}{10}$ etc.

4 Students should estimate solutions by rounding quantities to 1sf. Encourage them to use a different method to solve the problem, as outlined for question 3 above.

5 Students should realise that 85% of an amount is less than the original amount, so John's answer cannot be correct.

Plenary activity

Encourage students, working in pairs, to write one question for each of these five types of calculation: fractions, decimals, percentages, ratio and proportionality.
Share the questions with the class.
Emphasise the use of multiplicative methods and the relationship between multiplication and division.

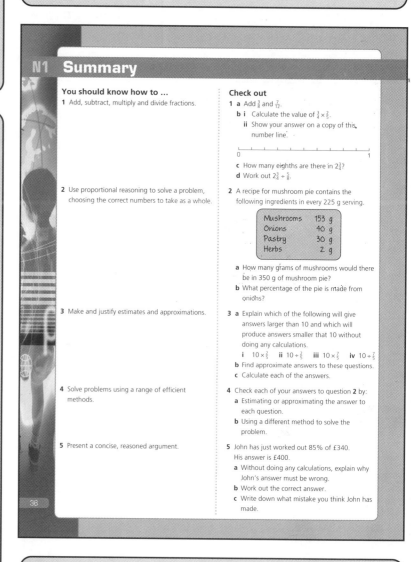

Development

Proportional problems are developed further in **A3**. The order of operations is revised and extended in **N2**.
Proportional reasoning in Shape (scale, ratio, enlargement) is developed in **S3** and **S4**.

Links

Proportional reasoning is a technique that can be developed across many topic areas. It can be used to emphasise that the techniques developed are transferable and that students will have many opportunities for using proportional reasoning in real situations.

Mental starters

Objectives covered in this unit:

▸ Order, add, subtract, multiply and divide integers.
▸ Know and use squares, cubes, roots and index notation.
▸ Recall multiplication and division facts to 10×10.
▸ Solve equations.
▸ Use formulae.
▸ Use metric units for calculations.
▸ Use metric units for estimation.
▸ Find highest common factors (HCF).
▸ Simplify fractions by cancelling.

Resources needed

* means class set needed
Essential:
A3.4OHP – similar rectangles
Calculators*

Useful:
A3.1OHP – expanding brackets
A3.2OHP – flow diagrams for equations
R27 – expression cards
A3.5ICT* – trial and improvement

A3   Solving equations

This unit will show you how to:

▸▸ Use rounding to make estimates.
▸▸ Distinguish between the different roles played by letter symbols in equations, identities, formulae and functions.
▸▸ Use index notation for integer powers and simple instances of the index laws.
▸▸ Construct and solve linear equations with integer coefficients.
▸▸ Use systematic trial and improvement methods to find approximate solutions.

▸▸ Solve problems involving direct proportion using algebraic methods, relating algebraic solutions to graphical representations.
▸▸ Solve increasingly demanding problems and evaluate solutions.
▸▸ Represent problems and interpret solutions in algebraic and graphical forms.
▸▸ Move from one form to another to gain a better perspective on the problem.
▸▸ Use trial and improvement where a more efficient method is not obvious.

500 kilos to port, NOW!

You also have to keep an equation in balance – the expressions on each side must be equal.

Before you start

You should know how to ...

1 Simplify algebraic expressions.

2 Solve simple equations.

3 Substitute values into formulae.

4 Expand brackets.
$3(x - 2) = 3 \times x - 3 \times 2 = 3x - 6$

Check in

1 Simplify:
  a $3x + 2y - 5x + 2x - 3y$
  b $3p - 2r + 7 - 2p + r$

2 Solve:
  a $3p + 4 = 19$ b $7n - 12 = 2$

3 Copy and complete the table for given values of x when $y = 2x - 1$.

x	-2	-1	0	1	2
y					

4 Expand and simplify:
  a $2(t - 3y)$ b $12 - 3(x - 4)$

37

Unit commentary

Aim of the unit

This unit revisits and extends algebraic skills, starting with expanding brackets and solving linear equations. Non-linear equations involving squares and square roots are introduced and students find estimates of solutions using systematic trial and improvement methods. They use algebra to solve direct proportion problems.

Introduction

Discuss these key words in the context of algebra:
solve, expand, substitute, simplify, evaluate.
Encourage students to represent situations algebraically. For example, write an expression for the amount each person pays when four people share this café bill equally: 4 coffees, 2 buns, 2 scones.

Framework references

This unit focuses on:
Teaching objectives pages:
57, 79, 113, 115, 123, 125, 133–137.
Problem solving pages:
7–9, 27, 29.

Differentiation

Support tier

Focuses on solving linear equations with variables on one or both sides

Extension tier

Focuses on solving equations and finding algebraic and graphical solutions to simultaneous equations.

Check in activity

Give students a variable and a value, for example $x = 2$.
Challenge them to write as many equations in x as possible that solve to give $x = 2$, in five minutes.
Compare and check the results.

Mental starter

Indices

Ask students to work out the value of:

3^2 5^3 10^5 4^3 9^2 etc.

Use flashcards or write the numbers on the board.

Develop to challenge students to find the value of:

$3^4 \times 3^2$ $5^4 \div 5^2$ etc.

Discuss strategies.

Useful resources

A3.1OHP – expanding brackets

R27 – expression cards

Introductory activity

Write these four expressions on cards or on the board. **R27** (expression cards) may be useful.

▶ $3(2n - 1)$

▶ $n + n + n + n$

▶ $8n + 7$

▶ $2(3 - 4n)$

Discuss how to multiply out the brackets.

Emphasise the use of a multiplication grid. **A3.1OHP** shows how to multiply out the brackets using a grid.

Ask students to work out the value of each card when $n = 2$.

Discuss which expressions will always have the same value.

Discuss how to write this.

Emphasise that the symbol ≡ shows when two expressions are equivalent and means the expressions will always take the same value.

Discuss how to add or subtract two of the expressions.

Emphasise that when you subtract an expression, you subtract each term.

Discuss the similar example in the Students' Book if more practice is needed.

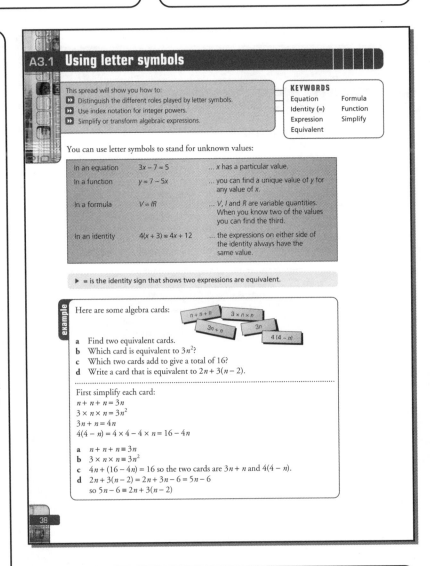

Plenary

Discuss question 5.

Encourage students to explain how they found the missing sides.

Discuss the difficulty in using the negative numbers.

Discuss how they found the perimeter: did they add the sides together?

Emphasise the strategy of working out:

$2 \times$ (length + width).

Challenge able students to draw an isosceles triangle with one side $3x + 2$ and perimeter $7x + 14$.
How many different triangles can they draw?

Differentiation

Core questions:
▶ Question 1 focuses on substituting to find equivalent expressions.
▶ Questions 2–5 focus on simplifying expressions.
▶ Questions 6 and 7 focus on laws of indices.

Extension tier: focuses on forming and solving equations.

Support tier: focuses on simplifying algebraic expressions.

Exercise A3.1

1 Here are some expression cards.

a Work out the value of each card when $a = 5$, $b = 6$ and $c = 2$.
b Copy the diagram and join pairs of expressions that have the same value when $a = 5$, $b = 6$ and $c = 2$.

2 Copy this diagram.
Join pairs of expressions that will always have the same value when $x = y = z$.

3 Simplify each of these expressions. The first is done for you.

a $3(n + 4) - 2(1 + 2n)$
  $= 3n + 12 - 2 - 4n$
  $= {}^-n + 10$
b $2n + 5 + 7n$
c $3n - 6 + 5 - n$
d $5(2n - 3) + 8n + 1$
e $n(n + 2) - 3n$
f $5n - 2(2n + 1)$
g $\frac{6n^2}{2}$
h $8n + \frac{1}{2}(12 - 10n)$
i $2(3n + 1) + 3(4n - 1)$
j $5(2n - 7) - 4(n - 3)$

4 Write an expression for the perimeter of each of these shapes. Find a value for x.

a
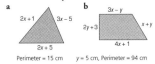
Perimeter = 15 cm

b
$y = 5$ cm, Perimeter = 94 cm

c

Perimeter = 17 cm

5 a Find the length of each missing side.

b What is the perimeter of the shape?

6 Simplify each of these expressions.

a $a^3 \times a^2$
b $a^7 \div a^3$
c $3a \times 2a^2$
d $\frac{6a^3}{2}$
e $a^2 \times 3a^2 \times 2a$
f $\frac{8a^4}{a^2}$
g $4(3a^3 - a^2)$
h $\frac{4a^7}{2a^3}$

Hint: write the expressions in full and combine or cancel fractions.

7 Work out the value of each expression in question 6 when $a = 10$.

39

Exercise commentary

The questions assess objectives on Framework Pages 113 and 115.

Problem solving
Questions 1 and 2 assess objectives on Framework Pages 7–9.
Questions 4 and 5 assess Page 27.

Group work
Questions 4 and 5 are ideal for paired work.

Misconceptions
Students may be tempted to oversimplify expressions, writing $y + z$ as yz. Encourage them to think of y as 'one lot of y'. Substituting values provides a check.
When expanding brackets, students often only multiply the first term and rarely take account of the effect of negative signs. Encourage them to use the grid method to help expand brackets until they have built up a better understanding.

Links
Perimeter: Framework Pages 235–237.

Homework

A3.1HW gives practice in simplifying expressions and writing and solving simple equations.

Answers

1 a $\frac{ab}{c} = a(c + 1) = 15$, $7a + 1 = b^2 = 36$, $2a + c = bc = 12$, $ac + b = 2(b + c) = 16$
  b Lines joining identical expressions as in *a*.
2 $2(x + y) = 4z$, $7(1 + 3y) = 21x + 7$, $yz = x^2$, $2\frac{xy}{z} = y + z$
3 b $9n + 5$ **c** $2n - 1$ **d** $18n - 14$ **e** $n^2 - n$ **f** $n - 2$ **g** $3n^2$ **h** $3n + 6$
  i $18n - 1$ **j** $6n - 23$ **4 a** $7x + 1$, $x = 2$ **b** $8x + 2y + 4$, $x = 10$ **c** $21 - 2x$, $x = 2$
5 a $6y - 8$, $18 - 4x$ **b** $10x + 16y + 6$
6 a a^5 **b** a^4 **c** $6a^3$ **d** $3a^3$ **e** $6a^5$ **f** $8a^2$ **g** $12a^3 - 4a^2$ **h** $2a^4$
7 a 100 000 **b** 10 000 **c** 6000 **d** 3000 **e** 600 000 **f** 800 **g** 11 600 **h** 20 000

Mental starter

Think of a number

Pose 'think of a number' questions such as:

▸ I think of a number, double it, add 3 and the answer is 15.

▸ I think of a number, halve it, add 6 and the answer is 17.

Ask students to describe how they worked out their answers.

Useful resources

A3.2OHP – flow diagrams for equations; Students' book example.

Introductory activity

Refer to the mental starter.

Discuss how to set up the problems as equations.

Emphasise that you use a letter to stand for the unknown number.

Discuss how to solve the equation, relating the method to the descriptions students gave in the mental starter.

Emphasise that to solve the equation you change both sides in the same way.

Discuss how to solve an equation with the unknown on both sides such as:

$18 - 2x = 3x - 2$.

Emphasise the strategy of collecting the unknowns on the side where there are most of them.

Encourage students to check answers by substituting.

A3.2OHP shows a flow diagram like the ones in question 6 that you can use to discuss how to form and then solve an equation.

Discuss the example in the Students' Book (shown on A3.2OHP).

Emphasise that opposite sides are equal so the expressions are equal.

Encourage students to suggest the relevant steps in the working.

Emphasise the need to work logically, keeping the equation in balance.

Encourage students to check their solutions.

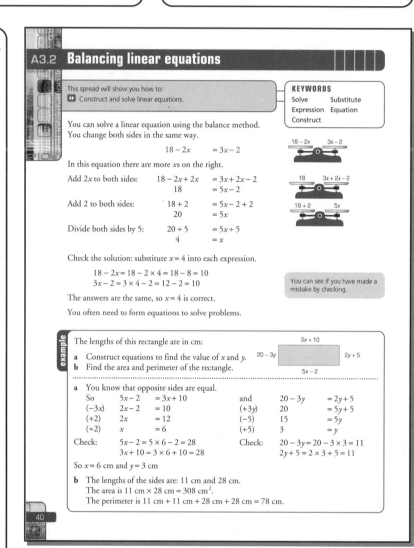

A3.2 Balancing linear equations

This spread will show you how to:

▸▸ Construct and solve linear equations.

KEYWORDS
Solve   Substitute
Expression Equation
Construct

You can solve a linear equation using the balance method. You change both sides in the same way.

$$18 - 2x = 3x - 2$$

In this equation there are more xs on the right.

Add $2x$ to both sides:
$$18 - 2x + 2x = 3x + 2x - 2$$
$$18 = 5x - 2$$

Add 2 to both sides:
$$18 + 2 = 5x - 2 + 2$$
$$20 = 5x$$

Divide both sides by 5:
$$20 \div 5 = 5x \div 5$$
$$4 = x$$

Check the solution: substitute $x = 4$ into each expression.
$$18 - 2x = 18 - 2 \times 4 = 18 - 8 = 10$$
$$3x - 2 = 3 \times 4 - 2 = 12 - 2 = 10$$

The answers are the same, so $x = 4$ is correct.

You can see if you have made a mistake by checking.

You often need to form equations to solve problems.

example

The lengths of this rectangle are in cm:

a Construct equations to find the value of x and y.

b Find the area and perimeter of the rectangle.

a You know that opposite sides are equal.

So	$5x - 2$	$= 3x + 10$	and	$20 - 3y$	$= 2y + 5$
$(-3x)$	$2x - 2$	$= 10$	$(+3y)$	20	$= 5y + 5$
$(+2)$	$2x$	$= 12$	(-5)	15	$= 5y$
$(+2)$	x	$= 6$	$(+5)$	3	$= y$

Check: $5x - 2 = 5 \times 6 - 2 = 28$ Check: $20 - 3y = 20 - 3 \times 3 = 11$
$3x + 10 = 3 \times 6 + 10 = 28$ $2y + 5 = 2 \times 3 + 5 = 11$

So $x = 6$ cm and $y = 3$ cm

b The lengths of the sides are: 11 cm and 28 cm.

The area is 11 cm $\times$ 28 cm = 308 cm^2.

The perimeter is 11 cm + 11 cm + 28 cm + 28 cm = 78 cm.

40

Plenary

Discuss how to solve question 7.

Encourage students to start by giving the geometrical facts they know.

Emphasise that to find the angles it is important to set up and solve an algebraic equation.

Check by asking questions that students' answers are sensible.

Emphasise that they are looking for the value of the expression not just the value of the unknown.

Further activities

Challenge students to make up similar problems to question 8 for a partner to solve.

Students could find the width and perimeter of a rectangle, given two equal sides and the area.

For example, $3x - 7$ $x + 3$

Differentiation

Core questions:

▶ Question 1 focuses on fairly simple equations.
▶ Questions 2–6 focus on forming and solving equations to find the unknown value.
▶ Questions 7 and 8 focus on forming and solving equations in more complex contexts.

Extension tier: focuses on constructing and solving equations using trial and improvement.

Support tier: focuses on substituting into expressions.

Exercise A3.2

1 Work out the value of x in each of these equations (use the balance method or another appropriate method).
  a $x + 5 = 9$ **b** $3x = 15$ **c** $16 = 8 + x$ **d** $3x - 5 = 28$
  e $5 + 2x = 13$ **f** $6x - 7 = 53$ **g** $18 - 2x = 4$ **h** $\frac{x}{4} + 1 = 5$
  i $2x + 1 = 3x - 2$ **j** $5 + 6x = 2x + 21$ **k** $9x + 3 = 45 - 12x$ **l** $\frac{3x}{2} - 7 = 11$

2 Use the balance method to solve these equations.
  a $8x - 6 = 3x + 9$ **b** $2(3x - 5) = 7x - 34$ **c** $\frac{x}{7} + 3 = 15$
  d $15 - 2x = 3x + 5$ **e** $5(2x + 7) = 3(4x - 5)$ **f** $8x - 2(5 + 2x) = 7x - 16$

3 If $y = 8$ what is the value of x in each of these equations?
  a $2y + 3x = 22$ **b** $4x = 3y - 8$ **c** $2(3x - y) = 5x + 7$
  d $3y - 2x = 5x - 4y$ **e** $7x + 2 = 3y - 4x$ **f** $3x - 8 = 5y$

4 Nina said, 'Multiplying my number by 4 then subtracting 5 gives the same answer as multiplying by 2 and adding 9'.
  a Call the number n and form an equation.   **b** Work out the value of Nina's number.

5 Find the value of the angle y in this triangle.

6 In these flow diagrams you get to the same finishing number whichever route you take.
Form equations and find the starting number x.

  a 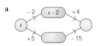   **b**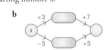

7 Work out the value of these angles.

  a   **b**   **c**

8 **a** The mean of three numbers is 18. If two of the numbers are 10 and 20, what is the third number?
  b The mean of three expressions is $2x + 8$.
    Two of the expressions are:
    What is the third expression?

41

Exercise commentary

There are a lot of questions in this exercise; it may not be appropriate for all students to answer them all. The questions assess objectives on Framework Pages 123 and 125.

Problem solving

Questions 4, 5, 7 and 8 assess objectives on Framework Page 27.

Group work

Questions 4–8 are appropriate for discussion in pairs.

Misconceptions

Students often make mistakes when solving equations, in particular:

▶ not doing the same to both sides, writing $2x + 1 = 15$ so $2x = 15$.
▶ using the wrong operation, writing $2x + 1 = 15$ so $2x = 16$.

Checking answers are correct by substituting will highlight errors. Encourage students to visualise the function machine for equations.

Links

Perimeter and area: Framework Pages 235–237.

Homework

A3.2HW focuses on solving linear equations, and writing and solving equations in the context of angle.

Answers

1 **a** 4 **b** 5 **c** 8 **d** 11 **e** 4 **f** 10 **g** 7 **h** 16
  i 3 **j** 4 **k** 2 **l** 12
2 **a** $x = 3$ **b** $x = 24$ **c** $x = 84$ **d** $x = 2$ **e** $x = 25$ **f** $x = 2$
3 **a** 2 **b** 4 **c** 23 **d** 8 **e** 2 **f** 16
4 **a** $4n - 5 = 2n + 9$ **b** 7
5 $y = 50°$ 6 **a** 7 **b** 11   7 **a** Both 65° **b** Both 68° **c** 110°, 70°
8 **a** 24 **b** $x + 20$

A3.3 Solving non-linear equations

Mental starter

Area of a square

Ask students to find the area of a square given the length of a side. Repeat a few times, changing the length and the measure used.

Challenge students to find the length of the side of a square given the area. Use different measures.

Useful resources

Calculators for the exercise

Introductory activity

Refer to the mental starter.

Check that students know how to find the square of a number and the square root of a number.

Pose the problem:
▶ I think of a number, square it and the answer is 64.

Expect students to answer 8.
Tell them that your number is not 8.
Discuss what it could be.
Emphasise that $^-8 \times {^-8}$ is also 64 and your answer is $^-8$.

Encourage students to set up the problem as an equation.

Discuss how to solve it.
Emphasise the use of the notation ± to show both solutions simultaneously.

Repeat with other problems until students feel comfortable with the idea.

Go on to more complex problems:
▶ I think of a number, add 5, square it and the answer is 36.

Encourage students to set up the equation. Discuss how many different answers there will be and how you know.
Emphasise that once you take the square root, you have two different options and you can set them out separately.

Emphasise the need to use a bracket to show a squared negative term: $(^-6)^2$.

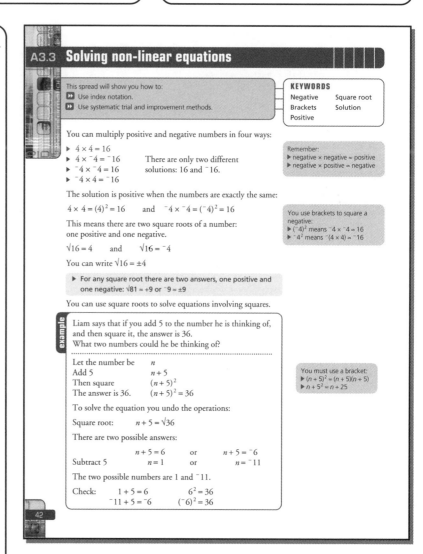

A3.3 Solving non-linear equations

This spread will show you how to:
▷ Use index notation.
▷ Use systematic trial and improvement methods.

KEYWORDS
Negative   Square root
Brackets   Solution
Positive

You can multiply positive and negative numbers in four ways:
▶ $4 \times 4 = 16$
▶ $4 \times {^-4} = {^-16}$ There are only two different
▶ $^-4 \times {^-4} = 16$ solutions: 16 and $^-16$.
▶ $^-4 \times 4 = {^-16}$

Remember:
▶ negative × negative = positive
▶ negative × positive = negative

The solution is positive when the numbers are exactly the same:
$4 \times 4 = (4)^2 = 16$ and $^-4 \times {^-4} = (^-4)^2 = 16$

This means there are two square roots of a number: one positive and one negative.

$\sqrt{16} = 4$ and $\sqrt{16} = {^-4}$

You can write $\sqrt{16} = \pm 4$

You use brackets to square a negative:
▶ $(^-4)^2$ means $^-4 \times {^-4} = 16$
▶ $^-4^2$ means $^-(4 \times 4) = {^-16}$

▶ For any square root there are two answers, one positive and one negative: $\sqrt{81} = +9$ or $^-9 = \pm 9$

You can use square roots to solve equations involving squares.

example

Liam says that if you add 5 to the number he is thinking of, and then square it, the answer is 36.
What two numbers could he be thinking of?

Let the number be n
Add 5 $n + 5$
Then square $(n + 5)^2$
The answer is 36. $(n + 5)^2 = 36$

To solve the equation you undo the operations:
Square root: $n + 5 = \sqrt{36}$

There are two possible answers:
$n + 5 = 6$ or $n + 5 = {^-6}$
Subtract 5 $n = 1$ or $n = {^-11}$
The two possible numbers are 1 and $^-11$.
Check: $1 + 5 = 6$ $6^2 = 36$
                $^-11 + 5 = {^-6}$ $(^-6)^2 = 36$

You must use a bracket:
▶ $(n + 5)^2 = (n + 5)(n + 5)$
▶ $n + 5^2 = n + 25$

42

Plenary

Discuss how to estimate square roots such as:
▶ $\sqrt{17}$ – why is it near 4?
▶ $\sqrt{24}$ – why is it near 5?
▶ $\sqrt{20}$ – is it nearer 4 or 5? How do you know?
Discuss why questions 7 and 8 can only have one solution even though they contain a squared term.

Further activities

Challenge students to solve:
$(x+2)^2 - 7 = 74$

Students could write an explanation of how $(-h)^2$ differs from $-h^2$.

Differentiation

Core questions:
- Questions 1 and 2 revise finding squares and roots.
- Questions 3–6 focus on estimating square roots and solving equations involving squared terms.
- Questions 7 and 8 involve forming and solving equations in context.

Extension tier: focuses on solving simultaneous equations algebraically.

Support tier: focuses on using inverse operations to solve equations.

Exercise A3.3

1 Calculate these:

  a 7^2 **b** $(^-5)^2$ **c** $(^-8)^2$ **d** 20^2

  e $(^-1)^2$ **f** $(^-12)^2$

2 Calculate these, giving two solutions each time:

  a $\sqrt{25}$ **b** $\sqrt{81}$ **c** $\sqrt{121}$ **d** $\sqrt{225}$

  e $\sqrt{900}$ **f** $\sqrt{1}$

3 For each of these questions, consider only the positive solution. Copy and complete this table.

Number	Value is between	The nearest whole number	Estimate to 1 dp	Actual answer on a calculator
$\sqrt{60}$	7 and 8	8	7.7	7.7459666
$\sqrt{20}$				
$\sqrt{39}$				
$\sqrt{48}$				
$\sqrt{7}$				
$\sqrt{56}$				
$\sqrt{84}$				
$\sqrt{110}$				

4 Work out the two possible values for x in each of these questions.

  a $x^2 = 36$ **b** $x^2 = 100$ **c** $x^2 = 64$ **d** $x^2 + 1 = 17$

  e $x^2 + 7 = 32$ **f** $x^2 - 10 = 26$ **g** $2x^2 = 50$ **h** $x^2 - 6 = 75$

  i $x^2 + 3.5 = 52.5$

5 Work out the two possible values for x in each of these questions.

  a $(x+1)^2 = 16$ **b** $(x-1)^2 = 100$ **c** $(x+3)^2 = 36$ **d** $(x-5)^2 = 49$

  e $(x+2)^2 = 64$ **f** $(x-7)^2 = 4$

6 Solve these equations:

  a $\frac{y^2}{3} = 3$ **b** $\frac{y^2}{6} = 6$ **c** $\frac{4}{y^2} = 1$ **d** $3 = \frac{12}{y^2}$

  e $5y^2 = 45$ **f** $\frac{32}{y^2} = 2$ **g** $(5+y)^2 = 100$ **h** $\frac{9}{y+1} = y+1$

7 The area of this square is 81 m².
  a What is the value of x?
  b Why can there only be one value for x in this case?

$(x-7)$ m

8 The area of this triangle is 50 cm².
  a Using the formula for area of a triangle, write out an equation.
  b Solve the equation to find the value of x.

$(x+1)$ cm
$(x+1)$ cm

Exercise commentary

The questions assess objectives on Framework Pages 57 and 133.

Problem solving

Question 5 assesses objectives on Framework Page 29.
Questions 7 and 8 assess Page 27.

Group work

Question 3 is appropriate for pairs.

Misconceptions

Students may make mistakes in questions 4–6 due to poor algebraic manipulation skills.

Encourage them to try to visualise the function machine to help them work through the steps logically.

It is important to emphasise the use of a check.

Students find square roots confusing as they lead to two solutions.

Encourage a systematic approach and simple layout as suggested in the Students' book.

Links

Perimeter and area: Framework Pages 235–237.

Homework

A3.3HW focuses on finding square roots and solutions to equations involving x^2.

Answers

1 a 49 **b** 25 **c** 64 **d** 400 **e** 1 **f** 144   **2 a** ±5 **b** ±9 **c** ±11 **d** ±15 **e** ±30 **f** ±1

3 Actual: 4.472135955, 6.244997998, 6.92820323, 2.645751311, 7.483314774, 9.16515139, 10.48808848

4 a ±6 **b** ±10 **c** ±8 **d** ±4 **e** ±5 **f** ±6 **g** ±5 **h** ±9 **i** ±7

5 a $^-5, 3$ **b** $^-9, 11$ **c** $^-9, 3$ **d** $^-2, 12$ **e** $^-10, 6$ **f** 5, 9

6 a $y = 3$ **b** $y = ±6$ **c** $y = ±2$ **d** $y = ±2$ **e** $y = ±3$ **f** $y = ±4$ **g** $y = ^-15$ or 5 **h** $y = 2$ or $^-4$

7 a 2 **b** You cannot have a negative length.   **8 a** $\frac{1}{2}(x+1)^2 = 50$ **b** $x = 9$ cm

A3.4 Solving proportional problems

Mental starter

Cancel

Give students practice at cancelling down fractions such as:

$$\frac{18}{30} \qquad \frac{24}{20} \qquad \frac{8 \times 12}{16} \qquad \frac{1.5}{12}$$

Discuss strategies.

Emphasise the use of the highest common factor.

Useful resources

A3.4OHP – similar rectangles

Calculators for the exercise

Introductory activity

Refer to the mental starter.

Discuss how many different fractions you can find that are equivalent to $\frac{2}{3}$.

Emphasise that any fractions that have the numerator and denominator in the same ratio will be equivalent.

Draw a 2 by 3 rectangle on the board.

Discuss the dimensions of similar rectangles – that is, enlargements.

Emphasise that if you double the width you also double the length:

4 by 6 is an enlargement.

Emphasise that the sides are in the same proportion.

Encourage students to make the link with equivalent fractions:

$\frac{2}{3} = \frac{4}{6}$

Emphasise also that the corresponding sides are in the same proportion:

$\frac{2}{4} = \frac{3}{6}$

Discuss how to use this idea of proportionality to help solve problems involving similar rectangles.

A3.4OHP shows pairs of similar rectangles for you to discuss finding missing lengths.

Encourage students to set up and solve equations to find the missing lengths.

Emphasise that you choose the proportion so that you start the equation with the unknown:

$\frac{x}{6} = \frac{2}{3}$

The final example on **A3.4OHP** is harder, involving a decimal length. It is useful for ensuring students understand how to solve the equation.

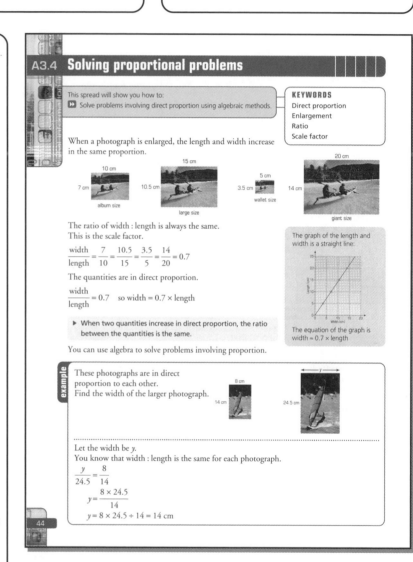

Plenary

Discuss answers to question 4.

Encourage students to share their strategies for approaching the questions.

Discuss when different strategies are appropriate.

Emphasise that when the numbers are easy you should use a mental method.

For other questions, discuss which proportions students chose to compare: length/width or corresponding lengths.

Less confident students could find similar rectangles to those in question 1 and show that they are similar using proportion.

Differentiation

Core questions:
▶ Questions 1 and 2 involve finding the ratio of lengths and plotting them on a graph.
▶ Questions 3 and 4 focus on using proportionality to solve problems.
▶ Questions 5 and 6 are more challenging as the proportions are harder to visualise.

Extension tier: focuses on solving simultaneous equations.

Support tier: focuses on constructing and solving equations using the balance method.

Exercise A3.4

1 Find the ratio between the widths and lengths of these photographs.
Which one is not in direct proportion to the other three?

a 4 cm 10 cm
b 7 cm 17.5 cm
c 3 cm 7.5 cm
d 4 cm 1.5 cm

2 Draw a graph to confirm your answer to question 1.
Plot width on the x-axis and length on the y-axis.
Explain how the graph confirms your answer.

3 Solve these algebraic equations:
a $\frac{x}{5} = \frac{17}{10}$ **b** $\frac{y}{9} = \frac{8}{3}$ **c** $\frac{z}{3} = \frac{15}{6}$ **d** $\frac{6}{15} = \frac{a}{10}$ **e** $\frac{12}{20} = \frac{b}{15}$ **f** $\frac{1.8}{2} = \frac{c}{5}$

4 Use algebra to find the missing width or length for each of these photographs.
Each pair is in direct proportion.

a 10 cm, 15 cm, x, 9 cm
b 5 cm, y, 8 cm, 4.8 cm
c 6 cm, x, 4 cm, 2.5 cm
d 10 cm, 12 cm, y, 9 cm

5 Light green paint is made by mixing 5 parts of blue paint with 12 parts of yellow paint.
Use algebra to find how many litres of:
a blue paint you would mix with 30 litres of yellow paint
b yellow paint you would mix with 12 litres of blue paint.

6 The model aircraft club make exact replicas of real aircraft.
Each dimension is in direct proportion to a real aircraft.
For the model of a Jumbo Jet the wing span is 48 cm.
The actual wing span of a Jumbo Jet is 64 m.
The actual length of the model was 56 cm.
How long is a real Jumbo Jet?

45

Exercise commentary

The questions assess objectives on Framework Pages 79 and 137.

Problem solving
Questions 4–6 assess objectives on Framework Page 5.
Question 2 assesses Page 27.

Group work
Questions 1 and 2 are suitable for discussion in pairs. Students can discuss an appropriate scale to use for the graph.

Misconceptions
This is a challenging exercise which many students will find difficult.
Emphasise that pairs of lengths are in proportion when the rectangles are enlargements.
Encourage students to start with the unknown and write it as a fraction of the other length in the rectangle. They should then write the lengths of the other rectangle the same way up.

Links
Enlargement: Framework Pages 213.

Homework

A3.4HW gives more practice in finding missing lengths in similar rectangles, and solving algebraic equations.

Answers

1 **a** 0.4 **b** 0.4 **c** 0.4 **d** 0.375, not in direct proportion
2 All points except **d** lie on a straight line.
3 **a** $x = 8.5$ **b** $y = 24$ **c** $z = 7.5$ **d** $a = 4$ **e** $b = 9$ **f** $c = 4.5$
4 **a** 6 cm **b** 3 cm **c** 9.6 cm **d** 7.5 cm
5 **a** 12.5 litres **b** 28.8 litres
6 $\frac{64}{48} \times 56 = 74$ m

Mental starter

Substitute

Have some flashcards with simple quadratic expressions on or write these expressions on the board:

x^2 $x^2 - 2$ $x^2 + 5$ $2x^2$ $3x^2$

Ask students to order the expressions when $x = 4, 5, 7$ etc.

Discuss solutions.

Ensure students understand that $2x^2$ is $2 \times x^2$.

Useful resources

Calculators for the exercise

Introductory activity

Discuss solutions to these linear equations:

$7x - 15 = 32$ $3x + 5 = 18.5$

Encourage students to give an estimate of the answer. Discuss their estimates and how they could be improved.

Discuss the solution to this quadratic equation: $x^2 = 44.89$.

Encourage students to suggest pairs of values that x^2 lies between, giving reasons for their suggestions.

Show suggestions in a table with these headings:

Lower estimate   Upper estimate

Discuss which of these estimates the value of x is closer to and why. [6 and 7, nearer to 7]

Encourage students to try the halfway number. [$6.5^2 = 42.25$]

6.5^2 is too small, so the value of x lies between 6.5 and 7. Therefore $x = 7$ to the nearest whole number.

Emphasise that the halfway number gives an estimate to the nearest whole number.

Discuss how to find the exact value.

Emphasise the strategy of considering the halfway between number (6.55).

Discuss the solution to $3x^2 = 172.3$

Emphasise that this is similar to the previous example.

Discuss the solution to:

$2x^2 + 3x = 72.08$

Emphasise the use of a table as in the Students' Book example to set out working.

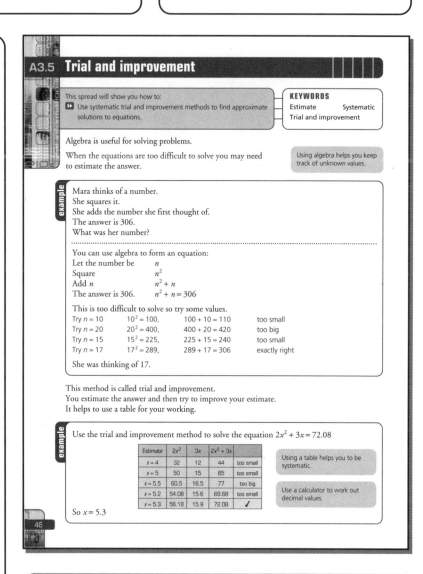

A3.5 Trial and improvement

This spread will show you how to:
▶▶ Use systematic trial and improvement methods to find approximate solutions to equations.

KEYWORDS
Estimate   Systematic
Trial and improvement

Algebra is useful for solving problems.

When the equations are too difficult to solve you may need to estimate the answer.

Using algebra helps you keep track of unknown values.

example

Mara thinks of a number.
She squares it.
She adds the number she first thought of.
The answer is 306.
What was her number?

You can use algebra to form an equation:
Let the number be n
Square n^2
Add n $n^2 + n$
The answer is 306. $n^2 + n = 306$

This is too difficult to solve so try some values.

Try $n = 10$	$10^2 = 100$,	$100 + 10 = 110$	too small
Try $n = 20$	$20^2 = 400$,	$400 + 20 = 420$	too big
Try $n = 15$	$15^2 = 225$,	$225 + 15 = 240$	too small
Try $n = 17$	$17^2 = 289$,	$289 + 17 = 306$	exactly right

She was thinking of 17.

This method is called trial and improvement.
You estimate the answer and then try to improve your estimate.
It helps to use a table for your working.

example

Use the trial and improvement method to solve the equation $2x^2 + 3x = 72.08$

Estimate	$2x^2$	$3x$	$2x^2 + 3x$	
$x = 4$	32	12	44	too small
$x = 5$	50	15	65	too small
$x = 5.5$	60.5	16.5	77	too big
$x = 5.2$	54.08	15.6	69.68	too small
$x = 5.3$	56.18	15.9	72.08	✓

Using a table helps you to be systematic.

Use a calculator to work out decimal values.

So $x = 5.3$

46

Plenary

Either:

▶ Review one of the questions, such as
$3x^2 + 7x - 15 = 49.08$

or:

▶ Discuss how to estimate the value of x when
$2x^2 - 5x = 7.5472$
where the answer has 2 dp.

In **A3.5ICT** students use a spreadsheet to investigate trial and improvement by repeated calculation.

Alternatively

Students can write equations for a partner to solve, using trial and improvement. In order that the equation has an exact solution, they should **start** by deciding on a value of x (either a whole number or to 1 dp).

Differentiation

Core questions:

▸ Question 1 focuses on substituting into quadratic expressions – part **g** has a negative solution.

▸ Questions 2 and 3 focus on using trial and improvement and setting work out in a table.

▸ Questions 4 and 5 are less structured so students have to devise their own tables.

Extension tier: focuses on constructing and solving simultaneous equations.

Support tier: focuses on solving problems involving proportionality.

Exercise A3.5

1 If $x = 6$, work out the value of each of these expressions:

   a $x^2 - 9$ **b** $2x^2 + 7$ **c** $3x^2 + 2x$ **d** $5x^2 - 8x$

   e $10x - x^2$ **f** $2x^2 - x + 1$ **g** $25 + x - x^2$ **h** $4x^2 + 3x - 7$

2 **Best guess**

Copy and complete the table.

For each equation:

▸ Estimate a value for x.

▸ Work out the value of the expression for your value of x.

▸ Find the difference between your estimate and the actual value.

Work out the total difference for your four guesses.

Equation	Expression	Estimate $x = ?$	Expression value	Actual value	Difference
$3x^2 + 7 = 82$	$3x^2 + 7$			82	
$180 - 2x^2 = 52$	$180 - 2x^2$			52	
$2x^2 + 3x = 119$	$2x^2 + 3x$			119	
$3x^2 - 2x = 180$	$3x^2 - 2x$		Total:	180	

3 Use trial and improvement to find the exact value of x in each equation. The first one is started for you.

   a $3x^2 + 7x = 516$

Estimate	$3x^2$	$+7x$	$3x^2 + 7x$	Too small or large
$x = 10$	300	70	370	too small
$x = 15$	675	105		
$x =$				

   b $2x^2 - 5x = 777$

Estimate	$2x^2$	$-5x$	$2x^2 - 5x$	Too small or large

   c $5x^2 + 3x - 2 = 1672$

4 Use trial and improvement to find an exact value of x for these expressions:

   a $2x^2 + x = 32.68$

   b $x^2 - 3x = 41.31$

   c $3x^2 + 7x - 15 = 49.08$

   d $300 - 3x^2 = 202.53$

5 For the equation $x^2 - 6x + 8.51 = 0$, there are two positive values for x. Use trial and improvement to find both values.

47

Exercise commentary

The questions assess objectives on Framework Pages 133–135.

Problem solving

Questions 2–5 assess objectives on Framework Page 29.

Group work

Questions 2 and 3 are suitable for pairs. Give students five seconds to work out an estimate and then they work out the difference.

Misconceptions

Students often think $2x^2$ means $2x \times 2x$. Emphasise that the ^{2} belongs only to the x term – encourage them to think of it as '2 lots of x^2'.

In trial and improvement, students often find it difficult knowing where to start. Emphasise that they can start anywhere but that the key idea is to improve on each estimate by looking at how much bigger or smaller the answer will be.

Links

Rounding: Framework Pages 43–47.

Homework

A3.5HW practises calculating the value of expressions, and solving equations by trial and improvement.

Answers

1 **a** 27 **b** 79 **c** 120 **d** 132

   e 24 **f** 67 **g** $^-5$ **h** 155

2 Good starting estimates would be: 80, 50, 120, 200.

3 **a** $x = 12$ **b** $x = 21$ **c** $x = 18$

4 **a** $x = 3.8$ **b** $x = 8.1$ **c** $x = 3.6$ **d** $x = 5.7$

5 2.3, 3.7

A3.6 Best estimate

Mental starter

Rounding

Ask students to round these numbers in turn:

81.3965   7.8549   0.0385

Start with writing correct to 1 dp, then to 2 dp, then to 3 dp.

Challenge students to find the smallest number that 3.6 rounded to 1 dp could be, if these were two figures after the decimal point.

Useful resources

Calculators

Introductory activity

Discuss the work from the previous lesson on trial and improvement.

Emphasise that although the numbers worked out exactly in the examples, this is not always the case.

Discuss the solution to
$3x^2 - 4x = 17.15$
Encourage students to suggest a possible solution. [Between 3 and 4.]
Discuss how to improve the estimate.

Encourage the use of a table to order results, using headings:

Estimate	$3x^2$	$-4x$	$3x^2 - 4x$	too big or small

Emphasise that 3.1 is too small but 3.2 is too big so the solution is somewhere in between.
Emphasise the strategy of checking the halfway value: 3.15
Discuss what the answer shows:
$x = 3.15$ gives a solution that is too big. This means the answer must lie between 3.10 and 3.15, so it must be 3.1 to 1 dp.

Encourage students to describe the steps in the working again.

Emphasise that you:
▸ Find the two values the solution is between to 1 dp.
▸ Consider the halfway value. If it is too big the solution is the lower of the two numbers; if it is too small the solution is the higher of the two.

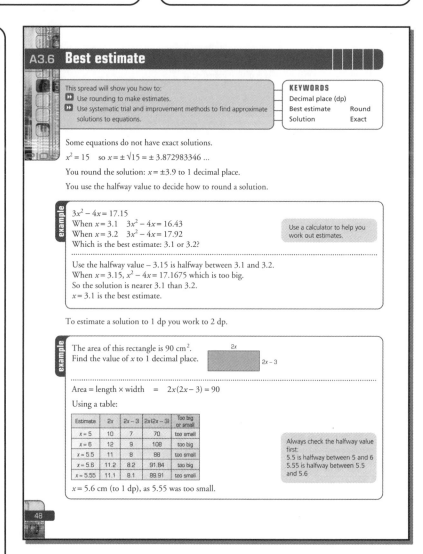

A3.6 Best estimate

This spread will show you how to:
▶▶ Use rounding to make estimates.
▶▶ Use systematic trial and improvement methods to find approximate solutions to equations.

KEYWORDS
Decimal place (dp)
Best estimate   Round
Solution   Exact

Some equations do not have exact solutions.
$x^2 = 15$ so $x = \pm \sqrt{15} = \pm 3.872983346 \ldots$
You round the solution: $x = \pm 3.9$ to 1 decimal place.
You use the halfway value to decide how to round a solution.

> **example**
> $3x^2 - 4x = 17.15$
> When $x = 3.1$ $3x^2 - 4x = 16.43$
> When $x = 3.2$ $3x^2 - 4x = 17.92$
> Which is the best estimate: 3.1 or 3.2?
>
> *Use a calculator to help you work out estimates.*
>
> Use the halfway value – 3.15 is halfway between 3.1 and 3.2.
> When $x = 3.15$, $x^2 - 4x = 17.1675$ which is too big.
> So the solution is nearer 3.1 than 3.2.
> $x = 3.1$ is the best estimate.

To estimate a solution to 1 dp you work to 2 dp.

> **example**
> The area of this rectangle is 90 cm². Find the value of x to 1 decimal place.
> (rectangle labelled $2x$ and $2x - 3$)
>
> Area = length × width   = $2x(2x - 3) = 90$
> Using a table:
>
> | Estimate | $2x$ | $2x - 3$ | $2x(2x-3)$ | Too big or small |
> |----------|------|----------|------------|------------------|
> | $x = 5$ | 10 | 7 | 70 | too small |
> | $x = 6$ | 12 | 9 | 108 | too big |
> | $x = 5.5$ | 11 | 8 | 88 | too small |
> | $x = 5.6$ | 11.2 | 8.2 | 91.84 | too big |
> | $x = 5.55$ | 11.1 | 8.1 | 89.91 | too small |
>
> *Always check the halfway value first:*
> *5.5 is halfway between 5 and 6*
> *5.55 is halfway between 5.5 and 5.6*
>
> $x = 5.6$ cm (to 1 dp), as 5.55 was too small.

48

Plenary

Discuss question 4.
Emphasise that they are looking to solve:

$x^2 + 3x - 5 = 0$

Encourage students to draw an accurate graph.
Discuss whether the graph is helpful.

Further activities

Encourage students to make a poster to illustrate the approach used to find a solution to the equation in question 4.

Differentiation

Core questions:
- Question 1 focuses on finding halfway values.
- Questions 2 and 3 focus on using trial and improvement to find solutions to 1 dp.
- Questions 4 and 5 focus on solving quadratic equations.

Extension tier: focuses on solving simultaneous equations graphically.

Support tier: focuses on substituting into and simplifying expressions involving indices.

Exercise A3.6

1 For each of these equations:
- ▸ Find the halfway value between the two estimates and substitute it into the equation.
- ▸ Decide which is the best estimate.
  Give a reason for your answer.

  a $x^2 + 4x = 19$; $x = 2$ and $x = 3$
  b $2x^2 + 3x = 120$; $x = 6$ and $x = 7$
  c $5x^2 - 8x = 200$; $x = 7$ and $x = 8$
  d $x^2 + 3x = 90$; $x = 8.1$ and $x = 8.2$

2 Use trial and improvement to find the value of x in these equations to 1 dp.
Copy and complete the tables to help you.

  a $x^2 + 5x = 114$

x	x^2	$5x$	$x^2 + 5x$	Too big/small

  b $2x^2 - 7x = 13$

x^2	$2x^2$	$7x$	$2x^2 - 7x$	Too big/small

3 The area of this rectangle is 108 cm^2.
Copy and complete the trial and improvement table to find an estimate (to 1 dp) for the value of x.

x	$5x$	$2x - 3$	$5x(2x - 3)$	Too big/small

4 The table shows values of x and y for the equation $y = x^2 + 3x - 5$.
  a Copy and complete the table:

x	-2	-1	0	1	2	3	4
y				-1	5	13	23

    The value of y is 0 for a value of x somewhere between 1 and 2.
  b Use trial and improvement to find the value of x, to 1 dp, that gives the value of y closest to 0.
  c Plot the coordinates on a graph.
    Join them with a smooth curve.
    Does the graph help you solve the question in part **b**?

5 Use trial and improvement to find the value of x, to 1 dp, that gives the value of y closest to 0 in each case [$x > 0$].
  a $y = 3x^2 - 2x - 17$
  b $y = x^2 - 7x + 3$

49

Exercise commentary

The questions assess objectives on Framework Pages 43 and 135.

Problem solving
The exercise assesses objectives on Framework Page 29. Question 4 assesses Page 27.

Group work
Questions 1–3 are suitable for work in pairs.

Misconceptions
Students need to understand that if the halfway value gives a solution that is too big then the lower bound is the appropriate solution. This can be a difficult concept to grasp.

Encourage students to use a number line to mark the bounds, halfway value and the solutions of each point, then the target solution so they can see how far away each one is.

It helps to use whole number values to illustrate the concept before moving on to decimals. Students can sketch the different points in question 1.

Links
Solving equations: Framework Pages 123–125.

Homework

A3.6HW gives more practice in using trial and improvement methods for equations with non-exact solutions.

Answers

1 **a** $x = 3$ **b** $x = 7$ **c** $x = 7$ **d** $x = 8.1$
2 **a** $x = 8.5$ **b** $x = 4.8$
3 $x = 4.1$
4 **a** -7, -7, -5   **b** $x = 1.2$
   c The solution is where the graph crosses the x-axis.
5 **a** $x = 2.7$ **b** $x = 6.5$

Summary

The key objectives for this unit are:

▶ Construct and solve linear equations with integer coefficients. (123–125)
▶ Use systematic trial and improvement methods to find approximate solutions. (133–135)

Check out commentary

1 Part **a** involves substitution, then solving linear equations. Students may need to be reminded how to deal with negative terms.
Students need to simplify by collecting like terms before solving, in part **b**.
In part **c**, encourage students to write the equation as $\frac{x}{n} =$, so that they can solve easily for x.

2 In part **a** a table is provided to help students work systematically. Encourage students to use a similar table for their working in part **b**.
Ensure that students have expanded the brackets correctly, in particular the negative term, and simplified the equation before using trial and improvement to solve it.

Plenary activity

Draw this isoceles triangle on the board. Tell students that $\angle B$ is 40° more than $\angle A$ and $\angle C$.
Encourage them to write and solve an equation to find the angles of the triangle. The area of the triangle is 18 cm². Discuss methods and find x to 1 dp.

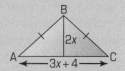

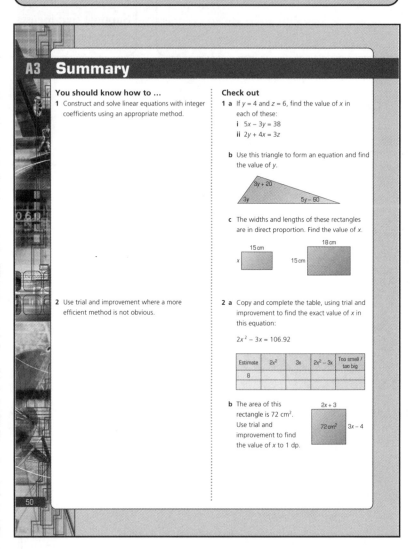

A3 Summary

You should know how to ...

1 Construct and solve linear equations with integer coefficients using an appropriate method.

2 Use trial and improvement where a more efficient method is not obvious.

Check out

1 **a** If $y = 4$ and $z = 6$, find the value of x in each of these:
  i $5x - 3y = 38$
  ii $2y + 4x = 3z$

  b Use this triangle to form an equation and find the value of y.

  c The widths and lengths of these rectangles are in direct proportion. Find the value of x.

2 **a** Copy and complete the table, using trial and improvement to find the exact value of x in this equation:

$$2x^2 - 3x = 106.92$$

Estimate	$2x^2$	$3x$	$2x^2 - 3x$	Too small / too big
8				

  b The area of this rectangle is 72 cm². Use trial and improvement to find the value of x to 1 dp.

Development

Techniques are revised in the context of graphs and formulae in A4 and A5. Equations are used in a problem-solving context in P1.

Links

Equations and formulae are used in other subject areas. For example, in Science, $V = IR$.

Mental starters

Objectives covered in this unit:

▶ Visualise, describe and sketch 2-D shapes.
▶ Recall and use formulae for areas of rectangles and triangles.
▶ Estimate and order acute, obtuse and reflex angles.
▶ Know and use tests for divisibility.
▶ Know or derive quickly factor pairs for a given number.
▶ Multiply and divide integers
▶ Derive products and quotients of multiples of 10, 100, 1000.

Resources needed

* means class set needed
Essential:
S1.2OHP – angles in octagons
S1.3OHP – regular shapes
S1.4OHP – alternate and corresponding angles
S1.6OHP – parts of a circle
R15 – special quadrilaterals
Compasses*   Rulers*
Protractors*   Plain paper
Useful:
S1.1OHP – labelling conventions
S1.5F – missing information angle problems
S1.6F – pie chart
S1.7ICT* – constructing triangles

S1 Geometrical reasoning and construction

This unit will show you how to:

▶▶ Distinguish between conventions, definitions and derived properties.
▶▶ Explain how to find, calculate and use:
– sums of the interior and exterior angles of quadrilaterals, pentagons and hexagons
– interior and exterior angles of polygons.
▶▶ Solve problems using properties of angles, of parallel and intersecting lines, and of triangles and other polygons.
▶▶ Know the definitions of a circle and its parts.
▶▶ Explain why inscribed regular polygons can be constructed by equal divisions of a circle.
▶▶ Use straight edge and compasses to construct a triangle, given right angle, hypotenuse and side (RHS).
▶▶ Use ICT to explore constructions of triangles and other 2-D shapes.
▶▶ Find the locus of a point that moves according to a simple rule.
▶▶ Explore connections in shape and space across a range of contexts.
▶▶ Represent problems and synthesise information in geometric form.
▶▶ Present a concise, reasoned argument.

Engineers use properties of shapes to design structures.

Before you start

You should know how to ...

1 Use angle facts:
▶ The angles in a triangle add up to 180°.
▶ The exterior angle of a triangle equals the sum of the two opposite interior angles.
▶ The angles on a straight line add to 180°.

2 Recognise special triangles and quadrilaterals and describe their properties.

Check in

1 Find the missing angles.

2 Name these shapes and describe their properties.
a   b

51

Unit commentary

Aim of the unit

The unit aims to develop students' ability to use precise geometrical reasoning to solve problems. Students are expected to justify their answers with diagrams and text. The unit develops to using straight-edge constructions and finding the locus of a set of points.

Introduction

Discuss geometrical shapes used in local landmarks and reasons for their use. Emphasise that it is not just aesthetics but also the properties of the shapes that makes them useful in all sorts of constructions.

Framework references

This unit focuses on:
Teaching objectives pages:
179, 183–187, 195, 197, 221–225.
Problem solving pages:
15, 17, 27, 31.

Check in activity

Can you?

Challenge students to sketch these shapes with an angle of 50°:

▶ Isosceles triangle
▶ Scalene triangle
▶ Right-angled triangle
▶ Equilateral triangle
▶ A triangle with one line of symmetry.

Encourage students to mark the other angles in the triangles.

Differentiation

Support tier

Focuses on angle facts, properties of shapes, constructions and loci.

Extension tier

Focuses on problem solving using angles, Pythagoras' theorem and circles and on construction and loci.

S1.1 Geometrical language

Mental starter

Angles
Draw six angles on the board or OHP. Label them **a–f**.
Ask students to:
▸ Order the angles from smallest to largest.
▸ State whether the angles are acute, obtuse or reflex.
▸ Estimate the size of each angle in degrees.

Useful resources

S1.1OHP – illustrations of labelling conventions
Plain paper for Further activities

Introductory activity

Refer to the mental starter.
Emphasise that each of the diagrams show two angles and that you need to label the one that you want so that everyone knows which one to find.

Discuss different ways of labelling an angle ABC (shown on **S1.1OHP**).
Emphasise that you trace the angle you want with your finger and give the letters of the vertices in order.
S1.1OHP also shows a line so you can discuss the labelling of the line segment.

Emphasise that the conventions are necessary so that everyone can understand which angle you mean.

S1.1OHP also shows a triangle and a parallelogram.
Encourage students to describe the equal angles using the labelling conventions.

Discuss how to show equal sides and equal angles.
Discuss how to show pairs of parallel sides.
Emphasise that you use single arrows for the first pair, double arrows for the second pair and so on.

Discuss how students know that there are 90° in a right angle.
Emphasise that '360° in a full turn' is a definition and that the angles in a quarter turn are derived from that.

Discuss other definitions and properties you can derive from them.

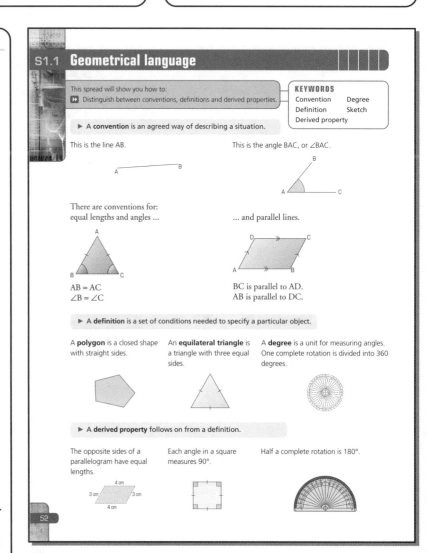

Plenary

Discuss answers to questions 2 and 3.
Emphasise that the definition needs to uniquely identify the shape.
Discuss why the definitions in question 3 do not do so.

Further activities

Students could cut any quadrilateral from paper, tear off the corners, and fit them together. Repeat for different quadrilaterals. What is the angle sum of a quadrilateral?

Differentiation

Core questions:

▶ Questions 1 and 2 are straightforward examples of illustrating and completing definitions.

▶ Questions 3–5 focus on distinguishing between definitions, conventions and derived properties.

▶ Question 6 is a challenging question, focusing on geometric reasoning.

Extension tier: focuses on definitions, derived properties and proof.

Support tier: focuses on congruence and correct use of vocabulary.

Exercise S1.1

1 Sketch a diagram to show each of these labelling conventions:
 a the line CD
 b the angle CAB
 c the triangle ABC
 d the parallelogram ABCD
 e the isosceles triangle XYZ where XY = YZ
 f the parallelogram EFGH where EF = HG
 g the trapezium ABCD where AB is parallel to DC
 h the equilateral triangle ABC
 i the trapezium ABCD where ∠A = ∠B = 90° and BC is parallel to AD
 j the triangle ABC with AC extended to D.

2 Copy and complete these definitions:
 a An isosceles triangle has two pairs of equal ___ and ___.
 b A ___ is a quadrilateral with one pair of parallel sides.
 c A ___ shape has equal angles and equal sides.
 d The vertex of a shape is ___.
 e A quadrilateral has ___ sides and ___.
 f A ___ has six sides.

3 Explain why these definitions are incomplete.
 Rewrite the sentences to make them into definitions.
 a A square has four sides of equal length.
 b A parallelogram has opposite sides of equal length.
 c A trapezium has two parallel sides.
 d A regular hexagon has six sides.
 e An equilateral triangle has three sides.

4 On a copy of this diagram, mark a pair of corresponding angles and a pair of alternate angles.

5 Copy and complete these sentences that describe some derived properties.
 a The angles of a triangle add up to ___.
 b Opposite angles of a parallelogram are ___.
 c A square has diagonals that are ___ in length.
 d Each interior angle in an equilateral triangle is ___.
 e Each interior angle in a square is ___.
 f Opposite sides of a parallelogram are ___ and ___.
 g The sides of a rhombus are ___.

6 Use a triangular piece of paper.

Fold the corners of your triangular piece of paper to a common point on the base. What does this show?

Does the result always work? Why? Explain and justify your reasoning.

Exercise commentary

The questions assess objectives on Framework Page 179.

Problem solving

Questions 3 and 6 assess objectives on Framework Page 31.

Group work

The exercise is suitable for group or paired work with the emphasis on the use of mathematical language.

Misconceptions

The use of geometric language can cause problems with students continuing to mix up names of shapes.

Having prominent displays of the main shapes and regular revision of their properties is important, as are regular spelling 'tests' to ensure students use the language confidently.

Some students have difficulty with the convention ABC for an angle.

Key Stage 3 questions tend to use a single letter, which is more straightforward.

Links

Geometric properties: Framework Pages 185–187.

Homework

S1.1HW focuses on using labelling conventions in sketches and writing definitions of mathematical terms.

Answers

1 Appropriate diagrams. 2 a Sides, angles b Trapezium c Regular d Its corner e Four, vertices f Hexagon

3 Must include: a four equal angles b opposite sides parallel c two parallel sides of different lengths d equal sides and equal angles e equal sides 4 Corresponding and alternate angles marked.

5 a 180° b equal c equal d 60° e 90° f equal and parallel g equal

6 Angles in a triangle sum to 180°, because they fit on a straight line.

S1.2 Angles in polygons

Mental starter

Multiples

Ask students to complete the 180 times table up to 10×180.

Discuss strategies.

Emphasise the link with the 9 times table.

Useful resources

S1.2OHP – octagons for the introductory activity, and a compound shape for the plenary

Introductory activity

Draw a triangle on an OHP.

Ask volunteers to show you different exterior angles of the triangle.

Emphasise that all exterior angles must be in the same direction.

Encourage students to rotate the triangle so they can see the direction is the same.

Emphasise interior + exterior = 180°.

Discuss the sum of the interior angles.

Discuss how students know this fact: it comes from the definition that there are 360° in a full turn.

Show a regular octagon (S1.2OHP).

Discuss the number of interior and exterior angles.

Encourage students to realise that the sizes of the angles are the same.

Discuss how to find the sum of the interior angles. Emphasise that you must start from facts you know – 180° in a triangle.

Encourage students to show how to spilt the octagon into triangles.

Emphasise the method of drawing diagonals from one vertex.

Refer to the mental starter for strategies of finding $6 \times 180°$.

Discuss a general rule for finding the sum of the interior angles.

Emphasise that there are six triangles because there are six diagonals.

Discuss whether this is true for irregular octagons (as on **S1.2OHP**).

Use the interior angles to find the exterior angles.

Discuss the general rule. Encourage students to derive the rule as shown in the Students' Book.

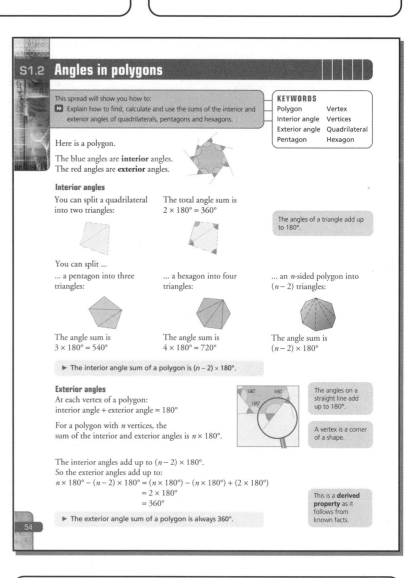

S1.2 Angles in polygons

This spread will show you how to:
▶ Explain how to find, calculate and use the sums of the interior and exterior angles of quadrilaterals, pentagons and hexagons.

KEYWORDS

Polygon	Vertex
Interior angle	Vertices
Exterior angle	Quadrilateral
Pentagon	Hexagon

Here is a polygon.

The blue angles are **interior** angles.
The red angles are **exterior** angles.

Interior angles

You can split a quadrilateral into two triangles:

The total angle sum is
$2 \times 180° = 360°$

The angles of a triangle add up to 180°.

You can split ...

... a pentagon into three triangles:

... a hexagon into four triangles:

... an n-sided polygon into $(n - 2)$ triangles:

The angle sum is
$3 \times 180° = 540°$

The angle sum is
$4 \times 180° = 720°$

The angle sum is
$(n - 2) \times 180°$

▶ The interior angle sum of a polygon is $(n - 2) \times 180°$.

Exterior angles

At each vertex of a polygon:
interior angle + exterior angle = 180°

For a polygon with n vertices, the
sum of the interior and exterior angles is $n \times 180°$.

The interior angles add up to $(n - 2) \times 180°$.
So the exterior angles add up to:
$n \times 180° - (n - 2) \times 180° = (n \times 180°) - (n \times 180°) + (2 \times 180°)$
$= 2 \times 180°$
$= 360°$

The angles on a straight line add up to 180°.

A vertex is a corner of a shape.

This is a **derived property** as it follows from known facts.

▶ The exterior angle sum of a polygon is always 360°.

54

Plenary

S1.2OHP shows a diagram made out of rhombuses and kites.

Discuss the properties of each of the shapes.

Challenge students to find angles, giving reasons for their choices.

Emphasise the need to start from facts they know.

Further activities

Students could investigate which regular polygons, tessellate (for example, rhombuses, hexagons). Encourage students to use their knowledge of angles to explain why the tessellations work. What are the interior angles of their regular polygons?

Differentiation

Core questions:
▶ Questions 1 and 2 focus on proving the angle facts for a triangle and quadrilateral.
▶ Questions 3–6 focus on finding interior and exterior angles.
▶ Questions 7 and 8 focus on combinations of shapes.

Extension tier: focuses on exterior/interior angles of polygons.

Support tier: focuses on angle facts for triangles.

Exercise S1.2

1 The diagram shows a quadrilateral.

Copy and complete:

$a + b + c =$ ___
$d + e + f =$ ___
The angle sum of a quadrilateral = ___

2 Use this diagram to prove that the sum of the three angles of a triangle is 180°.

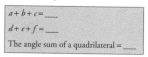

Hint: First look at the interior angles, then the angles on the straight line.

3 For this pentagon:

Copy and complete:

a You can split the pentagon into ___ triangles from one vertex.

b Each triangle has an angle sum of ___°.

c The angle sum of the pentagon is ___ × ___°.

4 Find the sum of the interior angles of each of these polygons.

a

b

c

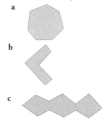

5 Find the sum of the interior angles of:
a an octagon
b a decagon
c a 30-sided polygon
d a 100-sided polygon.

6 Find the sum of the exterior angles of each polygon in question 5.

7 A regular polygon has equal sides and equal angles. This tessellation is made from regular octagons and regular quadrilaterals.

Draw a tessellation that uses a regular polygon and one other shape.

8 Use your knowledge of angles to explain why the tessellation in question 7 works.

Exercise commentary

The questions assess objectives on Framework Page 183.

Problem solving
Question 2 assesses objectives on Framework Page 31.

Group work
Questions 7 and 8 are suitable for paired or small group work.

Misconceptions
Students often find splitting up a shape into triangles confusing as it appears to create many more interior angles than at the start and it is difficult to see the correlation between what is created and what you are trying to find out.
One useful strategy is to mark the interior angles in a colour and then draw in the diagonals in pencil.
Emphasise that the triangles tessellate to create the interior angles of the shape.

Links
Geometric properties: Framework Pages 185–187.
Deriving formulae: Pages 139–143.

Homework

S1.2HW practises finding interior angles of polygons and investigates tessellations of two regular polygons.

Answers

1 180°, 180°, 360°
2 Angles on a straight line sum to 180°. The angles in the triangle fit on a straight line, so they too must sum to 180°.
3 three, 180°, 3 × 180°   4 a 900° b 720° c 1800°
5 a 1080° b 1440° c 5040° d 17 640°   6 All 360°
7 Student's own tessellation
8 Interior angle of square = 90°, interior angle of octagon = 135°
   90° + 135° + 135° = 360° = angle at a point

S1.3 Angles in regular polygons

Mental starter

Division

Write these numbers on the board:

88, 90, 100, 120, 150, 160, 200, 240.

Point to each one in turn and ask if it is divisible by 4.

Students hold up 'Y' or 'N' indicating what they think.

Repeat for division by 5 and 6.

Discuss strategies for dividing by 4, 5 and 6.

Useful resources

S1.3OHP – a regular quadrilateral, pentagon and hexagon

Introductory activity

Show the shapes on S1.3OHP.

Discuss the properties of the shapes.

Emphasise that they all have equal angles and equal sides.

Encourage students to identify other properties, such as symmetries.

Discuss what you call a shape with all sides equal and all angles equal.

Emphasise that a square is a regular quadrilateral.

Discuss whether there are any other regular quadrilaterals. Ask students to explain their reasoning.

Discuss the interior and exterior angles of a square.

Encourage students to explain their reasoning.

Emphasise that you divide the sum of the angles by four.

Repeat for the interior and exterior angles of a pentagon and a hexagon.

Discuss strategies for finding the interior angle in more detail.

Emphasise that it is easy to find the exterior angle then subtract from 180°.

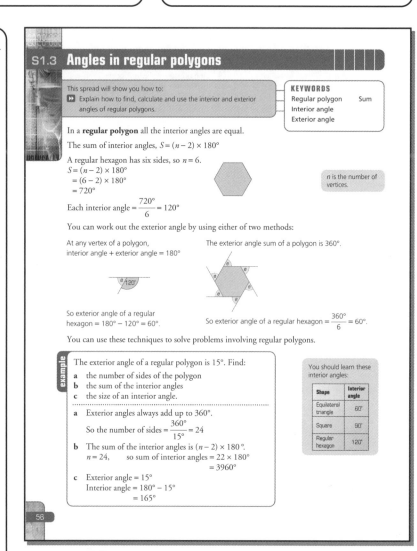

Plenary

Challenge students to state the maximum number of right angles you can have in a:

▸ Triangle
▸ Quadrilateral
▸ Pentagon.

Encourage students to explain their answers using angle calculations and diagrams.

Further activities

Students could investigate whether a regular polygon can have an interior angle of 100°. Encourage them to explain and justify their conclusion, using angle calculations and diagrams.

Differentiation

Core questions:

▸ Questions 1 and 2 focus on following a method for finding interior angles.
▸ Questions 3–7 focus on choosing a method to find interior and exterior angles.
▸ Question 8 is a more open task focusing on geometric reasoning.

Extension tier: focuses on problems using angle facts and properties of shapes.
Support tier: focuses on angles in parallel lines.

Exercise S1.3

1 The diagram shows a pentagon.

Copy and complete:

> You can split a regular pentagon into 3 triangles.
> The sum of the interior angles is $3 \times 180° = $ ___.
> Each interior angle is ___ ÷ 5 = ___.
> Each exterior angle is 180° − ___ = ___
> or $\dfrac{360°}{5} = $ ___.

2 The diagram shows an octagon.

Copy and complete:

> You can split a regular octagon into ___ triangles.
> The sum of the interior angles is ___ × 180° = ___.
> Each interior angle is ___ ÷ 8 = ___.
> Each exterior angle is 180° − ___ = ___
> or $\dfrac{360°}{8} = $ ___.

3 Find the sum of the interior angles of each of these polygons.

a   b   c

4 Use your answers to question 3 to work out the interior angle of each of these regular polygons:
  a regular hexagon
  b regular nonagon
  c regular decagon.

5 Find the exterior angle of a:
  a regular octagon
  b regular hexagon
  c regular decagon
  d regular nonagon.

6 Use your answers to question 5 to find the interior angle of a:
  a regular octagon
  b regular hexagon
  c regular decagon
  d regular nonagon.

7 In questions 4 and 6 you have used two methods to find the interior angle of a regular polygon. Which do you prefer? Give a reason for your choice.

8 **Investigation**
What is the maximum number of right angles you can have in an octagon?

What about other polygons?

Exercise commentary

The questions assess objectives on Framework Page 183.

Problem solving

Question 3 assesses objectives on Framework Page 27.
Question 8 assesses Page 17.

Group work

Questions 3–8 are suitable for students to discuss in pairs or groups.

Misconceptions

Students may mix up the formulae for interior and exterior angles, using the sum of interior angles as always 180°.
Encourage them to split the shape into triangles to help them visualise the angle sum, even if they use the exterior angles to calculate the interior ones.
Students may also draw diagonals from different vertices and find the result confusing.
Emphasise that you always draw from the same vertex, and that the diagonals should not cross.

Links

Geometric properties: Framework Pages 185–187.

Homework

S1.3HW gives more practice in calculating interior and exterior angles of regular polygons.

Answers

1 540°, 540° ÷ 5 = 108°, 180° − 108° = 72°, 72°
2 six, 6 × 180° = 1080°, 1080° ÷ 8 = 135°, 180° − 135° = 45°, 45°
3 a 1080°   b 720°   c 1440°   4 a 120°   b 140°   c 144°
5 a 45°   b 60°   c 36°   d 40°   6 a 135°   b 120°   c 144°   d 140°
7 Student's own answer plus reasoning.
    Either: $i = \dfrac{(n-2) \times 180°}{n}$ or $i = 180 - \dfrac{360}{n}$.
8 6 in an octagon. (4 in a square, 3 in a pentagon, 4 in a hexagon etc.)

S1.4 Lines and angles

Mental starter

Triangles and quadrilaterals

Ask students to draw triangles with:
▶ 1 right angle
▶ 2, then 3 equal angles
▶ 2, then 0 equal sides.

Ask them to draw quadrilaterals with:
▶ 1, then 2, then 3 right angles
▶ 1, then 2, then 0 lines of symmetry.

Useful resources

S1.4OHP – alternate and corresponding angles

Introductory activity

S1.4OHP shows angles in parallel lines.
Encourage students to tell you what they know about the angles formed.
Emphasise that:
▶ There are eight of them.
▶ They occur in pairs.
▶ The pairs add to 180°.
▶ Once you know one you know them all.

Discuss how to label them to show the equal angles. Mark the angles on the diagram.

Emphasise that there is terminology for the different equal angles:
▶ Vertically opposite angles,
▶ Corresponding angles and
▶ Alternate angles.
Discuss definitions for these terms.

On a different orientation of the diagram (on **S1.4OHP**), ask students to show pairs of angles that are corresponding or alternate.

Emphasise that the intersecting line (transversal) can be at any angle to the parallel lines to form the eight angles.

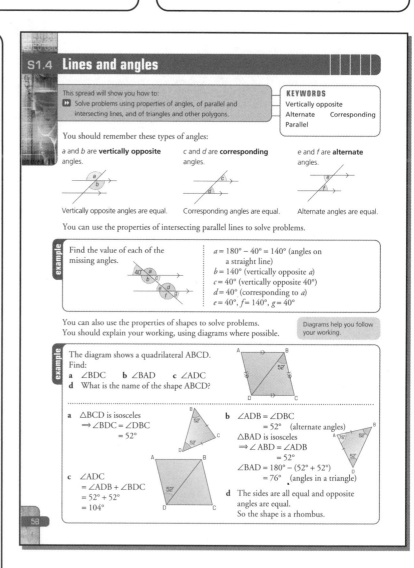

S1.4 Lines and angles

This spread will show you how to:
▶▶ Solve problems using properties of angles, of parallel and intersecting lines, and of triangles and other polygons.

KEYWORDS
Vertically opposite
Alternate   Corresponding
Parallel

You should remember these types of angles:

a and *b* are **vertically opposite** angles.

c and *d* are **corresponding** angles.

e and *f* are **alternate** angles.

Vertically opposite angles are equal.   Corresponding angles are equal.   Alternate angles are equal.

You can use the properties of intersecting parallel lines to solve problems.

example

Find the value of each of the missing angles.

$a = 180° − 40° = 140°$ (angles on a straight line)
$b = 140°$ (vertically opposite a)
$c = 40°$ (vertically opposite 40°)
$d = 40°$ (corresponding to a)
$e = 40°$, $f = 140°$, $g = 40°$

You can also use the properties of shapes to solve problems.
You should explain your working, using diagrams where possible.

Diagrams help you follow your working.

example

The diagram shows a quadrilateral ABCD.
Find:
a ∠BDC   **b** ∠BAD   **c** ∠ADC
d What is the name of the shape ABCD?

a △BCD is isosceles
⇒ ∠BDC = ∠DBC
= 52°

b ∠ADB = ∠DBC
= 52°   (alternate angles)
△BAD is isosceles
⇒ ∠ABD = ∠ADB
= 52°
∠BAD = 180° − (52° + 52°)
= 76°   (angles in a triangle)

c ∠ADC
= ∠ADB + ∠BDC
= 52° + 52°
= 104°

d The sides are all equal and opposite angles are equal.
So the shape is a rhombus.

58

Plenary

Draw a parallelogram on the board:
Encourage students to find the other angles.
Discuss what they notice. Does this apply to all parallelograms?
Repeat for an isosceles trapezium with one angle 125°.
Discuss what students know about angles in a quadrilateral.

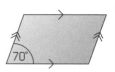

Further activities

Students can set angle problems for a partner to solve.

Emphasise that the problems should be solvable, and encourage students to give minimum but sufficient information in each diagram.

Differentiation

Core questions:

▶ Questions 1 and 2 revise geometrical language and conventions.

▶ Questions 3 and 4 focus on finding angles in parallel lines and geometric shapes.

▶ Questions 5 and 6 use the exterior angles of a triangle and will be challenging for most students.

Extension tier: focuses on Pythagoras' theorem.

Support tier: focuses on properties of quadrilaterals.

Exercise S1.4

1 Sketch these diagrams on squared paper and name them.
   a A shape with four straight sides, four right angles and two pairs of parallel sides.
   b A shape with four straight sides, no right angles and two pairs of parallel sides.
   c A shape with four straight sides, four right angles and four sides of equal length.

2 a Sketch an isosceles triangle PQR.
   b Mark the equal angles and sides and mark the angle PQR.
   c Extend the side PQ to S and mark the exterior angle of the triangle.

3 Find the angles marked with letters in these diagrams.

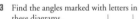
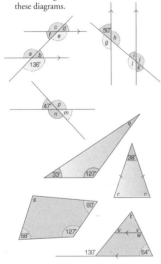

4 a Draw a pair of parallel lines and cross them with an intersecting line.
   b Label the parallel lines with arrowheads.
   c Label any pair of alternate angles with the letter *a*.
   d Label any pair of corresponding angles with the letter *c*.
   e Label any pair of vertically opposite angles with the letter *v*.

5 The diagram shows a rectangle ABEF resting on an equilateral triangle BCD. DE is a straight line passing through B. Show that triangle ABC is isosceles.

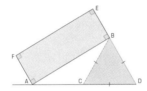

6 **Investigation**
   Change the equilateral triangle in question 5 to an isosceles triangle. Choose various values for the size of ∠CBD. Investigate the change to triangle ABC.

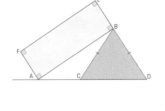

59

Exercise commentary

The questions assess objectives on Framework Pages 183–187.

Problem solving

Questions 3 and 6 assess objectives on Framework Page 17.
Question 5 assesses Page 31.

Group work

Questions 1, 2, 5 and 6 are suitable for students to discuss in pairs.

Misconceptions

Students tend to assume that angles which look equal are equal.

Emphasise that in Key Stage 3 papers questions usually have the wording 'not drawn to scale' which means they will need to work out the answer.

In addition, when asked to explain or give reasons for an answer, these must be geometric reasons.

The work on parallel lines can become very confusing with students unsure as to which the transversal is.

Encourage students to extend lines so that they can see the eight angles formed.

Links

Proof: Framework Page 179.

Homework

S1.4HW involves drawing quadrilaterals and identifying their properties, and 'missing angle' problems.

Answers

1 a Rectangle b Parallelogram c Square   2 Isosceles triangle PQR with exterior angle marked.   3 $a = 136°$, $b = 44°$, $c = 136°$, $d = 44°$, $e = 136°$, $f = 44°$, $g = 130°$, $h = 130°$, $i = 50°$, $j = 130°$, $k = 50°$, $l = 130°$, $q = 20°$, $r = 71°$, $s = 105°$, $t = 66°$, $u = 50°$, $v = 64°$, $w = 116°$

4 For example:

5 Angle C is 120°, angle B is 30° (angles on a straight line) angle A is 30° (angles in triangle ABD sum to 180°). So triangle ABC is isosceles.

6 As ∠CBD becomes smaller, AC becomes larger and triangle ABC becomes more scalene.

S1.5 Solving problems in shapes

Mental starter

Imaginings

Ask students to imagine a rectangular piece of paper.

Ask them to imagine cutting along the diagonal to form two triangles.

Challenge them to visualise all the different shapes they can make by fitting the two triangles together along an edge.

Discuss answers.

Useful resources

R15 – special quadrilaterals

S1.5F – missing information angle problems

Introductory activity

Refer to the mental starter.

Discuss the geometric properties of the different quadrilaterals formed.

Encourage students to list the:

▶ Angle properties,
▶ Side properties,
▶ Diagonal properties, and
▶ Symmetry properties.

Emphasise the need to work systematically.

Discuss the properties of other special quadrilaterals – use R15 as a prompt.

Emphasise that students need to know and be able to use these facts.

Discuss the second example in the Students' Book.

Emphasise that to solve problems you start by labelling the properties (angles) you know.

Discuss whether you can draw a quadrilateral with three equal sides and two equal angles.

Encourage students to explain their reasoning.

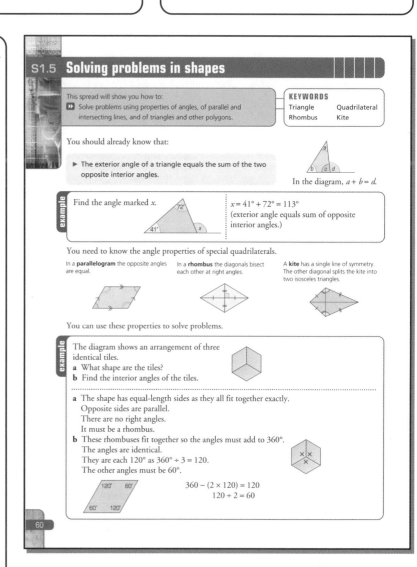

S1.5 Solving problems in shapes

This spread will show you how to:
▶▶ Solve problems using properties of angles, of parallel and intersecting lines, and of triangles and other polygons.

KEYWORDS
Triangle   Quadrilateral
Rhombus   Kite

You should already know that:

▶ The exterior angle of a triangle equals the sum of the two opposite interior angles.

In the diagram, $a + b = d$.

example

Find the angle marked x.

$x = 41° + 72° = 113°$
(exterior angle equals sum of opposite interior angles.)

You need to know the angle properties of special quadrilaterals.

In a **parallelogram** the opposite angles are equal.

In a **rhombus** the diagonals bisect each other at right angles.

A **kite** has a single line of symmetry. The other diagonal splits the kite into two isosceles triangles.

You can use these properties to solve problems.

example

The diagram shows an arrangement of three identical tiles.
a What shape are the tiles?
b Find the interior angles of the tiles.

a The shape has equal-length sides as they all fit together exactly.
 Opposite sides are parallel.
 There are no right angles.
 It must be a rhombus.
b These rhombuses fit together so the angles must add to 360°.
 The angles are identical.
 They are each 120° as 360° ÷ 3 = 120.
 The other angles must be 60°.

$360 - (2 × 120) = 120$
$120 ÷ 2 = 60$

60

Plenary

More imaginings

Ask students to imagine a square piece of paper.

Ask them to imagine making a symmetrical cut across one corner: what shape is left?

Ask them to make a series of parallel cuts: when does the shape left change, and what does it become?

Repeat with a rectangle.

Further activities

Students could investigate the minimum information they need to mark on the diagrams on S1.5F to allow a partner to find **all** the unmarked angles. They could choose values and solve the problems.

Differentiation

Core questions:
▶ Question 1 focuses on exterior angles of a triangle.
▶ Questions 2–5 focus on properties of quadrilaterals.
▶ Questions 6 and 7 are more challenging questions for confident students.

Extension tier: focuses on using Pythagoras' theorem to find the height/area of triangles.

Support tier: focuses on angle problems using angle and quadrilateral facts.

Exercise S1.5

1 Find the angles marked with letters in these diagrams.

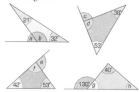

2 Sketch each of these shapes, marking any equal angles, equal sides and lines of symmetry:
  a rhombus
  b regular octagon
  c isosceles triangle
  d equilateral triangle
  e kite
  f trapezium
  g scalene acute-angled triangle
  h regular pentagon
  i irregular quadrilateral
  j isosceles trapezium.

3 Find the angles marked with letters in these quadrilaterals.

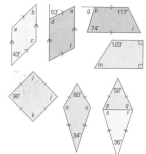

4 Name each of the quadrilaterals in question 3.

5 Write a LOGO program to draw each of these polygons with a side of 5 cm. The first one is started for you.
  a Regular pentagon
    FORWARD 50
    TURN RIGHT 72
    FORWARD 50
    TURN RIGHT 72
    FORWARD__
  b Equilateral triangle
  c Regular hexagon
  d Regular decagon
  e Square

6 The diagram shows a rhombus.

Find these angles:
  a ∠ABD
  b ∠ADB
  c ∠BDC
  d ∠BCD
  e ∠DBC

7 PQRS is an isosceles trapezium.

  a M is the midpoint of RS. If ∠QRS is 55°, calculate the size of the other angles.
  b Repeat with different values for ∠QRS.

Exercise commentary

The questions assess objectives on Framework Pages 185 and 187.

Problem solving
Question 5 assesses objectives on Framework Page 15.
Questions 1, 3, 6 and 7 assess Page 17.

Group work
Questions 5–7 are suitable for students to discuss in pairs.

Misconceptions
Students often find complex angle problems difficult.
Encourage them to label all the facts that they know on the shape and to work out those they can derive. Often this will give the next step to finding the required solution.
Students tend to mix up facts.
Encourage them to give reasons for their answers as these are usually required in Key Stage 3 tests. This will help to reinforce which fact should be used. It is important that students can recall facts and have regular opportunities to do so.

Links
Proof: Framework Page 179.

Homework

S1.5HW focuses on using angle facts to find angles in triangles and quadrilaterals.

Answers

1 $a = 53°$, $b = 127°$, $c = 91°$, $d = 89°$, $e = 95°$, $f = 85°$, $g = 50°$, $h = 90°$
2 Sketches of shapes.
3 $a = 137°$, $b = 43°$, $c = 137°$, $d = 117°$, $e = 63°$, $f = 117°$, $g = 74°$, $h = 106°$, $i = 63°$, $j = 96°$, $k = 84°$, $l = 84°$, $m = 57°$, $n = 133°$, $p = q = 64°$, $r = s = 72°$
4 Parallelogram, parallelogram, trapezium, rhombus, right-angled trapezium, kite, kite
5 fd 50 then **a** rt 72, fd 50 four times **b** rt 120, fd 50 twice
  c rt 60, fd 50 five times **d** rt 36, fd 50 nine times **e** rt 90, fd 50 three times
6 **a** 69° **b** 69° **c** 69° **d** 42° **e** 69°
7 **a** ∠S = 55°, ∠P = ∠Q = 125° **b** Always get two pairs of equal angles.

S1.6 Circle properties

Mental starter

Areas

Show a rectangle with length three and width five.
Ask for the area. Students should be able to quote the formula.
Ask for four rectangles with an area of 20 cm².
Show a triangle with height two and base five.
Ask for the area. Students should be able to quote the formula.
Ask for four triangles with an area of 10 cm².
Discuss the link between the two sets of answers.

Useful resources

S1.6OHP – parts of a circle
Compasses
Protractors
S1.6F – pie chart

Introductory activity

Discuss the definition of a circle.
Emphasise that it is a set of points that are a fixed distance (radius) from a fixed point (centre).
Discuss how to draw a circle – use compasses.

Encourage students to give everyday examples of circles:
▶ Car wheels, satellite dish, 10p coin.
Discuss the centre and radius of each of the examples.
Discuss the distance around the edge of the circle – the perimeter.
Emphasise that it has a special name: the circumference.
Encourage students to think of examples of the word circumference used in everyday life.

Discuss examples of circles in maths, in particular the use of pie charts.
Emphasise that a pie chart is split into sectors, each bounded by the radius.

S1.6OHP shows a circle broken into sectors and one broken into segments.
Discuss definitions of each label on each diagram.
Emphasise that the definitions must be precise and identify the term uniquely.
Emphasise that the diameter is double the length of the radius.

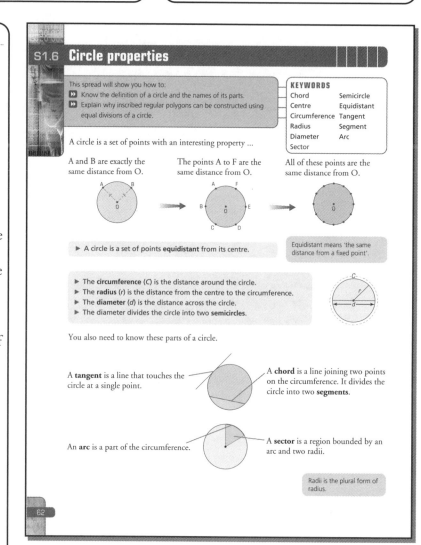

Plenary

Ask students to sketch a circle.
Ask them to draw and label these parts of the circle:
▶ Centre
▶ Diameter
▶ Radius
▶ Circumference
▶ Sector
▶ Arc.
Discuss any difficulties.

Further activities

Students could follow the instructions on **S1.6F** to construct a pie chart for a set of data.

Differentiation

Core questions:
▶ Questions 1 and 2 focus on drawing and labelling circles.
▶ Questions 3 and 4 focus on using a circle to construct a hexagon.
▶ Questions 5 and 6 focus on constructing a pentagon and the other polygons using circles.

Extension tier: focuses on constructing regular polygons in circles and solving problems involving circles and Pythagoras.

Support tier: focuses on constructing perpendiculars.

Exercise S1.6

1 Draw a circle with radius 4 cm. Label the centre, the radius and the circumference.

2 a Draw an arc with radius 4 cm.
On this arc, draw a sector with angle 60°.
b Draw an arc with radius 5 cm.
On this arc draw a sector with angle 120°.
c Draw a circle with radius 5 cm.
On this circle draw and label:
  i an arc
  ii a sector
  iii a radius
  iv a chord
  v a segment.

3 You can use a circle to construct a regular hexagon.
Follow these steps:
a Using compasses, draw a circle of radius 5 cm.

b Without changing your compass setting, put your compass point on the circle and mark off points. Put your compass point on each mark you have just made to make the next mark.

c When you have got back to the start, join the points up with chords. This will give you a regular hexagon.

4 Add these lines to the hexagon you drew in question 3.

Explain how you know that a regular hexagon is made up of six equilateral triangles.

5 Construct a regular pentagon by following these steps:
a Work out this angle first.

b Draw a circle of radius 6 cm. Draw in the radius.
c Measure the angle you found in part **a** from the radius.
Mark the point on the circumference. Join the centre to this point.
d Repeat part **c** from your new radius.
e Repeat again until you return to the start.
You should now be able to produce the pentagon.

6 Which other regular polygons could you construct by equal divisions of a circle?

Exercise commentary

The questions assess objectives on Framework Pages 195.

Problem solving
Questions 5 and 6 assess objectives on Framework Page 27.

Group work
All questions are suitable for group or paired discussion.

Misconceptions
Students often forget the meanings of the key words, particularly arc, sector and segment.
The plenary activity should give them a useful reminder. Encourage students to personalise their diagrams using colour and to keep them handy.
Emphasise that an orange splits into segments and visualising the shape of the segment should help them to remember the definition of the term.
Encourage students to discuss any other strategies they have for remembering the definitions.

Links
Polygons: Framework Page 183.

Homework

S1.6HW gives practice in constructing sectors and regular polygons.

Answers

1 Circle labelled as stated
2 2 arcs + sectors as stated, one circle, labelled as stated.
3 Student's own construction of hexagon
4 The radii are all the same length, so each triangle is isosceles.
The distances marked around the circumference were also equal to the radius. So each triangle has 3 equal sides.
5 a 72° **b–e** pentagon produced as shown.
6 All regular polygons can be constructed in this way.

Mental starter

Encourage students to discuss, in pairs, whether these triangles can be constructed:

▶ Sides 1 cm, 2 cm, 10 cm
▶ Sides 5 cm, 9 cm, 3 cm
▶ Angles 20°, 30°, 70°
▶ Triangle with two obtuse angles.

Compare results, encouraging students to give reasons for their answers.

Useful resources

Compasses
Rulers
Protractors

Introductory activity

Ask students to sketch a triangle with **sides 3 cm, 4 cm, 5 cm.**
Discuss answers.
Encourage students to explain how they decided what to draw.
Emphasise that the longest side will be opposite the largest angle.

Discuss how to construct the triangle using compasses.
Encourage them to start by drawing the longest side (5 cm).
Emphasise that the end of the 4 cm side will be 4 cm away from the end of the longest side.
Emphasise that you can construct all the points 4 cm away by a circle of radius 4 cm.
Repeat for 3 cm. Emphasise that the third point of this triangle is where these circles meet. Students can draw arcs rather than full circles each time.
Discuss which is the largest angle.
Emphasise that it is opposite the longest side.

Students may notice it is a right angle.
Discuss how to construct a right angle without compasses.

Discuss how to draw a triangle with lengths 6 cm, 8 cm, 10 cm.
Emphasise that you use the same method.
Encourage students to notice that all the lengths are doubled so it is an enlargement of the previous triangle.
Discuss what this means – the angles will be the same.

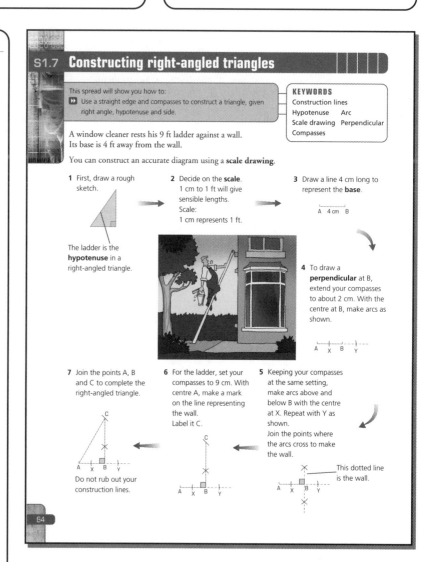

S1.7 Constructing right-angled triangles

This spread will show you how to:
▶ Use a straight edge and compasses to construct a triangle, given right angle, hypotenuse and side.

KEYWORDS
Construction lines
Hypotenuse   Arc
Scale drawing Perpendicular
Compasses

A window cleaner rests his 9 ft ladder against a wall. Its base is 4 ft away from the wall.

You can construct an accurate diagram using a **scale drawing.**

1 First, draw a rough sketch.

The ladder is the **hypotenuse** in a right-angled triangle.

2 Decide on the **scale**. 1 cm to 1 ft will give sensible lengths. Scale: 1 cm represents 1 ft.

3 Draw a line 4 cm long to represent the **base**.
A 4 cm B

4 To draw a **perpendicular** at B, extend your compasses to about 2 cm. With the centre at B, make arcs as shown.
A X B Y

5 Keeping your compasses at the same setting, make arcs above and below B with the centre at X. Repeat with Y as shown. Join the points where the arcs cross to make the wall. This dotted line is the wall.

6 For the ladder, set your compasses to 9 cm. With centre A, make a mark on the line representing the wall. Label it C.

7 Join the points A, B and C to complete the right-angled triangle. Do not rub out your construction lines.

Plenary

Challenge students to construct these triangles:

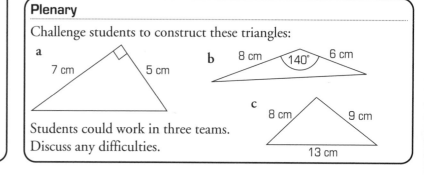

a 7 cm, 5 cm (right angle)
b 8 cm, 6 cm, 140°
c 8 cm, 9 cm, 13 cm

Students could work in three teams.
Discuss any difficulties.

Further activities

In **S1.7ICT** students use a geometry package to construct right-angled triangles.

Alternatively

Students can make up impossible triangles for partners to try to construct.

Differentiation

Core questions:

▶ Questions 1 and 2 focus on constructing and measuring right-angled triangles.
▶ Questions 3–5 focus on constructing triangles.
▶ Question 6 focuses on geometrical reasoning.

Extension tier: focuses on constructing triangles and deciding when a given triangle is unique.

Support tier: focuses on constructing triangles.

Exercise S1.7

1 Construct the scale drawing described on page 64.
Use your diagram to measure:
a the angle between the ladder and the ground
b how far up the wall the ladder reaches.

2 Construct these triangles.

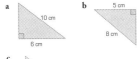

3 Construct these triangles.

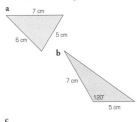

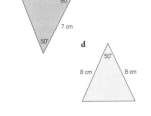

4 A window cleaner has a 12 metre ladder. Kings Castle is surrounded by a 4 metre moat. Use a scale drawing to investigate the maximum height of windows that can be cleaned.

5 Construct these triangles.

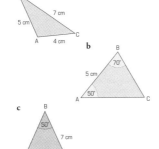

6 Can you construct triangles with these measurements?
Construct each triangle if possible. If not possible, give a reason.
a ∠BAC = 50°, ∠ABC = 60°, ∠ACB = 70°
b BC = 6 cm, AC = 4 cm, AB = 2 cm
c AC = 8 cm, BC = 6 cm, ∠ACB = 40°
d BC = 6 cm, AC = 10 cm, ∠ABC = 80°

65

Exercise commentary

The questions assess objectives on Framework Pages 221 and 223.

Problem solving

Question 4 assesses objectives on Framework Page 27.
Question 6 assesses Page 31.

Group work

The exercise is suitable for paired work.

Misconceptions

There are many steps involved in constructions and some students lose track of their working.
Encourage them to work systematically, drawing a sketch of the shape on the same page as the construction so they can see what they need to do.
Emphasise the need to leave construction marks in place.
Encourage students to check their drawings by checking that the longest side is opposite the largest angle.

Links

Loci: Framework Page 225.

Homework

S1.7HW gives practice in constructing triangles, with and without right angles. Students will need compasses, rulers and protractors.

Answers

1 a 64°   b 8.1 m
2, 3 Triangles constructed as shown
4 11.3 m
5 Triangles constructed as shown.
6 a Yes   b No, AB + AC must be more than BC.   c Yes   d Yes

Mental starter

Pizza delivery

Ask students to mark a point P on a piece of paper.

Ask them to mark any point on the paper that is 3 cm away from P.

Students repeat this until they have 10 marks 3 cm away from P.

Students should hold up their paper at this point.

Discuss any difficulties.

Useful resources

Compasses
Rulers

Introductory activity

Refer to the mental starter.

Discuss the pattern that the points made – a circle, centre P, radius 3 cm.

Emphasise that the circle is the locus of points 3 cm away from P.

Discuss this problem:

▶ The catchment area for a school is all the houses within 4 km of the school.

▶ Students who live more than 3 km from a school are entitled to a free bus pass.

Encourage students to show the area where students are entitled to a free bus pass.

Emphasise that they will need to use a scale – 1 cm for 1 km is sensible.

Emphasise that each locus is a set of points a fixed distance away from a fixed point. This is a circle.

Ask students to draw two points, P and Q on a piece of paper – they must be more than 2 cm apart.

Ask them to mark a point that is the same distance from both P and Q.

Encourage them to mark more equidistant points until they can see a pattern.

Discuss students' explanations of the pattern.

Emphasise that it is the perpendicular bisector of the line joining P and Q.

Discuss how to construct the perpendicular bisector of a line AB.

Emphasise that the points must be the same distance from A and from B so you use circles of equal radius.

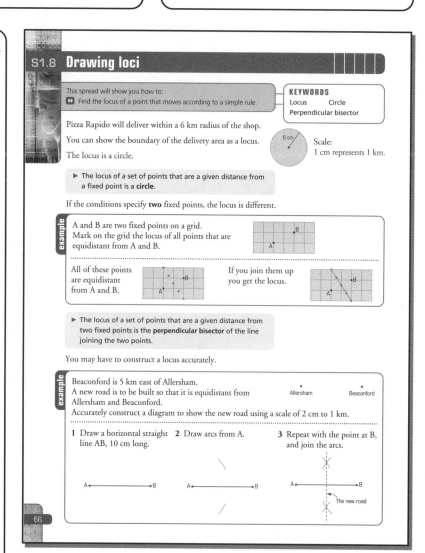

Plenary

Challenge students to visualise and describe this locus:

▶ A piece of string 30 cm long is held vertically.

▶ A wasp flies so that it is always 10 cm away from the string.

Discuss students' suggestions.

Emphasise that the locus is a cylinder with a hemisphere at each end.

Challenge students to draw the locus of a point that moves so that it is always 2 cm away from a line RS, which is 4 cm long.

Differentiation

Core questions:
▶ Question 1 involves finding a locus on a grid which can be done by counting squares.
▶ Questions 2 and 3 focus on constructing a locus.
▶ Questions 4 and 5 focus on 3-D loci.

Extension tier: focuses on loci in threee dimensions.

Support tier: focuses on constructing circles and perpendicular bisectors.

Exercise S1.8

1 Copy the diagrams and draw the locus of all points which are the same distance from the marked points.

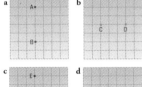

2 Pizza Rapido delivers within a 6 km radius. Pizza Quik delivers within a 4 km radius. The shops are 5 km apart. Draw a scale diagram to show the region which can receive pizzas from both outlets.

Start by drawing R and Q 5 km apart. A scale of 1 cm to 1 km is suitable.

3 Use a straight edge and compasses to draw the locus of all the points that are the same distance from these pairs of points.

4 A spider is motionless.
A fly is buzzing so that it is always 8 cm from the spider.

Describe the locus of the fly.

Hint:
The fly moves in 3-D space!

5 Describe two other situations which would give a locus of the same shape as the one in question 4.

67

Exercise commentary

The questions assess objectives on Framework Page 225.

Problem solving
Question 2 assesses objectives on Framework Page 15.

Group work
Questions 4 and 5 are suitable for paired work.

Misconceptions
Students will often draw a locus by eye instead of constructing it, particularly for perpendicular bisectors.
Emphasise the need for precision.
Students can mix up the different loci, drawing a set of points 3 cm away from a fixed point as a straight line 3 cm away from the point.
Encourage students to mark a few points that satisfy the rule before drawing the locus.

Links
Constructions: Framework Pages 221–223.

Homework

S1.8HW focuses on constructing circular and perpendicular bisector loci. Question 5 involves a 3-D locus. Students will need compasses and rulers.

Answers

1 Loci drawn as shown.
2 Scale diagram similar to:

3 Three perpendicular bisectors drawn.
4 Sphere with radius 8 cm
5 Examples: conker on the end of a string, ball on the end of a piece of string, inside wheel of a gyroscope.

S1.9 More loci

Mental starter

Ask students to mark a point on a piece of paper that is the same distance away from both vertical edges.

Ask them to repeat this until they have 10 marks the same distance away from both vertical edges.

Students should hold up their paper at this point.

Discuss any difficulties.

Useful resources

Compasses
Rulers
Plain paper

Introductory activity

Refer to the mental starter.

Discuss the pattern that the points made – a line parallel to the edges, and exactly halfway between them.

Repeat the mental starter activity.
This time, students should mark points that are equidistant from adjacent edges.

Encourage students to mark as many points as they need to before they can see the pattern.

Discuss the pattern that the points make.

Emphasise that the locus is a set of points a fixed distance away from each edge.

Discuss the properties of this line.

Emphasise it is the bisector of the angle between the edges.

Discuss how to construct an angle bisector.

Emphasise that using a protractor is not as accurate as using a pair of compasses.

Discuss the locus of the vertex of a square that is rolling along a straight line as in the Students' Book example.

Discuss why part of the locus is more than 1 cm high.

Encourage students to focus on the basic shape of the locus.

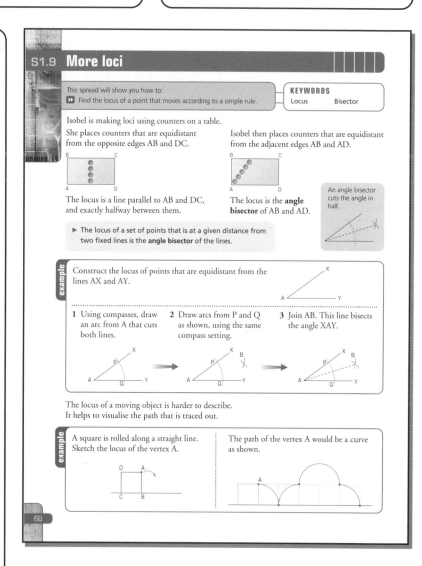

S1.9 More loci

This spread will show you how to:
▶ Find the locus of a point that moves according to a simple rule.

KEYWORDS
Locus   Bisector

Isobel is making loci using counters on a table.

She places counters that are equidistant from the opposite edges AB and DC.

Isobel then places counters that are equidistant from the adjacent edges AB and AD.

The locus is a line parallel to AB and DC, and exactly halfway between them.

The locus is the **angle bisector** of AB and AD.

An angle bisector cuts the angle in half.

▶ The locus of a set of points that is at a given distance from two fixed lines is the **angle bisector** of the lines.

example

Construct the locus of points that are equidistant from the lines AX and AY.

1 Using compasses, draw an arc from A that cuts both lines.

2 Draw arcs from P and Q as shown, using the same compass setting.

3 Join AB. This line bisects the angle XAY.

The locus of a moving object is harder to describe. It helps to visualise the path that is traced out.

example

A square is rolled along a straight line. Sketch the locus of the vertex A.

The path of the vertex A would be a curve as shown.

68

Plenary

Challenge students to visualise and describe the locus of the vertex of a rectangle 1 cm high and 2 cm long that is rolling along a straight line.

Encourage students to use squared paper.

Discuss what will happen to the locus as the dimensions change.

Further activities

Students could consider the locus of other points on the square in question 5. Challenge students to draw the locus of a point P that moves at a fixed distance 2 cm from a square ABCD of side 4 cm.

Differentiation

Core questions:
▸ Question 1 involves bisecting an angle on a grid which can be done by counting squares.
▸ Questions 2–4 focus on constructing angle bisectors.
▸ Questions 5–7 focus on harder problems with irregular loci.

Extension tier: focuses on scale drawings of combinations of loci.

Support tier: focuses on Logo instructions and accurate constructions.

Exercise S1.9

1 Copy the diagrams and draw the locus of all points which are the same distance from both lines.

a

b

c

d

2 On plain paper, draw three diagrams with two straight lines similar to those in question 1.
Construct the locus of all points which are the same distance from both lines for each diagram.

3 Using only compasses, a ruler and a pencil:
   a Construct an angle of 90°.
   b Construct an angle of 45°.

4 Using only compasses, a ruler and a pencil:
   a Construct an equilateral triangle.
   b Bisect each angle.
   c Describe the different shapes made inside the triangle by the angle bisector.

5 Look at the last example on page 68. Copy and continue the locus of the point A as the square is rolled along a straight line.

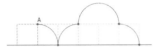

6 An isosceles right-angled triangle is rolled along a straight line:

Copy and continue the locus of the vertex A.

7 Investigate the locus of a fixed point A for other regular polygons rolled along a straight line.

Exercise commentary

The questions assess objectives on Framework Page 225.

Problem solving
Questions 3 and 4 assess objectives on Framework Page 27.
Question 7 assesses Page 15.

Group work
The exercise is particularly suitable for group work.

Misconceptions
Students will often draw a locus by eye instead of constructing it, particularly for angle bisectors.
Emphasise the need for precision.
Key Stage 3 questions usually require working to be shown and a slight error in measuring could lead to no marks awarded.
Students forget how to construct angle bisectors.
Discuss strategies for remembering as a class so useful methods can be shared.

Links
Constructions: Framework Pages 221–223.

Homework

S1.9HW gives more practice in constructing angle bisectors. Students need compasses, ruler and plain paper.

Answers

1 Four angle bisectors
2 Three more examples of angle bisectors
3 Angles constructed as given, 45° by bisecting 90°
4 **a, b** Triangle constructed and angles bisected.   **c** Right-angled triangles
5 Pattern repeated as shown.
6 Pattern repeated as shown.
7 Student's own investigation.

The key objectives for this unit are:
▶ Solve problems using properties of angles, of parallel and intersecting lines, and of triangles and other polygons. (185–189)
▶ Present a concise and reasoned argument using symbols and explanatory text. (31)

Plenary activity

Pose this problem for students to solve:
▶ A tessellation uses a regular hexagon and one other shape.
▶ Find the other shape and draw a sketch to show why the tessellation works. [It's an equilateral triangle.]

Check out commentary

1 Emphasise that the aim is to calculate the angles, not measure them.
Parts **a** and **b** establish that all angles are 60°, so ABC is equilateral, which leads to **c** and **d**.
In part **e** students do not need to calculate the area. They should realise that DC < 10 cm, so area $= \frac{1}{2} \times DC \times 10$ is less than 50.

2 Students often find it difficult to explain answers to problems.
Emphasise that the explanation could be as simple as a diagram, or involve geometrical reasoning.
To show an answer is false, encourage students to use a counter-example.

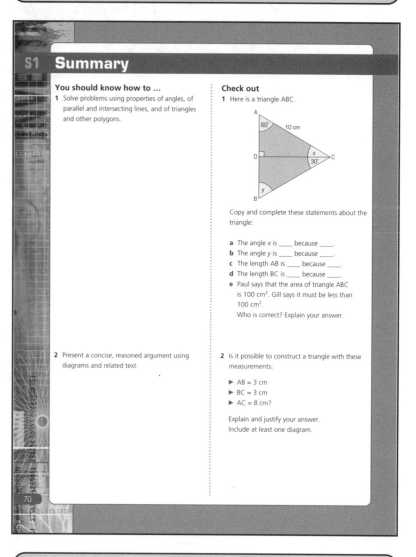

S1 Summary

You should know how to ...

1 Solve problems using properties of angles, of parallel and intersecting lines, and of triangles and other polygons.

2 Present a concise, reasoned argument using diagrams and related text.

Check out

1 Here is a triangle ABC.

Copy and complete these statements about the triangle:

a The angle x is _____ because _____.
b The angle y is _____ because _____.
c The length AB is _____ because _____.
d The length BC is _____ because _____.
e Paul says that the area of triangle ABC is 100 cm². Gill says it must be less than 100 cm².
Who is correct? Explain your answer.

2 Is it possible to construct a triangle with these measurements:

▶ AB = 3 cm
▶ BC = 3 cm
▶ AC = 8 cm?

Explain and justify your answer.
Include at least one diagram.

Development

The work on circles is developed in S2, S3 and S4 develop geometric reasoning further.

Links

The work on reasoning has strong links to algebraic proof, with students moving away from making judgements based on numerical examples.

Mental starters

Objectives covered in this unit:
▶ Order, add, subtract, multiply and divide integers.
▶ Add and subtract several small numbers.
▶ Discuss and interpret graphs.
▶ Calculate a mean using an assumed mean.

Resources needed

* means class set needed
Essential:
R36 – handling data cycle

Useful:
D1.2OHP – statistical averages
D1.3OHP – graphs and charts
D1.4OHP – interpreting graphs and charts
D1.5OHP – population pyramid
D1.6OHP – misleading statistics
D1.3ICT* – chart types
Newspapers or magazines
Compasses*

D1 Handling data

This unit will show you how to:

▶▶ Suggest a problem to explore using statistical methods, frame questions and raise conjectures.
▶▶ Discuss how data relate to a problem and identity possible sources.
▶▶ Design a survey to capture the necessary data.
▶▶ Determine the sample size and degree of accuracy needed.
▶▶ Design, trial, and if necessary refine data collection sheets.
▶▶ Select suitable graphical representation to progress an enquiry.

▶▶ Find summary values that represent the raw data, and select the statistics most appropriate to the problem.
▶▶ Interpret graphs and diagrams and draw inferences.
▶▶ Compare two or more distributions and make inferences.
▶▶ Communicate interpretations and results of a statistical enquiry.
▶▶ Represent problems and synthesise information in graphical form.

Difference in average surface temperature, comparison with 1962–90 average. Global and Central England, degrees C.

You can see the relationship between sets of data on a graph.

Before you start

You should know how to ...
1 Calculate the mean, median, mode and range of a set of raw data.

2 Draw graphs and charts to represent data.

Check in
1 Write these numbers in size order, starting with the smallest:
a 1, 7, 8, 6, 2, 3, 7
b 1.2, 1.4, 1.3, 1.9, 0.6, 1.5, 0.8, 1.2

2 The table shows the favourite colours of 8C.

Colour	Red	Blue	Black	Purple
Number	6	9	5	10

Draw a suitable chart to represent this data.
Give a reason for your choice of diagram.

Unit commentary

Aim of the unit

This unit aims to consolidate and extend understanding of the handling data cycle in preparation of the Key Stage 3 test. There is an emphasis on developing a good understanding of the whole cycle and developing skills by working through varied problems.

Introduction

Emphasise that a good understanding of the handling data cycle is essential for the Key Stage 3 tests, and also for work in other subjects such as Science and Geography. Ask students to think of examples of use of statistics in other subject areas and in the media, and to discuss ways in which statistics could be used wrongly to support different conclusions.

Framework references

This unit focuses on:
Teaching objectives pages:
249–253, 257 and 261–275.
Problem solving pages:
25, 27 and 29.

Check in activity

Use the numbers from question 1 of the Check in.
Ask students to find the:
▶ mean
▶ median
▶ mode.
Ask what sort of chart they could best represent the data on.
Discuss answers.

Differentiation

Support tier

Focuses on using the handling data cycle, calculating statistics and drawing and interpreting charts and diagrams.

Extension tier

Focuses on the handling data cycle, extending to cumulative frequency graphs and lines of best fit.

Mental starter

Definitions

Write the five keywords from the Student's book on the board and ask questions about each one.

▶ Ask for a simple definition, a sentence that uses the word, or synonyms.

▶ Discuss the definitions – include practical examples.

▶ Relate each word to an appropriate stage of the handling data cycle.

Useful resources

R36 – handling data cycle

Introductory activity

Refer to the mental starter.

Remind students of the handling data cycle, on **R36**. Emphasise that it is a useful guide to carrying out a statistical project. Discuss the examples in the Students' Book for each stage of the cycle. Ask students for examples from previous project work. Discuss responses and problems faced.

Emphasise that students need:

▶ A clear testable hypothesis

▶ Good data collection

▶ Appropriate diagrams and statistics

▶ To make sense of their work, referring back to the hypothesis.

Discuss the second example again.

Challenge students to come up with a strategy Liska could use to collect data.

Discuss methods and strategies. Emphasise:

▶ Use of both primary and secondary data is important.

▶ Use of a pilot survey to help you trial and refine your questionnaire.

▶ A suitable sample size and degree of accuracy.

▶ Appropriate questions – need to provide options for questions that will give many variations in the answer.

▶ Design of tables to collect data in the clearest way.

Emphasise that:

▶ Students must interpret their work, not reproduce standard charts.

▶ The Key Stage 3 test may contain unfamiliar wording.

▶ Writing clear, concise explanations is an important test technique to practise as students work through the exercise.

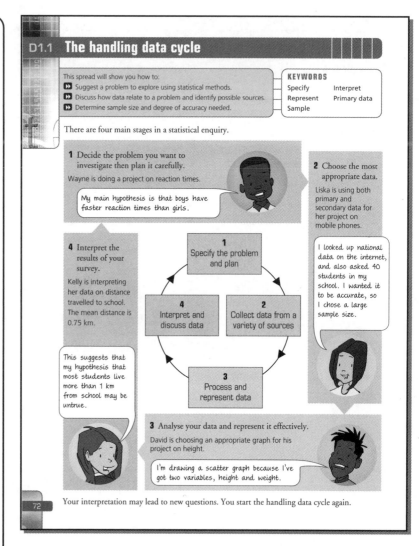

Plenary

Review the focus of the lesson – collecting data as part of the handling data cycle.

Discuss how often the word 'explain' occurs in the questions.

Choose some of the questions and discuss answers.

Focus on what students say and what they actually wrote down.

Challenge students to discuss if the written answer captures all the main points of the explanation.

Make a list on the board of 'good words' that students use in their explanations.

Exercise D1.1

1 Penny decides to find out how accurately people can throw. She tests people's accuracy in throwing a beanbag.

  a Make a list of the factors that influence people's accuracy in throwing a beanbag, and write a hypothesis that Penny could test with an experiment.

  b Design an experiment and data collection sheet to test this hypothesis. Explain what data to collect, describe the accuracy needed in recording the data, and explain a good sample size to use.

> ▸ Too small a sample may give unrepresentative results.
> ▸ A large sample may be expensive and take a long time.

2 Jenny investigates people's attitudes to organic fruit and vegetables. She decides to carry out a survey.

  a Suggest some hypotheses that Jenny could test in her survey.

  b Design a questionnaire for a survey, based on these hypotheses.

  c Explain how Jenny could carry out a pilot survey.

  d Explain how Jenny should select the people to take part in her survey.

3 Jodie was asked to write a project with the title 'Teenagers and mobile phones'.

  a Think of three different questions that she could investigate for the project, and write a hypothesis for each one.

  b Explain how she could collect the information needed to test each of the hypotheses. Remember to include:
    ▸ Whether she would use primary or secondary data.
    ▸ How and where to collect the data.
    ▸ How big a sample size she would need.

4 A group of students was doing a project to find out whether people in the UK had healthy lifestyles.

  a One question was:

> What is your age (in years)?
> ☐ 0–15 ☐ 15–30 ☐ 30–45 ☐ 45+

  Explain why this question needs to be changed.

  b Another question was:

> Do you eat lots of vegetables?
> ☐ None ☐ A few ☐ Lots

  Explain why this question needs to be changed, and write a better version.

  c The students discuss who they will give their questionnaire to. One student said:

> 'Let's ask everybody in our class to fill in a copy.'

  Give one advantage and one disadvantage of this suggestion.

5 Gill and Paul see a magazine article that says: '60% of teenagers now own a mobile phone'. They decide to test this claim.

  a Gill says: 'We could ask 10 people in Year 9'. Give two reasons why Gill's method might not give reliable results.

  b Paul says: 'We could go into town, and watch people walking past the shops. We could make a note of how many of the teenagers are carrying mobile phones'. Give two reasons why Paul's method might not give reliable results.

73

Answers

1 **a** Examples: age or gender, suitable hypothesis   **b** Sample experiment and collection sheet.

2 Student's own answers.

3 Student's own answers.

4 **a** Categories overlap/too personal   **b** Categories are vague. Need more specific amounts: 'Up to 3 portions per day', 'Up to 5 portions per day' and 'More than 5 portions per day'.
  c Advantages: quick and easy. Disadvantages: small sample and unrepresentative.

5 **a** Small sample and unrepresentative.   **b** Examples: Phones may not be on show. It may not be obvious who are teenagers.

Mental starter

Write the numbers 1, 4, 5, 5, 8, 9 and 20 on the board, along with the words mean, median, mode and range.
Challenge students to describe how to find each statistic.
Discuss answers.
Challenge students to find all the values.

Useful resources

D1.2OHP – Students' Book examples

Introductory activity

Refer to the mental starter.
Remind students that this lesson will revise finding and using statistics.

Emphasise that in the Key Stage 3 test, students will not only have to calculate statistics, but will also need to understand how and when to use them.

Discuss the first example from the Students' Book, on D1.2OHP.
Emphasise that the mean, median and mode are averages, but the range is a measure of spread.
Encourage students to notice that all three averages are similar, and it makes little difference which one is used in this case.

Discuss the second example, also on D1.2OHP. Emphasise that the averages vary, and students need to make a suitable choice.
Discuss what is unusual about part **b** of the second example. Emphasise that the extreme value causes the data set to be skewed and the mean to be distorted.
Discuss the best way to summarise the data. Emphasise the median as the best average and the range as a good measure of spread.

Emphasise that for continuous or grouped discrete data you work out the modal class instead of the mode.

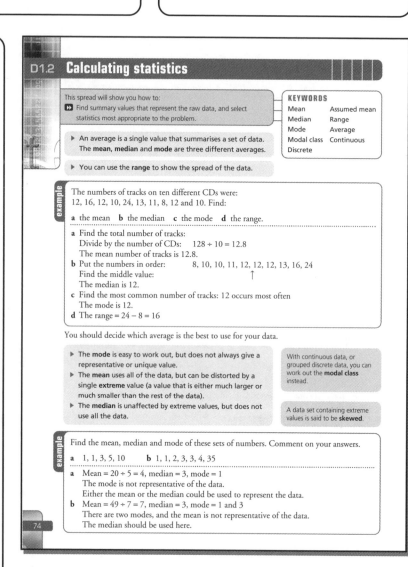

D1.2 Calculating statistics

This spread will show you how to:
▶▶ Find summary values that represent the raw data, and select statistics most appropriate to the problem.

KEYWORDS

Mean	Assumed mean
Median	Range
Mode	Average
Modal class	Continuous
Discrete	

▶ An average is a single value that summarises a set of data. The **mean**, **median** and **mode** are three different averages.

▶ You can use the **range** to show the spread of the data.

example

The numbers of tracks on ten different CDs were:
12, 16, 12, 10, 24, 13, 11, 8, 12 and 10. Find:
a the mean **b** the median **c** the mode **d** the range.

a Find the total number of tracks:
Divide by the number of CDs: $128 \div 10 = 12.8$
The mean number of tracks is 12.8.
b Put the numbers in order: 8, 10, 10, 11, 12, 12, 12, 13, 16, 24
Find the middle value: ↑
The median is 12.
c Find the most common number of tracks: 12 occurs most often
The mode is 12.
d The range = $24 - 8 = 16$

You should decide which average is the best to use for your data.

▶ The **mode** is easy to work out, but does not always give a representative or unique value.
▶ The **mean** uses all of the data, but can be distorted by a single **extreme** value (a value that is either much larger or much smaller than the rest of the data).
▶ The **median** is unaffected by extreme values, but does not use all the data.

With continuous data, or grouped discrete data, you can work out the **modal class** instead.

A data set containing extreme values is said to be **skewed**.

example

Find the mean, median and mode of these sets of numbers. Comment on your answers.
a 1, 1, 3, 5, 10   **b** 1, 1, 2, 3, 3, 4, 35

a Mean = $20 \div 5 = 4$, median = 3, mode = 1
The mode is not representative of the data.
Either the mean or the median could be used to represent the data.
b Mean = $49 \div 7 = 7$, median = 3, mode = 1 and 3
There are two modes, and the mean is not representative of the data.
The median should be used here.

Plenary

Discuss answers to question 8, and strategies for deciding on the best average:
a There is no mode and the mean and median are similar.
b A single large value makes the mean larger than the median and the two modes.
c There is no mode and the mean is smaller than the median.
For **b** and **c** it may be best to state the median and range.

Further activities

Challenge students to work in pairs to develop more questions similar to questions 4 and 5. Encourage them to focus on sets of conditions that produce unique solutions.

Differentiation

Core questions:
▶ Question 1 practises finding and using a mean.
▶ Questions 2–5 provide further practice with averages.
▶ Questions 6–8 extend to finding means using assumed means and frequency tables, and justifying choices of averages.

Extension tier: focuses on calculating statistics from raw data and diagrams.

Support tier: focuses on comparing averages and deciding which is best to use.

Exercise D1.2

1 The table shows the amount of money Joe paid for his lunch each day one week.

Monday	Tuesday	Wednesday	Thursday	Friday
£3.45	£4.50	£3.75	£4.25	£3.90

Joe says: *On average, I spent less than £4 each day.*

Is Joe correct? Explain your answer.

2 To qualify for the final of a gymnastics competition, Polly needs a mean score of at least 9.0 points over four rounds. Her points for the first three rounds are shown in the table.

	Round 1	Round 2	Round 3	Round 4
Points	9.2	8.6	8.8	

How many points does Polly need to score in Round 4?

3 a Jodie played four holes of Crazy Golf. She scored 6 on each of the first three holes, and 2 on the last one. What was Jodie's mean score over four holes?
b Katryn only played two holes. Her mean score was 7, and the range of her scores was 4. What were Katryn's scores on each hole?
c Laura played three holes of Crazy Golf. She also had a mean score of 7, with a range of 4. What could Laura's scores have been on each hole? Explain your reasoning.

4 Sammy has three number cards. You cannot see the numbers, but you can work them out from the clue given.

Clue
The mean is 7
The mode is 8

What are the numbers on Sammy's cards?

5 Find sets of whole numbers that meet these conditions:
a three numbers with a range of 6, a median of 8 and a mean of 8
b three numbers with a mode of 4, a median of 4 and a mean of 5
c four numbers with a mode of 4, a median of 4, a mean of 4 and a range of 6.

6
> You can use an assumed mean to make calculations easier:
> ▶ Subtract the assumed mean from each value.
> ▶ Find the mean of the new values.
> ▶ Add on the assumed mean to give the actual mean.

Calculate the mean of each of these sets of numbers, using an appropriate **assumed mean**. Explain your working carefully.
a 32, 36, 38, 31, 30, 31, 32, 35, 34, 38
b 102, 98, 97, 96, 105, 101, 104, 99, 94, 94
c 5.26, 5.39, 5.01, 5.47, 5.66

7 The table shows the scores achieved by 20 students who played a game.

Score	0	1	2	3	4	5
Frequency	4	9	4	2	0	1

Calculate the mean score for the 20 students.

8 For each data set, state which measure of average you would use. Give a reason for your choice.
a 7, 9, 14, 26, 29, 33, 37
b 1, 1, 3, 3, 4, 24
c 1, 31, 33, 35

75

Exercise commentary

The questions assess objectives on Framework Pages 257 and 261.

Problem solving
The exercise assesses objectives on Framework Page 25.

Group work
Questions 4, 5 and 8 are suitable for group work.

Misconceptions
Students may need further practice at justifying choices in writing.
Students may have difficulty calculating averages.
Mean: Emphasise the need to keep a clear track of working, estimate answers and check answers when complete.
Median: Emphasise the need to order the data clearly, and that the median is between two values if there are an even number of values.
Mode: Emphasise that there may be several modes, or none.

Links
This exercise links to practical investigations in Science.

Homework

D1.2HW gives more practice in finding averages, and in finding data values given an average or the range.

Answers

1 Yes, the mean is £3.97 (or the median is £3.90).
2 9.4   **3 a** 5   **b** 5 and 9   **c** 5, 7, 9   **4** 5, 8, 8
5 a 5, 8, 11   **b** 4, 4, 7   **c** 1, 4, 4, 7
6 a 33.7 (assumed meaning of 30)   **b** 99 (100)   **c** 5.358 (5)
7 1.4
8 a Mean (as evenly spread)
    b Median (and range as one skew value)
    c Median (and range as one skew value)

D1.3 Representing data

Mental starter

Charts

Sketch a simple bar chart on the board. For example, colours of cars: black [5], white [18], red [9], blue [4].

Label bars with frequencies if necessary.

Ask questions based on the chart: What is the modal colour? What percentage was white? How many cars altogether? etc.

Redraw the data as a pie chart and ask the same questions.

Discuss which of the questions are easier with each type of chart.

Useful resources

R36 – handling data cycle

D1.3OHP – Students' Book examples

Introductory activity

Remind students of the handling data cycle, on **R36**, and explain that in the Key Stage 3 test they will be expected to produce a range of appropriate statistical diagrams.

Refer to the mental starter.

Discuss when bar charts are useful – to compare categories with each other.

Discuss when pie charts are useful – to compare categories with the whole. Discuss the difference between a graph and a chart:

▸ A graph shows pairs of values plotted on a grid.

▸ Any other statistical diagram is a chart.

Discuss other charts and graphs that students may know. The examples in the Students' Book are on **D1.3OHP**.

▸ Tree diagram

▸ Stem-and-leaf diagram

▸ Frequency diagram

▸ Line graph

▸ Scatter graph.

Discuss features of the charts and graphs.

Emphasise that:

▸ Scatter graphs use paired values to compare two different measures. You can sometimes draw a line of best fit on a scatter graph.

▸ Time series graphs show change over time.

Discuss examples of project data that would lead to each of these graphs.

Revise the procedures for drawing different types of chart if necessary.

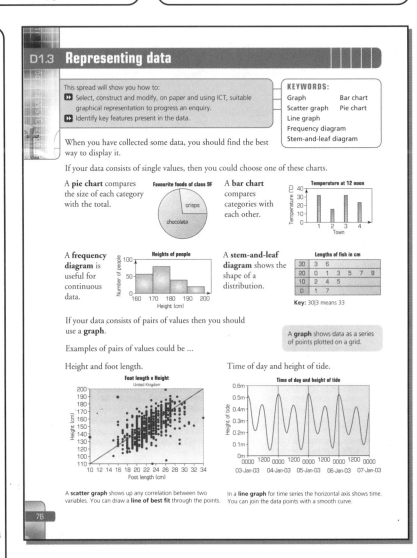

D1.3 Representing data

This spread will show you how to:

▸▸ Select, construct and modify, on paper and using ICT, suitable graphical representation to progress an enquiry.

▸▸ Identify key features present in the data.

KEYWORDS:
Graph   Bar chart
Scatter graph   Pie chart
Line graph
Frequency diagram
Stem-and-leaf diagram

When you have collected some data, you should find the best way to display it.

If your data consists of single values, then you could choose one of these charts.

A **pie chart** compares the size of each category with the total.

A **bar chart** compares categories with each other.

A **frequency diagram** is useful for continuous data.

A **stem-and-leaf diagram** shows the shape of a distribution.

If your data consists of pairs of values then you should use a **graph**.

Examples of pairs of values could be …

Height and foot length.

Time of day and height of tide.

A **graph** shows data as a series of points plotted on a grid.

A **scatter graph** shows up any correlation between two variables. You can draw a **line of best fit** through the points.

In a **line graph** for time series the horizontal axis shows time. You can join the data points with a smooth curve.

Plenary

Discuss questions 1 and 2, and ask students to discuss their methods for drawing a pie chart. Emphasise that students need this skill for the Key Stage 3 test.

Encourage students to discuss their answers to question 6, explaining their choices of appropriate statistical diagram for each. Discuss methods and strategies for choosing different diagrams.

Collate the reasons for choosing each type of diagram into a table with 'pros' and 'cons', to clearly show the features of each diagram.

Further activities

In **D1.3ICT** students consider different types of charts and graphs using a spreadsheet package.

Alternatively

Challenge students to draw a line of best fit on their scatter graph from question 3. Then encourage students to use this line to estimate the weight of a book with 500 pages. Discuss how confident they are that their prediction is correct.

Differentiation

Core questions:

▶ Questions 1 and 2 practise drawing pie charts.
▶ Questions 3–4 provide further practice at drawing different types of graphs and diagrams.
▶ Questions 5 and 6 extend to deciding on the best form of diagram for different data sets.

Extension tier: focuses on estimating statistics from a cumulative frequency graph.

Support tier: focuses on drawing and interpreting pie charts.

Exercise D1.3

1 The table shows the number of animals staying in a vet's surgery one night.

Cats	Dogs	Rabbits	Hamsters	Birds
4	2	1	3	2

Draw a pie chart to represent the data.

2 There are 29 students in Katie's class, and seven of them wear glasses.
Katie wants to show this information on a pie chart.
What angle will Katie need to use for the sector representing students who wear glasses?
Show your working clearly.

3 Ten books were weighed and the number of pages in each was recorded.

Number of pages	660	317	224	222	472	255	419	206	602	437
Weight (g)	453	231	199	230	318	137	426	311	448	333

Draw a scatter graph to represent the data.

4 The table shows the heights of a group of Year 9 students.

Height (cm)	Number of students	Height (cm)	Number of students
$145 < h < 150$	1	$165 < h < 170$	23
$150 < h < 155$	2	$170 < h < 175$	17
$155 < h < 160$	18	$175 < h < 180$	5
$160 < h < 165$	32	$180 < h < 185$	2

Represent this data on a frequency diagram.

5 The table shows the temperature of the contents of a test tube during a scientific experiment.

Time (s)	5	10	15	20	25	30	35	40	45	50	55	60	65	70	75	80	85	90
Temp (°C)	18	18	19	24	63	140	189	211	231	244	239	210	177	152	130	112	97	86

Represent this data on a suitable graph.

6 Sketch the type of diagram that you would use for these sets of data.
Explain the reasons for your choice in each case (there may be more than one possibility).
a A list of the weights (in kg) of the students in a class.
b A table showing the height (in cm) of a group of students, together with their personal best times for the 100 m sprint.
c A data collection sheet recording the eye colour for a group of students.
d A table showing the finishing times for 100 runners in a marathon.
e A questionnaire recording the numbers of children in the respondents' families.

Exercise commentary

The questions assess objectives on Framework Pages 263–267.

Problem solving

This exercise assesses objectives on Framework Page 27.

Group work

Questions 6 is suitable for group work or discussion in pairs.

Misconceptions

Students may confuse bar charts with frequency diagrams.
Emphasise that:

▶ Bar charts are for discrete or categorical data, so only for data that can be separated out.
▶ Frequency diagrams are only for continuous data.

Links

This topic links to practical investigations in other subject areas.

Homework

D1.3HW requires students to give examples of data that could be shown on different statistical diagrams.

Answers

1 Cats 120°, Dogs 60°, Rabbits 30°, Hamsters 90°, Birds 60°
2 87°   3 Appropriate scatter graph.
4 Frequencies: 1, 2, 18, 32, 23, 17, 5, 2 on an appropriate diagram.
5 Appropriate scatter graph
6 a Frequency diagram or stem-and-leaf diagram   b Scatter graph
   c Pie chart or bar chart   d Frequency diagram or stem-and-leaf diagram
   e Bar chart or pie chart

D1.4 Interpreting graphs and charts

Mental starter

Sketch a varying line graph on the board, but do not label the axes. Ask students to suggest what the graph could represent. For each suggestion, ask what the axes represent and how they should be labelled.

Repeat with other types of chart.

Discuss key features of the charts, such as whether the data represented is discrete or continuous.

Useful resources

R36 – handling data cycle
D1.4OHP – Students' Book examples
Compasses for Further activities.

Introductory activity

Remind students of the handling data cycle, on **R36**, and emphasise that the 'interpret and discuss data' stage is a crucial part of the cycle. Emphasise that in the Key Stage 3 test students will be expected to interpret a range of familiar and unfamiliar diagrams.

Discuss the charts and graphs in the Students' Book. The examples are on D1.4OHP.

Discuss the first example. Encourage students to read it in the same way as a pie chart, even though it may look unfamiliar. Emphasise that unfamiliar chart types can often be related to charts that students already know.

Challenge students to identify information that they can find out from the chart and from that information write down inferences.

Discuss inferences and whether they can be justified using the information provided in the chart.

Emphasise that pie charts show proportions, not actual values, so inferences can be made about relative values but not absolute data.

Discuss the second example.

Emphasise that scatter graphs show absolute data.

Encourage students to identify the general trend of the graph, and the anomaly.

Emphasise that an anomaly is a value that does not conform to a rule or general trend.

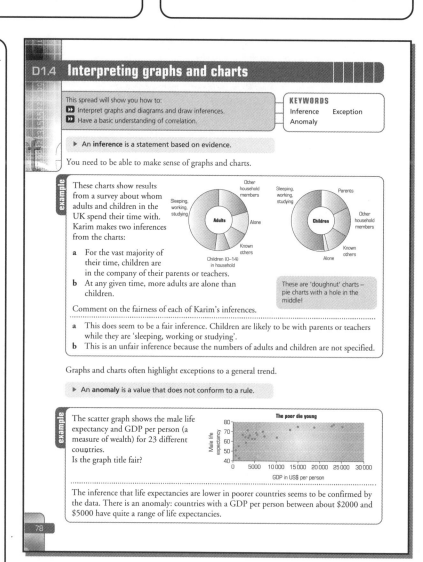

Plenary

Discuss answers to question 2.

Ask students to form hypotheses to interpret the features of the graph. Discuss if the dip in life expectancy for people born in the 1920s might relate to the fact that these people were young adults at the start of World War II. Emphasise that further information would be needed to confirm this hypothesis.

Discuss question 4, and encourage students to state what sort of correlation they find in the scatter graphs.

Further activities

Challenge students to redraw the data from question 1 as a pair of pie charts. Some of the smaller values will need to be combined into an 'other' category. Encourage students to discuss the features that are most clearly shown by each type of chart.

Differentiation

Core questions:
▶ Question 1 practises interpreting data from a comparative bar chart.
▶ Questions 2–4 provide further practice at interpreting different types of graphs.
▶ Question 5 extends to interpreting a time series graph.

Extension tier: focuses on interpreting cumulative frequency graphs and comparing distributions.

Support tier: focuses on drawing appropriate charts for data.

Exercise D1.4

1 The chart shows the amount of time that people in the UK spend on different activities in a typical day.

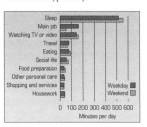

Describe the main differences between the way people use their time during weekdays and weekends.
Suggest reasons for the differences.

2 The graph shows the life expectancies of people born in the UK in the years from 1901.

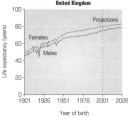

Explain the main features of the graph.

3 The chart shows temperature information for a village in England.

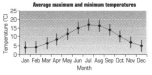

Explain how the graph works, and describe its main features.

4 Sketch a scatter graph for each of these relationships.
a Televisions with bigger screens cost more money.
b Older cars cost less than new cars.
c Cakes take less time to cook if the oven is hotter.
d The distance you can throw a tennis ball does not depend on your height.
e Students who do well in a history test usually do well in geography.

5 The graph shows the number of people at a railway station one morning.

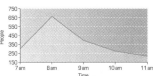

Are these statements true or false?
Explain your answers.
a The number of people in the station more than doubled between 7 am and 8 am.
b The number of people in the station halved between 8 am and 9 am.

79

Exercise commentary

The questions assess objectives on Framework Pages 269–271.

Problem solving
The exercise assesses objectives on Framework Page 27.

Group work
All questions are suitable for group work or discussion in pairs.

Misconceptions
Students' reports on charts and graphs often only comment on one of the variables rather than making comparisons between the variables.
Encourage students to fully describe what is happening to both variables.

Encourage students to use correct terminology where appropriate, such as trend and correlation.

Links
Interpreting graphs: Framework Pages 173–177.
This topic also links to practical investigations in other subject areas.

Homework

D1.4HW focuses on interpreting pie charts and line graphs.

Answers

1 At weekends, more time sleeping, eating, social life. Less time working, travelling, studying.
2 Generally rising trend, with female life expectancy higher than male. Big dip around 1920 due to WWII, smaller ones later.
3 Bars show the average values of the monthly maximum and minimum temperatures; points show the midpoints of the bars; the line shows the trend.
4 Scatter graph showing: **a** positive correlation **b** negative correlation **c** negative correlation **d** no correlation **e** positive correlation
5 **a** True, it went from 300 to 650. **b** False, it went from 650 to 400.

D1.5 Comparing distributions

Mental starter

Challenge students to say which group of five students did best in a test. Here are their marks:

Group 1: 2, 3, 5, 7, 8   Group 2: 4, 4, 5, 5, 7   Group 3: 5, 6, 6, 6, 7

Ask students to justify their choice using statistics.

Discuss the mean, median, mode and range of each group and the significance of each statistic.

Use an assumed mean if necessary or useful.

Useful resources

D1.5OHP – Students' Book example

Introductory activity

Refer to the mental starter.

Emphasise that comparing distributions involves looking at key features of data and calculating statistics.

Discuss the example in the Students' Book, shown on **D1.5OHP**. Discuss what sort of data is shown, and encourage students to discuss what the hypothesis might be.

Emphasise that the data are ages, and the table shows grouped discrete data.

Check by asking questions that students understand the data in the table.

The chart shown is a population pyramid. Discuss the benefits and disadvantages of this chart, for example:

▶ Allows direct comparison of the actual value for each group.

▶ Doesn't show total population.

Challenge students to think of other ways of showing this data, and list the benefits and disadvantages:

▶ Pie chart. [Only shows proportions, not actual data.]

▶ Stacked histogram or frequency diagram. [Can be hard to compare values, but does give total for each group.]

Encourage students to list the key features of the chart, and discuss the features given in the example.

Discuss the statistics used. Emphasise that the modal class is used as the median and mean cannot be easily calculated.

Emphasise that the range cannot be calculated without the actual data.

Emphasise that it is important to choose and use appropriate statistics to compare distributions.

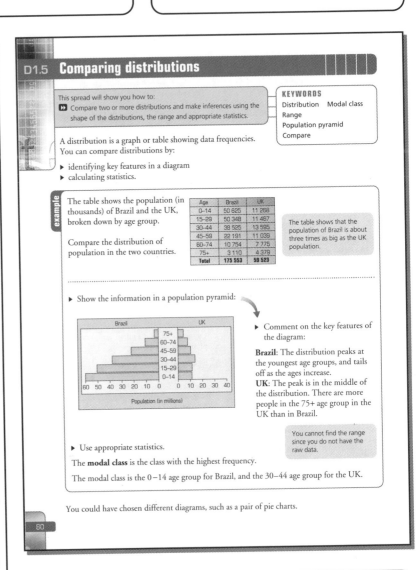

Plenary

Discuss answers to question 6.

Emphasise that this is a typical Key Stage 3 question. It has an unfamiliar type of diagram, but can be read reasonably easily.

Discuss the two statements in the question, and emphasise that **a** is definitely true, but **b** cannot be decided.

Encourage students to make up other statements based on the chart, and discuss reasoning.

Further activities

Challenge students to take the data from question 3 and pair it (the first two scores, 70 and 50, belong to Student A, and so on). Then encourage them to draw a scatter diagram and comment on the pattern.

Differentiation

Core questions:
▶ Questions 1 and 2 practise finding and interpreting the mean.
▶ Questions 3 and 4 focus on comparing distributions using appropriate statistics.
▶ Questions 5 and 6 involve interpreting charts and comparing distributions.

Extension tier: focuses on scatter graphs and lines of best fit.

Support tier: focuses on reading and interpreting tables and charts.

Exercise D1.5

1 The customer rating of two types of car, from 0 (worst) to 10 (best) is:

Type A	7	8	7	7	9	8	7	8
Type B	2	1	5	8	10	7	4	0

a Find the average rating for each car.
b Find the range for each car.
c Which type of car were customers happier with? Explain your answer.

2 A group of students investigated four different brands of crisps. For each brand, they opened ten packets of crisps, and counted the number of crisps in the packet. The results are shown in the table.

Brand A	19	17	19	17	18	19	18	18	17	18
Brand B	17	16	14	20	19	20	19	17	17	18
Brand C	21	21	21	21	20	23	22	20	20	21
Brand D	15	15	17	15	16	18	17	18	15	21

a For each brand, find the average number of crisps per packet.
b Find the range of the numbers of crisps per packet.
c It would not be sensible to say 'The brand with the highest average number of crisps in a packet represents the best value for money'. Explain why not.

3 A class took two different tests on the same day.
The results are shown in the table.

Test A	70 81 69 72 81 74 63 82 73 88 75 72 70 71 63 77 70 86 68 76 85 73 71 72 78
Test B	50 61 62 68 44 68 59 54 47 54 51 54 58 55 57 75 74 57 57 47 75 47 43 59 36

a Explain why the mean would be a suitable average for these sets of data.
b Calculate the mean of each set, using an appropriate assumed mean.
c Find the range of each set of marks.
d Explain in words which test you think was more difficult.

4 20 boys and 20 girls took part in a sports tournament in which the aim was to score points. The results are shown in the table.

Number of points	5	6	7	8	9	10	11	12	13	14
Number of boys	1	3	1	2	2	2	2	3	1	3
Number of girls	0	0	4	2	4	3	3	3	1	0

Use the information in the table to compare the performance of the boys and the girls. Comment on the distribution of the scores, and calculate appropriate statistics.

5 There are 30 students in class 9A, and 12 of them own cats.
a Draw a pie chart to show this data.
b When a similar chart is drawn for the students in class 9B, the angle for cat owners is 180°. Can you say 'There must be more cat owners in class 9B than there are in class 9A'? Explain your answer.
c There are 30 students in class 9C. The angle for cat owners on a pie chart for class 9C is 168°. Is it possible to say 'People in class 9C own more cats than people in class 9A'? Explain your answer.

6 The chart shows the heights of a set of adults.
Use the information in the chart to decide whether these statements are true or false, or whether it is impossible to tell. Explain your answers.

Heights (in cm) of a set of adults

a The shortest female was shorter than the shortest male.
b The tallest male was taller than the tallest female.

81

Exercise commentary

The questions assess objectives on Framework Page 273.

Problem solving

Questions 5 and 6 assess objectives on Framework Page 27.

Group work

All questions are suitable for group work or discussion in pairs. Explanations can be developed in paired discussions.

Misconceptions

Students can give too little information when comparing distributions. Emphasise that there are generally three aspects to cover – an appropriate average, the range of each set of data, and a description of key features of the distribution.

Links

Interpreting graphs: Framework Pages 173–175.
This topic also links to practical investigations in other subject areas.

Homework

D1.5HW requires students to compare two sets of data.

Answers

1 a A 7.625, B 4.625   b A 2, B 10   c On the whole, people were happier with A (higher mean). However, some people were very happy with B (large range).
2 a Mean: 18, 17.7, 21, 16.7   b 2, 6, 3, 6   c Size (weight) and quality of crisps is also important.
3 a There are no extreme values.   b 74.4, 56.48   c 25, 39   d Test B
4 Means: boys 9.85, girls 9.6. Ranges: boys 9, girls 6. Boys marks slightly higher, but more widely spread.
5 a Cat owners 144°   b No. The proportion is higher, but 9B may be a smaller class.
c No, there are more cat owners, but we do not know how many cats they own.
6 a True; there is at least one female in the category 151–160 cm   b Impossible to tell

Mental starter

Averages

Write the number 1, 1 and 10 on the board.

Encourage students to calculate the three different averages for this data. Discuss which average gives an impression that the numbers are large, and which that the numbers are small.

Repeat the activity for other sets of data, for example, 1, 1, 2, 5, 21.

Useful resources

D1.6OHP – Students' Book examples
Newspapers or magazines for Further activities

Introductory activity

Refer to the mental starter.

Discuss how to use statistics to give a fair impression of 'difficult' data sets similar to those in the starter activity.

Emphasise that statistics and forms of representation can be used deliberately to give a biased or misleading impression.

Discuss the first example in the Students' Book, shown on **D1.6OHP**.

Encourage students to give their first impressions of the chart.

Discuss the raw data and the ways in which a misleading impression was created.

Discuss other ways of distorting statistics.

Emphasise that choice of scales on axes can also be misleading.

Discuss the second example, also on **D1.6OHP**. Emphasise that the two graphs show different aspects of the same set of data – the first graph is the last part of the second graph, on an enlarged scale.

Encourage students to describe the features of each graph separately and then contrast the two impressions.

Discuss the techniques used to create a misleading impression.

Discuss the third example, and how the claim may be misleading. Encourage students to list possible reasons why the claim may not be fair. Discuss answers.

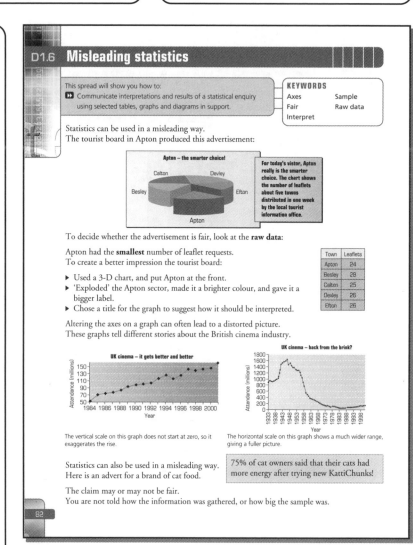

Plenary

Discuss answers to question 2.

Emphasise that this is not a deliberate attempt to mislead, but shows the danger of misinterpreting a graph. The manager has not considered the reason behind the statistics, which is the change in weather.

Encourage students to look at any published statistics or diagrams in a critical way. Use real-life examples if possible.

Further activities

Challenge students to produce their own misleading charts. Encourage them to use spreadsheets and computer charts.

Alternatively, challenge students to find statistics in newspapers or magazines and comment on whether they are fair or misleading, or if more information is required to be certain.

Differentiation

Core questions:

▶ Question 1 focuses on criticising and redrawing misleading statistical diagrams.

▶ Question 2 asks students to criticise incorrect reasoning from a scatter diagram.

▶ Question 3 provides further practice at selecting and calculating averages.

Extension tier: focuses on misleading graphs and charts.

Support tier: focuses on comparing distributions.

Exercise D1.6

1 Each of these statements is supported by a misleading statistical diagram. Explain what is wrong with each one, and draw a fairer diagram to represent the data.

a 'Sales of *The Daily Bugle* just get better and better!'

Month	Average daily sale
Jan	500
Feb	550
Mar	650
Apr	680
May	690
Jun	720
Jul	740

b 'Customers love our great service.'

Customer	Ratings
Poor	28%
Fair	52%
Good	8%
Superb	12%

□ Good
□ Superb

c 'All the local beaches got great marks for cleanliness, but Apton's famous beach really leads the way!'

Clean beach scores	
Apton	87%
Besley	91%
Calton	92%
Devley	91%
Efton	95%

2 The Sandwell Bay Tourist Board records the number of people on the beach and in the pool each day one month in a scatter graph.

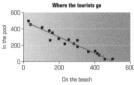

Where the tourists go

(In the pool vs On the beach)

The leisure pool has to close for one day for maintenance. The manager of a beach café says: 'With the pool shut, we will expect about 500 people on the beach.' Explain why the manager may be wrong.

3 For each of these sets of numbers, work out the mean, the median and the mode.

Set 1
1, 1, 2, 2, 2, 4, 5, 7, 9, 48

Set 2
0, 45, 45, 46, 48

Set 3
502, 513, 519, 1208

Set 4
29, 33, 48, 21, 33, 56, 62

Explain which of these averages you would use with each set:

a to give the impression that the numbers were large

b to give the impression that the numbers were small

c to give as fair an impression as possible.

Exercise commentary

The questions assess objectives on Framework Pages 273 and 275.

Problem solving

Questions 1 and 2 assess objectives on Framework Page 27.

Group work

Questions 1 and 2 are particularly appropriate for group work.

Misconceptions

Students may find it difficult to pinpoint the wrong or misleading conclusions from published statistics.

Emphasise that when any chart is drawn, decisions are made about how the data is represented.

Encourage students to consider choice of title, scale, axes, shading and style when looking at a chart. Also encourage them to think about what information is not supplied, or has not been investigated.

Links

This topic links to practical investigations in other subject areas.

Homework

D1.6HW requires students to write a help-sheet about how statistics can be presented in a misleading way.

Answers

1 a No scales or labels; vertical axis does not start from zero. b Pie chart should include poor and fair ratings. c Perspective has been used to make comparison difficult. A 2-D bar chart should be used.

2 People use the beach on sunny days and the pool on cloudy days. If the pool is closed on a cloudy day, the people will still not go on the beach.

3 Means: 8.1, 36.8, 685.5, 40.3; Medians: 3, 45, 516, 33; Modes: 2, 45, none, 33

  a mean, median/mode, mean, mean b mode, mean, median, median/mode

  c median, median/mode, median, median/mode

Summary

The key objectives for this unit are:

▶ Design a survey or experiment to capture the necessary data from one or more sources. (253)

▶ Determine the sample size and degree of accuracy needed. (253)

▶ Design, trial and, if necessary, refine data collection sheets. (253)

▶ Communicate interpretations and results of a statistical enquiry using selected tables, graphs and diagrams in support. (273–275)

Check out commentary

1 Students may not remember that primary data is data they collect themselves, whereas secondary data is from a 'published' source. Emphasise that secondary data may be from a larger set and more reliable, but sometimes is not available or available in the correct form.

2 Students may not realise the need for realistic surveys in their investigations. Emphasise that Ben's sample size is too large to collect individually, and that his measurements are to a higher degree of accuracy than is needed. Tom's sample size is too small and also biased towards his friends.

3 a Students often do not understand the concept of a pilot survey saving time and ensuring more accurate data. From the pilot you are able to revise or rephrase questions, or add new questions.
b Students may forget that options are used when free choice answers would give too wide a variety of results.

4 a Students may only see the attractive benefits of 3-D charts. Emphasise that 3-D charts can be difficult to read and interpret, and can give misleading impressions.
b Students may not highlight all misleading aspects of a graph. Emphasise the misleading use of scales, labels, shading, etc. to give a wrong impression.

Plenary activity

Discuss examples of graphs, charts, statistics, etc. used in newspapers, magazines and travel brochures.
Are the charts and statistics used misleading? How could they be improved? What other type of chart could be used to represent this data?

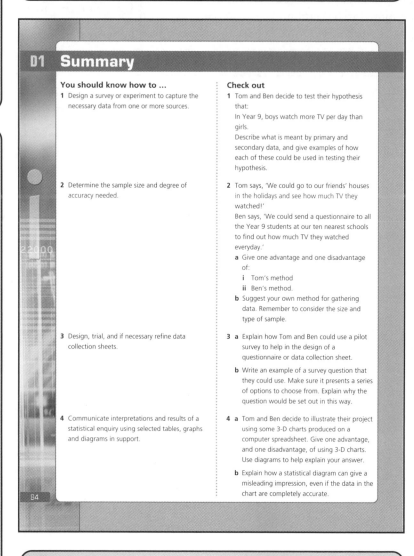

Development

The themes of this unit are developed in **D3** and **D4**. Specifically in **D3**, students use the handling data cycle to create their own statistical investigation and report.

Links

Handling data links to work in many other subjects such as Science, Geography and PSHE.

Mental starters

Objectives covered in this unit:

▶ Visualise, describe and sketch 2-D and 3-D shapes.
▶ Use metric units for calculations.
▶ Use metric units for estimation.
▶ Convert between metric units.
▶ Multiply and divide integers.
▶ Use jottings to support multiplication.
▶ Use knowledge of place value to multiply and divide decimals.
▶ Use approximation to estimate answers.
▶ Recall and use formulae for areas.
▶ Calculate volumes of cuboids and prisms.

Resources needed

* means class set needed

Essential:
S2.1OHP – finding areas
Circular objects
String   Compasses*
Calculators*   Set of solids

Useful:
S2.3OHP – area of a circle
S2.4OHP – circle examples
S2.5OHP – cubic conversions
S2.6OHP – prisms
R16 – 3-D shapes
S2.4F – areas of sectors
S2.5ICT* – dimensions and volume

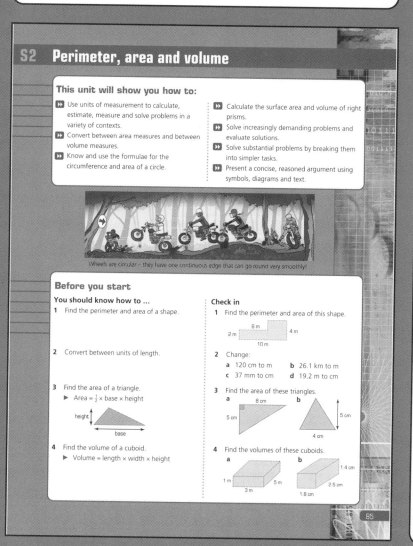

S2   Perimeter, area and volume

This unit will show you how to:

▶▶ Use units of measurement to calculate, estimate, measure and solve problems in a variety of contexts.

▶▶ Convert between area measures and between volume measures.

▶▶ Know and use the formulae for the circumference and area of a circle.

▶▶ Calculate the surface area and volume of right prisms.

▶▶ Solve increasingly demanding problems and evaluate solutions.

▶▶ Solve substantial problems by breaking them into simpler tasks.

▶▶ Present a concise, reasoned argument using symbols, diagrams and text.

Wheels are circular – they have one continuous edge that can go round very smoothly!

Before you start

You should know how to ...

1 Find the perimeter and area of a shape.

2 Convert between units of length.

3 Find the area of a triangle.
   ▶ Area = $\frac{1}{2}$ × base × height

4 Find the volume of a cuboid.
   ▶ Volume = length × width × height

Check in

1 Find the perimeter and area of this shape.

2 Change:
   a 120 cm to m   b 26.1 km to m
   c 37 mm to cm   d 19.2 m to cm

3 Find the area of these triangles.
   a   b

4 Find the volumes of these cuboids.
   a   b

85

Unit commentary

Aim of the unit

This unit aims to develop students' understanding of area and volume, including using appropriate units. The unit extends to the area of a circle and students go on to find volumes of more complex prisms.

Introduction

Discuss any objects or buildings that students know are circular. For example, the London Eye, a ferris wheel, water wheels, plates and bowls, car wheels. Discuss why these objects are circular. Emphasise that circles are very useful for engineers and designers as they move very smoothly along their edge.
Plates and bowls were originally made of ceramic materials, which are easier to make as a circle on a wheel.

Framework references

This unit focuses on:
Teaching objectives pages:
229, 235–237, 239–241.
Problem solving pages: 19, 29, 31.

Check in activity

Challenge students to find as many shapes as they can with an area of 12 cm^2.

Students should work in pairs or small groups.

Encourage them to come up with at least one example of each of these shapes:

▶ Rectangle
▶ Triangle
▶ Parallelogram.

Differentiation

Support tier

Focuses on coordinates in all four quadrants, areas of plane shapes, volume and surface area of cuboids.

Extension tier

Focuses on areas of sectors, the formula for the midpoint of a line, and volume and surface area of prisms and cylinders.

Mental starter

Estimating

Ask students to estimate in cm the lengths of 10 objects in the classroom.

Ask them to convert the lengths to m.

Extend to estimating the area of some rectangular objects in cm^2 or in m^2.

Useful resources

S2.1OHP – finding areas of simple shapes

Introductory activity

Refer to the mental starter.

Discuss the formula for the area of a rectangle.

Emphasise that you multiply the two perpendicular lengths together.

Discuss how you can use this formula to find the area of a:

▸ Triangle
▸ Parallelogram
▸ Trapezium.

Discuss how to use the formulae with some simple examples (on **S2.1OHP**).

Encourage students to state the units in their answers.

Emphasise that the units must be the same to use the formulae.

Ask students to work out one of the areas in different units, that is, to convert between squared units.

Discuss students' strategies.

Emphasise that 1 m = 100 cm but that there are two dimensions in areas.

Encourage students to work from first principles:

▸ Change all the lengths to the required units and then find the area.

Encourage students to generalise:
1 m^2 = 10 000 cm^2

Emphasise that:
1 m^2 is 1 m × 1 m = 100 cm × 100 cm

Discuss how to change 25.6 mm^2 to cm^2 and 64 000 cm^2 to m^2.

Emphasise the strategy of visualising a rectangle with a length of 1 cm or 1 m then finding the other length as in the Students' Book example.

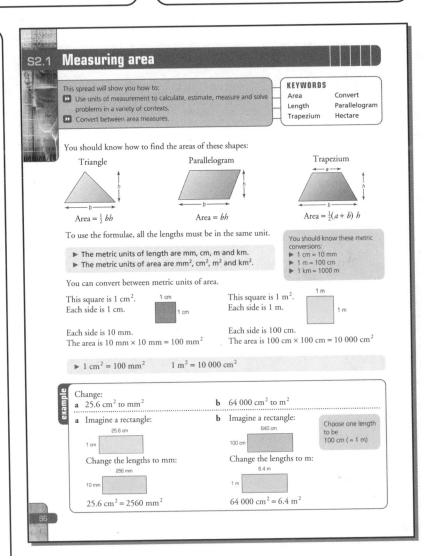

Plenary

Ask students to estimate the area of the front of their textbook in cm^2, then mm^2, then m^2.

Discuss answers.

Ask them to measure the sides of the book and calculate the area in cm^2 exactly.

Discuss what the area in mm^2 and m^2 must be.

Further activities

Students could investigate possible dimensions for fields of different areas, as in question 8. They could compare the perimeters of their possible fields.
What do they notice about the shape of the field with the smallest perimeter for a given area?

Differentiation

Core questions:
▶ Question 1 focuses on using area formulae.
▶ Questions 2–6 focus on converting between units of area.
▶ Questions 7 and 8 are harder questions involving proof and a more open-ended task on area.

Extension tier: focuses on area problems, including converting between metric units.

Support tier: focuses on plotting points on coordinate grids.

Exercise S2.1

1 Calculate the areas in cm² of each of these shapes.

a

5 cm
4 cm

b

12.2 cm
15 cm

c

7 cm
6 cm
9 cm

2 Change these areas to mm².
  a 6 cm²   b 26 cm²
  c 0.6 cm²   d 14.6 cm²
  e 240 cm²

3 Change these areas to cm².
  a 4 m²   b 7.3 m²
  c 0.56 m²   d 17.2 m²
  e 256 m²

4 Change these areas to m².
  a 60 000 cm² b 125 000 cm²
  c 6000 cm²   d 2 000 000 cm²
  e 450 cm²

5 Change these areas to cm².
  a 600 mm²   b 7500 mm²
  c 85 mm²   d 120 000 mm²
  e 44 mm²

6 Calculate the area in cm² of each shape.

a

1.2 m
96 cm

b

63 cm
3 m

c
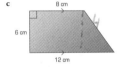
8 cm
6 cm
12 cm

d
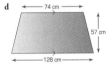
74 cm
57 cm
128 cm

  e Change each of your answers to:
    i mm²   ii m²

7 Use diagrams to show why the formulae for the area of a triangle, parallelogram and trapezium work.

8 **Investigation**
A mathematician has a field with an area of 1 hectare. Investigate possible dimensions for his field.

> 1 hectare = 10 000 m²

87

Exercise commentary

The questions assess objectives on Framework Page 229.

Problem solving
Question 7 assesses objectives on Framework Page 31.
Question 8 assesses Pages 19 and 29.

Group work
Questions 7 and 8 are suitable for paired work.

Misconceptions
Students often mistake the slant height for the perpendicular height in the formulae. Emphasise that the formulae derive from the rectangle where the sides are perpendicular.
Many students mix up the different metric conversions.
Emphasise cent means 100 and kilo 1000 – regular revision will help.
Commonly students will divide by 100 to convert between cm² and m².
Encourage them to visualise the square or rectangle for the second dimension, and to check that an answer is sensible.

Links
Enlargement: Framework Page 213.

Homework

S2.1HW gives more practice in calculating areas and using units of area.

Answers

1 a 10 cm² b 183 cm² c 48 cm²
2 a 600 mm² b 2600 mm² c 60 mm² d 1460 mm² e 24 000 mm²
3 a 40 000 cm² b 73 000 cm² c 5600 cm² d 172 000 cm² e 2 560 000 cm²
4 a 6 m² b 12.5 m² c 0.6 m² d 200 m² e 0.045 m²
5 a 6 cm² b 75 cm² c 0.85 cm² d 1200 cm² e 0.44 cm²
6 a 5760 cm² b 18 900 cm² c 60 cm² d 5757 cm²
  e i 576 000 mm², 1 890 000 mm², 6000 mm², 575 700 mm² ii 0.576 m², 1.89 m², 0.006 m², 0.5757 m² 7 Diagram of shapes as stated 8 For example, 100 m²

S2.2 Circumference of a circle

Mental starter

Three times

Ask students to multiply these numbers by 3 as quickly as they can:

4   14   23   56   67   79

Discuss strategies and ensure students have the correct outcomes.

Ask students to work out the same numbers multiplied by 3.1.

Encourage use of jottings.

Discuss strategies.

Useful resources

Circular objects

String

Compasses

Calculators

Introductory activity

Show students a circular object such as a clock or tin lid.

Discuss what you call the distance around and across the shape.

Encourage students to draw a circle then estimate and then measure the diameter and the circumference.

Discuss strategies for measuring the circumference – use string!

Encourage students to measure accurately.

Discuss the relationship between the circumference and the diameter – keep a table of results on the board.

Emphasise that the circumference is about three times the diameter.

Discuss what students understand by the term 'pi', or symbol π.

Emphasise that it stands for the exact number that links the diameter and circumference.

Encourage students to explore the value of π on a calculator: it is 3.14 (to 2 dp), or you can use $\frac{22}{7}$.

Encourage students to use this information to derive the formula for the circumference.

Discuss how the formula changes when you use the radius.

Emphasise that the circumference is a length and so the units will be cm, etc.

Ask students for the circumference given the diameter or the radius.

Emphasise that they can estimate using $3 \times$ diameter or $3.1 \times$ diameter.

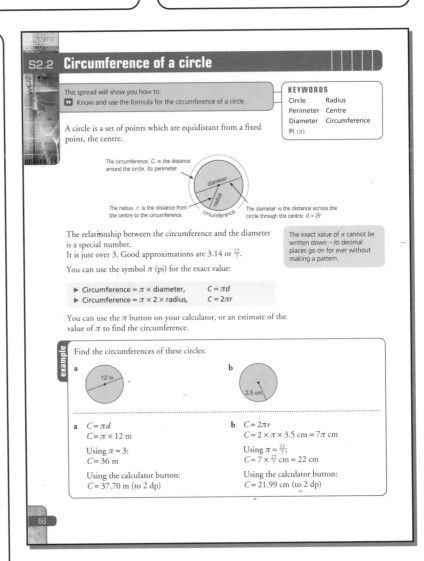

S2.2 Circumference of a circle

This spread will show you how to:

▶ Know and use the formula for the circumference of a circle.

KEYWORDS

Circle   Radius

Perimeter   Centre

Diameter   Circumference

Pi (π)

A circle is a set of points which are equidistant from a fixed point, the centre.

The circumference, C, is the distance around the circle, its perimeter.

The radius, r, is the distance from the centre to the circumference.

The diameter is the distance across the circle through the centre: $d = 2r$

The relationship between the circumference and the diameter is a special number.

It is just over 3. Good approximations are 3.14 or $\frac{22}{7}$.

You can use the symbol π (pi) for the exact value:

The exact value of π cannot be written down – its decimal places go on for ever without making a pattern.

▶ Circumference = $\pi \times$ diameter, $C = \pi d$

▶ Circumference = $\pi \times 2 \times$ radius, $C = 2\pi r$

You can use the π button on your calculator, or an estimate of the value of π to find the circumference.

example

Find the circumferences of these circles:

a   12 m

b   3.5 cm

a $C = \pi d$

$C = \pi \times 12$ m

Using $\pi = 3$:

$C = 36$ m

Using the calculator button:

$C = 37.70$ m (to 2 dp)

b $C = 2\pi r$

$C = 2 \times \pi \times 3.5$ cm $= 7\pi$ cm

Using $\pi = \frac{22}{7}$:

$C = 7 \times \frac{22}{7}$ cm $= 22$ cm

Using the calculator button:

$C = 21.99$ cm (to 2 dp)

Plenary

Challenge students to investigate this problem:

▶ What happens to the circumference of a circle when you double the radius?

Encourage students to work in small groups.

Encourage them to generalise and to explain their reasoning.

Discuss answers as a class.

Further activities

Students could estimate the distance they travel to school, and the diameter of a car/bus/scooter/bicycle/roller skate wheel. How many revolutions does this wheel make on their journey to school?

Differentiation

Core questions:

▶ Question 1 focuses on identifying radius and diameter of a circle.
▶ Questions 2–7 focus on using the formula for the circumference.
▶ Questions 8 and 9 are more challenging, requiring students to use efficient methods.

Extension tier: focuses on area and circumference of circles.

Support tier: focuses on area of a triangle.

Exercise S2.2

1 Write down the radius and diameter of each of these circles.

a 6 cm
b 16 cm
c 9 m
d 27 cm

2 Find the circumference of each of these circles.

a 11 cm **b** 7 cm **c** 4.2 cm **d** 21.2 cm

3 A big wheel has a diameter of 30 m.

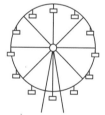

How far do you travel in one revolution of the wheel?

4 The radius of a bicycle wheel is 15 inches. What is the circumference of the wheel?

5 To find the diameter of a circle from its circumference, you rearrange the formula:

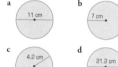

$$C = \pi d$$
$$so \ \frac{C}{\pi} = d$$

Find the diameter of a circle with circumference:
a 27 cm **b** 14 cm **c** 27.1 m

6 The largest big wheel in Scarborough has a circumference of 60 m. Find the radius of the wheel.

7 The Golden Dragon Restaurant has a round table with a diameter of 2.7 m. How many people can sit round the table? Assume each person needs 45 cm of space.

8 Find the perimeter of each of these shapes.

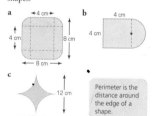

Perimeter is the distance around the edge of a shape.

9 **Challenge**
The diameter of the wheel of a racing bike is 60 cm. How many rotations does the wheel make in a 50 km race?

Exercise commentary

The questions assess objectives on Framework Page 235.

Problem solving
Questions 3, 4 and 6–8 assess objectives on Framework Page 19.
Question 8 and 9 assess Page 29.

Group work
The exercise is suitable for pair work.

Misconceptions
Students mix up the diameter and the radius.
Emphasise that the circumference is about $3 \times$ diameter which is a useful check.
Students often make mistakes when using rearranged formulae, particularly as they have to divide by π.
Encourage them to estimate by using $\pi = 3$ in the standard formula before working out the answer using π.
In questions 7 and 9, students should be encouraged to draw diagrams and work systematically.

Links
Measures: Framework Page 229.

Homework

S2.2HW focuses on finding the circumference of a circle in a range of contexts.

Answers

1 **a** 6 cm, 12 cm **b** 8 cm, 16 cm **c** 9 m, 18 m **d** 13.5 cm, 27 cm
2 **a** 34.6 cm **b** 44.0 cm **c** 26.4 cm **d** 66.6 cm
3 94 m 4 94.2 inches
5 **a** 8.6 cm **b** 4.5 cm **c** 8.6 m
6 9.5 m 7 18 people
8 **a** 28.6 cm **b** 18.3 cm **c** 37.7 cm 9 26 526

89

Mental starter

Ask students to estimate the circumference of a circle, diameter 8 cm.

Emphasise that $\pi = 3$ gives a reasonable estimate.

Ask them what is half the circumference, and to draw a sketch showing half the circumference.

Repeat for a quarter.

Challenge them to find the perimeter of a quarter sector of the circle.

Useful resources

S2.3OHP – area of a circle
Calculators

Introductory activity

Draw a circle on the board or OHP – use a (cm) squared background.

Discuss how to find the area of the circle.

Emphasise that the area is less than d^2 as that is the square surrounding the circle.

Encourage students to sketch the size of r^2 – a square of side r.

Discuss how many r^2 would make the area of the circle.

Encourage students to count squares.

Emphasise that the relationship is about 3 again.

Encourage students to consider whether it could be π.

S2.3OHP shows a circle split into lots of sectors rearranged to make a rectangle as in the Students' Book.

Refer to the mental starter – you found half the circumference by dividing by 2 so it is πr instead of $2\pi r$.

Encourage students to derive the formula: πr^2.

Discuss how to work out values on a calculator: work out r^2 then multiply by π.

Work through a couple of examples – one with a radius given and one with a diameter.

Emphasise that area uses square units.

Encourage students to use checking procedures.

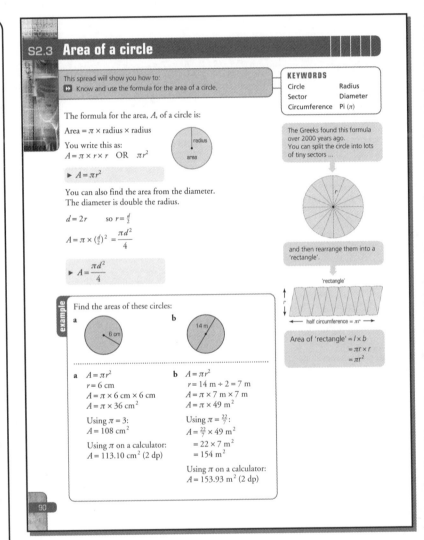

S2.3 Area of a circle

This spread will show you how to:
▶▶ Know and use the formula for the area of a circle.

KEYWORDS
Circle Radius
Sector Diameter
Circumference Pi (π)

The formula for the area, A, of a circle is:

Area = $\pi \times$ radius $\times$ radius

You write this as:
$A = \pi \times r \times r$ OR πr^2

▶ $A = \pi r^2$

You can also find the area from the diameter. The diameter is double the radius.

$d = 2r$ so $r = \frac{d}{2}$

$A = \pi \times (\frac{d}{2})^2 = \frac{\pi d^2}{4}$

▶ $A = \frac{\pi d^2}{4}$

The Greeks found this formula over 2000 years ago.
You can split the circle into lots of tiny sectors ...

and then rearrange them into a 'rectangle'.

'rectangle'

← half circumference = πr →

Area of 'rectangle' = $l \times b$
= $\pi r \times r$
= πr^2

example

Find the areas of these circles:

a 6 cm

b 14 m

a $A = \pi r^2$
$r = 6$ cm
$A = \pi \times 6$ cm $\times 6$ cm
$A = \pi \times 36$ cm^2

Using $\pi = 3$:
$A = 108$ cm^2

Using π on a calculator:
$A = 113.10$ cm^2 (2 dp)

b $A = \pi r^2$
$r = 14$ m $\div 2 = 7$ m
$A = \pi \times 7$ m $\times 7$ m
$A = \pi \times 49$ m^2

Using $\pi = \frac{22}{7}$:
$A = \frac{22}{7} \times 49$ m^2
$= 22 \times 7$ m^2
$= 154$ m^2

Using π on a calculator:
$A = 153.93$ m^2 (2 dp)

Plenary

Challenge students to find the area and perimeter of a sector of a circle with angle 60° and radius 8 cm.

Further activities

Students could give possible dimensions for a square, rectangle and triangle with perimeter 10 cm. If a circle has circumference 10 cm, which of these four shapes will have the largest area?

Differentiation

Core questions:
▶ Question 1 revises the circumference of a circle.
▶ Questions 2–5 focus on finding the area of a circle, quarter and semicircles.
▶ Question 6 challenges students to investigate how area changes with radius.

Extension tier: focuses on perimeters and areas of sectors.

Support tier: focuses on area of triangles, rectangles, parallelograms and trapezia.

Exercise S2.3

1 Find the circumference of each of these circles.

a
8 cm

b
26 mm

c
2.1 m

d
20 m

2 Find the area of each circle in question 1.

3 Use π as 3 to estimate the circumference and the area of each of these circles.

a
10 cm

b
8 cm

c
4 mm

d
20.7 cm

4 Find the shaded areas.

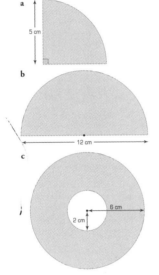

a
5 cm

b
12 cm

c
6 cm
2 cm

5 A small pizza has a diameter of 22 cm. A large pizza has a diameter of 32 cm.
  a Find the area of the top of each pizza.
  b The small pizza costs £5. The large pizza costs £9.
     Which is better value and why?
  c Choose a suitable size and price for a medium pizza. Explain your reasoning.

6 **Challenge**
  ▶ What happens to the area of a circle if you double the radius?
  ▶ What happens to the area of a circle if you multiply the radius by 3?
  Explain and justify your answers.

91

Exercise commentary

The questions assess objectives on Framework Page 237.

Problem solving
Questions 4 and 5 assess objectives on Framework Page 19.
Question 6 assesses Page 31.

Group work
Questions 4–6 are suitable for group work.

Misconceptions
Students mix up the formulae for circumference and area.
Emphasise that the area has two dimensions: r^2.
Students often use the diameter in the area formula.
Encourage them to find the radius of the circle first. Checking that the area is less than d^2 is a useful strategy.
Many students evaluate $\pi \times 7^2$ by working out $\pi \times 7$ then squaring.
Checking procedures should help.

Links
Measures: Framework Page 229.

Homework

S2.3HW practises finding circumference, area of circles and area of sectors.

Answers

1 a 50.3 cm b 81.7 mm c 13.2 m d 62.8 m
2 a 201 cm^2 b 531 mm^2 c 13.9 m^2 d 314 m^2
3 a 30 cm, 75 cm^2 b 24 cm, 48 cm^2 c 12 mm, 12 mm^2 d 62.1 cm,
    approx. $3 \times 10^2 = 300$ cm^2 4 a 19.6 cm^2 b 56.5 cm^2 c 100.5 cm^2
5 a 380 cm^2, 804 cm^2 b Large, it is 1.1p per cm^2 compared with 1.3p.
  c Example: 27 cm, £7
6 Double the radius: multiply the area by 4. Multiply the radius by 3: multiply the area by 9.

S2.4 Circle problems

Mental starter

Ask students to estimate the answers to questions based on area and circumference of a circle:

▶ Find the circumference/area of a circle with radius/diameter 8 cm.
▶ Find the radius/diameter of a circle with circumference 36 cm.

After estimating, encourage students to work out the exact answers on a calculator.

Useful resources

S2.4OHP – circle examples from the Students' Book
Calculators
S2.4F – areas of sectors

Introductory activity

Refer to the mental starter.
Check by asking questions that students know these names of the parts of a circle: radius, diameter, centre and circumference.
Discuss the meaning of π and its approximate value.

Encourage students to describe the relationship between the radius and the diameter and give the formulae for the area and circumference.

Discuss units.
Emphasise that area uses squared units.
Radius, diameter and circumference are all lengths.
Discuss strategies for remembering which is which.

Recap efficient calculator sequences.

Discuss the examples in the Students' Book (shown on **S2.4OHP**).
Encourage students to start with the facts they know.
Emphasise the need to:
▶ Work systematically.
▶ Estimate before calculating.
▶ Use the calculator efficiently.
▶ Use a sensible degree of accuracy.
▶ Check that answers are reasonable.

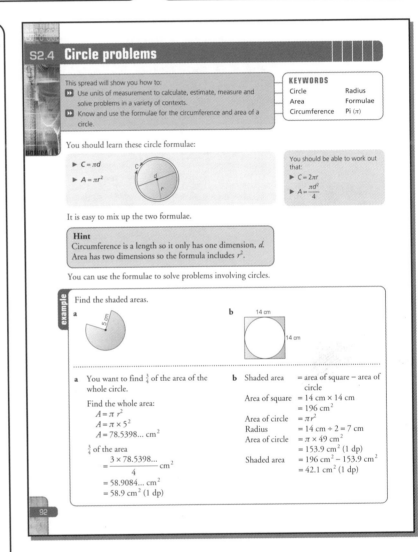

S2.4 Circle problems

This spread will show you how to:
▶▶ Use units of measurement to calculate, estimate, measure and solve problems in a variety of contexts.
▶▶ Know and use the formulae for the circumference and area of a circle.

KEYWORDS
Circle   Radius
Area   Formulae
Circumference   Pi (π)

You should learn these circle formulae:

▶ $C = \pi d$
▶ $A = \pi r^2$

You should be able to work out that:
▶ $C = 2\pi r$
▶ $A = \dfrac{\pi d^2}{4}$

It is easy to mix up the two formulae.

Hint
Circumference is a length so it only has one dimension, d.
Area has two dimensions so the formula includes r^2.

You can use the formulae to solve problems involving circles.

example

Find the shaded areas.

a

b   14 cm / 14 cm

a You want to find $\frac{3}{4}$ of the area of the whole circle.

Find the whole area:
$A = \pi r^2$
$A = \pi \times 5^2$
$A = 78.5398...\ cm^2$

$\frac{3}{4}$ of the area
$= \dfrac{3 \times 78.5398...}{4}\ cm^2$
$= 58.9084...\ cm^2$
$= 58.9\ cm^2\ (1\ dp)$

b Shaded area = area of square − area of circle
Area of square = 14 cm × 14 cm
= 196 cm²
Area of circle = πr^2
Radius = 14 cm ÷ 2 = 7 cm
Area of circle = $\pi \times 49\ cm^2$
= 153.9 cm² (1 dp)
Shaded area = 196 cm² − 153.9 cm²
= 42.1 cm² (1 dp)

92

Plenary

Challenge students to answer these questions:

a Find the area and circumference of a circle of diameter 8 m.
b Find the shaded area of this shape:

Discuss solutions and strategies.

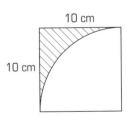

10 cm / 10 cm

Further activities

S2.4F is a structured activity on calculating areas of sectors of circles.

Differentiation

Core questions:

▶ Question 1 and 2 recap area and circumference of a circle.
▶ Questions 3–7 are Key Stage 3 type questions, focusing on solving problems involving circles.
▶ Questions 8 and 9 focus on the relationship between perimeter and area. They could lead to an extended piece of work.

Extension tier: focuses on calculating midpoints of lines.

Support tier: focuses on counting cubes and using the formula to calculate the volume of a cuboid.

Exercise S2.4

1 The radius of a big wheel is 37 m.
Joe starts at the bottom. The big wheel stops when he is at the top.
How far has he travelled to reach the top?

2 a Find the area of a circle with radius 6 m.
b Find the area of a semicircle with radius 6 m.

3 The minute hand of this clock is 10 cm long.

a How far does the tip of the minute hand travel in 1 hour?
b The hour hand is 4 cm long. How far will the tip of the hour hand travel in
i 1 hour   ii a day?

4 Find the shaded areas.

a

b

c

5 A dance record is made from vinyl.

The diameter of the record is 30 cm.
The hole in the middle has a diameter of 0.9 cm.
a Find the circumference of the record.
b Find the area of the hole.
c Find the area of the vinyl.

6 a Calculate the area of this church door.
b Calculate the perimeter of the door.

7 A dining room table is a rectangle with a semicircle at each end.

Calculate the area of the dining table.

8 You have 160 m of fencing to enclose a field.
What area will you enclose if:
a the field is square
b the field is circular?

9 Repeat question 8 for different lengths of fencing. What do you notice?

Exercise commentary

The questions assess objectives on Framework Page 235–237.

Problem solving
Questions 1, 3, 4, 5, 6 and 7 assess objectives on Framework Page 19.
Questions 8 and 9 assess Page 29.

Group work
The exercise is suitable for pair or group work.

Misconceptions
Students mix up the diameter and the radius, especially in area calculations. Emphasise that the word 'diameter' is longer than the word 'radius' and is also the longer measure.
Encourage them to check that the area is less than d^2.
Students also mix up the formulae. Emphasise that the area has two dimensions: r^2.

Links
Measures: Framework Pages 229.

Homework

S2.4HW provides more practice in circle problems in a range of contexts.

Answers

1 116 m   2 a $113 \, m^2$ b $56.5 \, m^2$
3 a 62.8 cm   b i 2.09 cm   ii 50.3 cm
4 a $66.0 \, cm^2$ b $85.8 \, cm^2$ c $30.9 \, cm^2$
5 a 94.2 cm   b $0.64 \, cm^2$ c $706 \, cm^2$
6 a $3.78 \, m^2$ b 8.83 m   7 $16 \, 110 \, cm^2$ or $1.61 \, m^2$
8 a $1600 \, m^2$ b $2037 \, m^2$
9 The circular area is always bigger.

S2.5 Measuring volume

Mental starter

Areas

Ask students for:

▶ Three rectangles with an area of 40 m².
▶ Three parallelograms with an area of 40 m².
▶ Three triangles with an area of 20 m².

Students sketch their shapes on paper and mark in dimensions and units clearly.

Compare answers. Refer to formulae.

Useful resources

S2.5OHP – conversions between cubic units

Introductory activity

Refer to the mental starter.

Discuss the metric units of length and their equivalences: mm, cm, m and km.
Emphasise that area has two dimensions: length and width or base and height, and that they are perpendicular to each other in the formulae.
Emphasise that to find the area the lengths must be in the same units.

Discuss what 40 m² is in cm².
Encourage students to use supporting diagrams.
Discuss how to convert 40 m² to mm².
Emphasise that you convert it to cm² first.

Discuss what students understand by the term 'volume'.
Emphasise that it has three dimensions: length, width and height.
Discuss how to find the volume of a cuboid.
Encourage students to derive the formula: $l \times w \times h$.

Discuss the units you use to measure volume: cubic units, cm³, m³ etc.
S2.5OHP shows a centimetre cube and a metre cube which you can use to discuss converting between units.

Discuss how to convert 25.3 cm³ to mm³ and 640 000 cm³ to m³.
Encourage students to set two dimensions to be one of the units they are converting between (1 cm or 1 m).

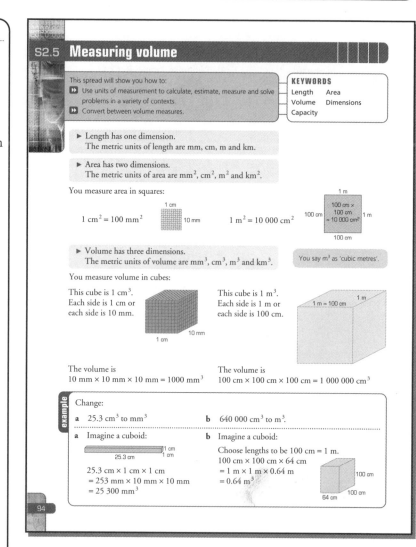

Plenary

Challenge students to:
▶ Find a cuboid with a volume of 1000 cm³
▶ Find another shape with a volume of 1000 cm³.
Discuss answers. Emphasise the variety of shapes with the same volume.

Further activities

In **S2.5ICT** students practise finding dimensions and volumes for containers of different shapes and sizes using a spreadsheet.

Alternatively

Students could work in pairs to estimate the volume of water in the local swimming pool, or a bath, or sink. Encourage them to make sensible estimates of the dimensions.

Differentiation

Core questions:

▶ Question 1 recaps volume of a cuboid.
▶ Questions 2–8 involve converting between cubic units.
▶ Questions 9 and 10 focus on investigating capacity of different containers.

Extension tier: focuses on calculating average speed and converting between measures.

Support tier: focuses on using nets to find surface area and volumes of cuboids.

Exercise S2.5

1 Calculate the volume of each of these cuboids in cubic centimetres.

a

5 cm, 12 cm, 7 cm

b

6.2 cm, 8.9 cm, 5.3 cm

c

5.3 cm, 6.3 cm, 2 m

2 Give your answers to question 1 in cubic millimetres.

3 Calculate the volume of each of these cuboids in cubic centimetres.

a

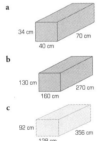
34 cm, 70 cm, 40 cm

b
130 cm, 270 cm, 160 cm

c
92 cm, 356 cm, 128 cm

4 Give your answers to question 3 in cubic metres.

5 Change these volumes to cubic millimetres.
a 6 cm³   **b** 26 cm³
c 0.7 cm³   **d** 14.6 cm³
e 250 cm³

6 Change these volumes to cubic centimetres.
a 3 m³   **b** 6.5 m³
c 0.63 m³   **d** 15.6 m³
e 46 m³

7 Change these volumes to cubic centimetres.
a 6000 mm³   **b** 25 000 mm³
c 700 mm³   **d** 56 000 mm³
e 75 mm³

8 Change these volumes to cubic metres.
a 6 000 000 cm³   **b** 17 600 000 cm³
c 450 000 cm³   **d** 450 cm³
e 70 cm³

9 **Investigation**

1 litre = 1000 cm³

A container in the shape of a cuboid has a capacity of 1 litre.

Investigate possible dimensions for the container.

10 **Challenge**
A can in the shape of a cylinder has a capacity of 1 litre. Investigate possible dimensions for the container.

Area of a circle = πr^2.

95

Exercise commentary

The questions assess objectives on Framework Page 229.

Problem solving

Questions 9 and 10 assess objectives on Framework Page 29.

Group work

Questions 9 and 10 are suitable for pair or group work.

Misconceptions

Students need to know the metric conversions of length to be able to answer the questions.

Discuss strategies of remembering as a class so good ideas are shared. Regular recaps and prominent displays of the conversions should help.

When converting between units, students often divide or multiply just once as for length.

Encourage them to visualise the cuboid as in the example so that they can see there are three dimensions.

Students will often use the wrong units in an answer. Emphasise that the little number shows how many dimensions there are.

Links

Volume: Framework Pages 239–241.

Homework

S2.5HW focuses on calculating volumes and converting between units.

Answers

1 a 420 cm³   **b** 292 cm³   **c** 6678 cm³   **2 a** 420 000 mm³   **b** 292 000 mm³
  c 6 678 000 mm³   **3 a** 95 200 cm³   **b** 5 616 000 cm³   **c** 4 192 256 cm³
4 a 0.0952 m³   **b** 5.616 m³   **c** 4.19 m³
5 a 6000 mm³   **b** 26 000 mm³   **c** 700 mm³   **d** 14 600 mm³   **e** 250 000 mm³
6 a 3 000 000 cm³   **b** 6 500 000 cm³   **c** 630 000 cm³   **d** 15 600 000 cm³   **e** 46 000 000 cm³
7 a 6 cm³   **b** 25 cm³   **c** 0.7 cm³   **d** 56 cm³   **e** 0.075 cm³
8 a 6 m³   **b** 17.6 m³   **c** 0.45 m³   **d** 0.000 45 m³   **e** 0.000 07 m³
9 For example, 100 cm × 10 cm   **10** For example, diameter = 3.18 cm, length = 100 cm

Mental starter

Visualise

Students work in pairs, sitting back to back with each other.
They take it in turns to describe a shape from a set of solids.
The partner must sketch and name the shape described.
Students compare answers.

Useful resources

R16 – 3-D shapes
S2.6OHP – prisms and surface area
Set of solids for the mental starter

Introductory activity

Check by asking questions that students can recall the formulae for the area of a rectangle, parallelogram, triangle and circle.

Refer to the mental starter.
Ask students for a solid that has a rectangular face.
Repeat for a parallelogram, trapezium, triangle and circle. (**R16** shows 3-D shapes.)

Discuss what the shapes they describe have in common.
Emphasise that some taper to a point but others have a constant cross-section.
Discuss what to call each category.
Encourage students to explain what the terms 'prism' and 'pyramid' mean in their own words.
Emphasise that you name a prism by its end face.

Emphasise that a cuboid is a prism with a rectangular end face.
Discuss how to find the volume of a prism.
Encourage students to think of the prism as lots of layers of the end face.

Discuss how to find the surface area of a 3-D shape.
Emphasise that it is the total area of all its faces and that you can use the net.

Discuss the examples from the Students' Book (on **S2.6OHP**).
Encourage students to work out the surface area efficiently, using pairs of faces where possible.

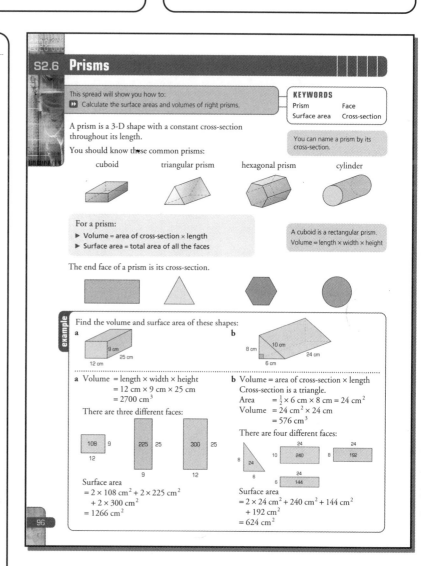

Plenary

Challenge students to find three prisms with a volume of 800 cm^3.
Encourage them to produce a varied range of answers.
Discuss strategies.

Further activities

Students could find the volumes of the shapes in question **3c–e** by first finding the area of the cross-section (by splitting it into rectangles).

Core questions:

▶ Question 1 recaps volume of a cuboid.
▶ Questions 2–5 involve finding the volume and surface area of prisms.
▶ Questions 6 and 7 are open-ended questions investigating possible dimensions for a given volume.

Extension tier: focuses on calculating cross-sectional area, volumes and lengths of prisms.

Support tier: focuses on converting between metric and Imperial measures.

Exercise S2.6

1 Work out the volumes of these cuboids.

a

5 cm 12 cm 6 cm

b

8.6 cm 3.7 cm 3.1 cm

c
1.2 m 5.3 m 1.4 m

2 Calculate the surface areas of the cuboids in question 1.

3 Work out the volumes of these prisms.

a
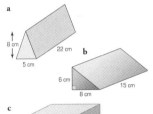
8 cm 22 cm 5 cm

b
6 cm 8 cm 15 cm

c
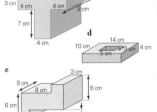
3 cm 4 cm 4 cm 9 cm 7 cm 4 cm

d
14 cm 10 cm 5 cm 3 cm 4 cm

e
3 cm 9 cm 8 cm 6 cm 6 cm 2 cm 2 cm 2 cm

Hint: split parts **c–e** into cuboids.

4 Find the surface areas of the prisms in question 3 parts **c** and **e**.

5 Find the lengths marked with letters.

a

a 7 cm 10 cm

volume = 420 cm³

b
8 cm b 10 cm

volume = 240 cm³

c
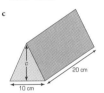
c 10 cm 20 cm

volume = 1600 cm³

6 **Investigation**
a A cuboid has a volume of 600 cm³. Investigate its possible dimensions.
b Change the volume and investigate possible dimensions.

7 **Investigation**
a A prism has a volume of 600 cm³. Investigate its possible dimensions.
b Change the volume and investigate possible dimensions.

97

Exercise commentary

The questions assess objectives on Framework Pages 239–241.

Problem solving
Questions 3 and 5 assess objectives on Framework Page 19.
Questions 6 and 7 assess Page 29.

Group work
Questions 3–7 are suitable for pair or group work.

Misconceptions
Students tend to multiply three lengths together without considering what they are trying to find, so in question 3b they will find the area of the cuboid.
Emphasise that they should always find the area of the end face first.
The number of steps involved in some of the compound shapes questions may lead to mistakes.
Encourage students to work systematically through problems.

Links
Nets: Framework Page 199.

Homework

S2.6HW focuses on finding volumes of a variety of prisms.

Answers

1 **a** 360 cm³ **b** 98.6 cm³ **c** 8.904 m³
2 **a** 324 cm² **b** 139.9 cm² **c** 30.92 m²
3 **a** 440 cm³ **b** 360 cm³ **c** 576 cm³ **d** 500 cm³ **e** 486 cm³
4 **c** 524 cm² **e** 450 cm²   5 **a** 6 cm **b** 6 cm **c** 16 cm
6 **a** For example, 6 × 10 × 10 cm **b** For example, Volume of 500 cm³, dimensions of 25 × 5 × 4 cm
7 **a** For example a triangular prism: base = 12 cm, height = 10 cm, length = 10 cm
  b Student's own answer.

Summary

The key objectives for this unit are:
▸ Know and use the formulae for the circumference and area of a circle. (235–237)
▸ Solve substantial problems by breaking them into simpler tasks. (29)
▸ Present a concise and reasoned argument using symbols and explanatory text. (31)

Check out commentary

1 Students need to calculate the perimeter of the circle and then divide to see how many it can seat.
   Emphasise that they must work in consistent units.
   Students may not realise that in part **b** the corners are quarter circles and in part **c** the ends are semicircles.
   Emphasise the importance or working systematically and being careful with units.

2 Emphasise that students should start by labelling/noting all the facts they know about a rhombus – parallel equal sides, etc.
   They may remember from previous work that opposite angles of a rhombus are equal.
   If not, they can extend side BC and consider angles in parallel lines.
   Emphasise the need to explain their reasons for each step clearly.

3 Encourage students to sketch diagrams and explain clearly the steps they follow in this calculation. They will need to estimate the amount of space each person needs, or they could use the 70 cm measurement for question 1.

Plenary activity

Ask students to find three different prisms with a volume of 600 cm³ including a cylinder.
Challenge them to work out which one has the smallest surface area.
Discuss why that information might be important to a manufacturer. [Less material needed.]

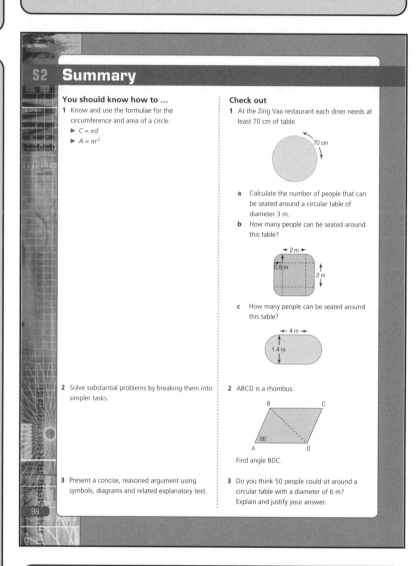

Development

The work on prisms is developed in S4.

Links

The work on area and volume uses formulae, providing a link to algebra, particularly when students change the subject of formulae.

Mental starters

The objectives covered are:
▸ Order, add, subtract, multiply and divide integers.
▸ Use squares, cubes, roots and index notation.
▸ Use jottings to support addition, subtraction, multiplication and division.
▸ Recall multiplication and division facts to 10 × 10. Derive products and quotients of multiplies to 10, 100, 1000.
▸ Use knowledge of place value to multiply and divide decimals by multiples of 0.1 and 0.01.
▸ Round integers and decimals.
▸ Use approximations to estimate answers.

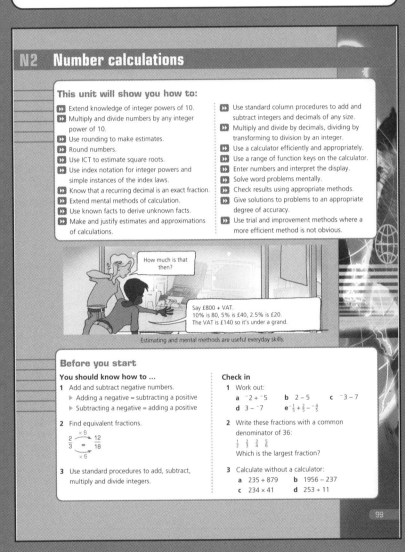

N2 Number calculations

This unit will show you how to:

▸▸ Extend knowledge of integer powers of 10.
▸▸ Multiply and divide numbers by any integer power of 10.
▸▸ Use rounding to make estimates.
▸▸ Round numbers.
▸▸ Use ICT to estimate square roots.
▸▸ Use index notation for integer powers and simple instances of the index laws.
▸▸ Know that a recurring decimal is an exact fraction.
▸▸ Extend mental methods of calculation.
▸▸ Use known facts to derive unknown facts.
▸▸ Make and justify estimates and approximations of calculations.

▸▸ Use standard column procedures to add and subtract integers and decimals of any size.
▸▸ Multiply and divide by decimals, dividing by transforming to division by an integer.
▸▸ Use a calculator efficiently and appropriately.
▸▸ Use a range of function keys on the calculator.
▸▸ Enter numbers and interpret the display.
▸▸ Solve word problems mentally.
▸▸ Check results using appropriate methods.
▸▸ Give solutions to problems to an appropriate degree of accuracy.
▸▸ Use trial and improvement methods where a more efficient method is not obvious.

How much is that then?

Say £800 + VAT.
10% is 80, 5% is £40, 2.5% is £20.
The VAT is £140 so it's under a grand.

Estimating and mental methods are useful everyday skills.

Before you start

You should know how to ...

1 Add and subtract negative numbers.
  ▸ Adding a negative = subtracting a positive
  ▸ Subtracting a negative = adding a positive

2 Find equivalent fractions.
$$\frac{2}{3} \xrightarrow{\times 6} \frac{12}{18}$$

3 Use standard procedures to add, subtract, multiply and divide integers.

Check in

1 Work out:
  a $^-2 + ^-5$ b $2 - 5$ c $^-3 - 7$
  d $3 - ^-7$ e $\frac{1}{5} + \frac{2}{5} - \frac{4}{5}$

2 Write these fractions with a common denominator of 36:
  $\frac{1}{2}$ $\frac{2}{9}$ $\frac{3}{4}$ $\frac{5}{6}$
  Which is the largest fraction?

3 Calculate without a calculator:
  a 235 + 879   b 1956 − 237
  c 234 × 41   d 253 ÷ 11

99

Check in activity

Encourage students to invent three different problems that can be solved using either multiplication or division. One of the problems should require a mental method, one a written method, and one should best be solved using a calculator. Choose some of their problems and give these to the rest of the class to solve.

Resources needed

* means class set needed

Essential:
N2.2OHP – powers of 10
N2.3OHP – doughnut problem
N2.8OHP – calculations and answers
R34 – multiplication pairs
R5* – number ladders
Scientific and non-scientific calculators*

Useful:
R1 – number cards or dice
R6 – number lines
N2.7OHP – written division
Food packaging showing weights of contents
N2.3ICT* – number lines and square roots
Reference books, Internet access

Unit commentary

Aim of the unit

This unit continues to develop techniques for multiplying and dividing, using mental, written and calculator methods.

Introduction

Discuss situations in everyday life and in other subjects where students are required to multiply and divide. Emphasise the use of very large and very small numbers in subjects such as science.

Framework references

This unit focuses on:
Teaching objectives pages:
37, 39, 43, 45, 57, 59, 65, 83, 89, 93, 97–109, 133, 139.
Problem solving pages: 3, 7, 21, 27, 31.

Differentiation

Support tier

Focuses on mental, written and calculator methods for the four operations, and methods for checking answers.

Extension tier

Focuses on consolidating mental methods and extends to surds, standard form and recurring decimals.

N2.1 Powers and roots

Mental starter

Ask the students a series of quick-fire mental questions, focusing on powers and roots:

4^2, 17^2 [289], $\sqrt{256}$ [16], 3^4, $(^-2)^3$, $\sqrt{361}$ [19], $^-5^2$, x^3 when $x = 5$

Between what numbers does $\sqrt{200}$ lie? [14 and 15]

Students can answer by various methods:

holding up cards, all answering together, writing answers down.

Useful resources

R6 – number lines

Introductory activity

Check by asking questions that students:

▸ **Know squares of the first 10 numbers and square roots of the first 10 squares:**
  ▸ 7^2, $\sqrt{27}$
▸ **Know how to calculate numbers raised to different powers:**
  ▸ 2^5, $\sqrt[3]{64}$

Put these multiples of 4 on the board:
4^3, 4^2, 4^5, 4^1, 4^6, 4^0

Challenge students to investigate how to multiply or divide these numbers in index form.

Remind students how to use the $\boxed{x^y}$ key on a calculator to help them.

Emphasise that any number raised to the power of zero is one: $4^0 = 1$.

Encourage students to justify and check their answers:

▸ Can you use algebra to show that this works for any number?
▸ What about $4^2 \times 3^4$?

Emphasise that you add the indices when multiplying, and subtract the indices when dividing.

Challenge students to discuss the meaning of negative powers from division calculations: $4^3 \div 4^5 = 4^{-2} = \frac{1}{4^2}$

Challenge students to find $\sqrt{30}$ to 1 dp. Discuss methods used. Emphasise the use of trial and improvement.

Use a number line (**R6**) to show the position of their estimates.

Identify strategies for determining the final answer to 1 dp.

$5.5 > x$, $5.45 < x$ so $x = 5.5$ to 1 dp.

Extend to finding the root to 2 dp.

Emphasise that a positive integer has two square roots, one positive and one negative: $\sqrt{144} = 12$ or $^-12$.

N2.1 Powers and roots

This spread will show you how to:
▸ Use index notation for integer powers and simple instances of the index laws.
▸ Use a calculator efficiently and appropriately.
▸ Use trial and improvement.

KEYWORDS
Cube number   Power
Indices   Index form
Square root   Cube root
Index notation

You use index notation to represent powers of a number.

Positive powers

$17^4 = 17 \times 17 \times 17 \times 17 = 83\,521$
$(^-3)^5 = ^-3 \times ^-3 \times ^-3 \times ^-3 \times ^-3 = ^-243$

Negative powers

$10^{-2} = \frac{1}{10^2} = \frac{1}{10 \times 10} = \frac{1}{100} = 0.01$

▸ Any number raised to the power of zero is 1:
  $10^0 = 1$ $4^0 = 1$

You can multiply and divide numbers written in index form.

Add the indices when multiplying:
$5^3 \times 5^4 = 5^{3+4} = 5^7$

$5^3 \times 5^4 = (5 \times 5 \times 5) \times (5 \times 5 \times 5 \times 5)$
$= 5 \times 5 \times 5 \times 5 \times 5 \times 5 \times 5$
$= 5^7$

Subtract the indices when dividing:
$4^2 \div 4^5 = 4^{2-5} = 4^{-3}$

$4^2 \div 4^5 = \frac{(4 \times 4)}{(4 \times 4 \times 4 \times 4 \times 4)}$
$= \frac{(\cancel{4} \times \cancel{4})}{(4 \times 4 \times \cancel{4} \times \cancel{4} \times 4)}$
$= \frac{1}{4^3} = 4^{-3}$

You can input powers on a calculator using the $\boxed{x^y}$ key:

$17^4 = 17 \boxed{x^y} 4$ $(^-3)^5 = 3 \boxed{+/-} \boxed{x^y} 5$ $10^{-2} = 10 \boxed{x^y} 2 \boxed{+/-}$

▸ A positive integer has two square roots, one positive and one negative.
  $\sqrt{144} = 12$ or $^-12$
▸ A positive integer has a positive cube root and a negative integer has a negative cube root.
  $\sqrt[3]{27} = 3$ and $\sqrt[3]{^-27} = ^-3$

You can use trial and improvement to estimate a square root.

example

Estimate $\sqrt{30}$ to 1 decimal place.

$5^2 = 25$ so $5 < x$
$6^2 = 36$ so $6 > x$
$5.5^2 = 30.25$ so $5.5 > x$
$5.4^2 = 29.16$ so $5.4 < x$
$5.45^2 = 29.7025$ so $5.45 < x$
so $\sqrt{30} = 5.5$ (1 dp)

So $5.45 < x < 5.5$

100

Plenary

Challenge students to spot the mistakes in these problems:

▸ $7^2 \times 7^2 = 14^2$
▸ $3^2 \times 2^3 = 6^5$
▸ $4^5 \times 3^5 = 12^5$ (no mistake)
▸ $3^6 \div 3^2 = 3^3$
▸ $5^2 \div 5^5 = 5^3$

Discuss responses, encouraging correct solutions.

Challenge students to make up their own 'errors' to fool the class and discuss them.

Further activities

Students could choose a target number and challenge a partner to estimate the square root, checking using a calculator. They could devise a points system, for example 1 point if the whole number part is correct, 2 points if the estimate is correct to 1 dp, etc. and play a game.

Differentiation

Core questions:
- ▶ Questions 1–4 practise squares, roots and prime factor decomposition.
- ▶ Questions 5–8 focus on laws of indices and trial and improvement methods.
- ▶ Question 9 extends to representing a problem algebraically and geometrically.

Extension tier: focuses on calculations involving whole number and fractional powers.

Support tier: focuses on squares, cubes and their roots.

Exercise N2.1

1 Calculate:
  - a 5^2
  - b 3^4
  - c 2^8
  - d $(^-3)^4$
  - e 0.1^2
  - f $\sqrt{121}$
  - g $\sqrt[3]{27}$
  - h 17^2
  - i 25^2
  - j $15^2 + 16^2$

2 Use prime factor decomposition to:
  - a Write each of these numbers using index notation, e.g. $25 = 5^2$
    - i 196
    - ii 1728
  - b Find the square roots of:
    - i 576
    - ii 1296

3 **Puzzle**
Find two consecutive whole numbers whose squares differ by 49.

4 Calculate, using your calculator where necessary:
  - a 13^3
  - b 5^{-2}
  - c 10^{-1}
  - d 17^0
  - e 15^4
  - f $\sqrt[3]{4913}$
  - g $\sqrt[3]{^-3375}$

5 Calculate, leaving your answer in index form where appropriate:
  - a $3^2 \times 3^4$
  - b $4^3 \times 4^2$
  - c $5^6 \div 5^4$
  - d $7^6 \div 7^3$
  - e $3^2 + 3^3$
  - f $6^4 \times 6^5$
  - g $8^3 - 8^2$
  - h $13^8 \div 13^5$
  - i $4^3 \times 3^2$
  - j $4^4 \times 4^2 \div 4^8$

6 a Use a trial and improvement method to estimate to 2 decimal places:
    - i $\sqrt{20}$
    - ii $\sqrt[3]{90}$
    - iii $\sqrt{1000}$
  - b Use the square root and cube root keys on your calculator to check your answers.

7 **Puzzle**
Axel says that 'Adding two numbers and then finding the square root is always the same as finding the square root of each number and then adding'.

Morrisey says that 'Adding two numbers and then finding the square root is never the same as finding the square root of each number and then adding'.

Who do you think is correct? Explain and justify your answer.

8 a Write the value of x and y if $256 = 16^2 = 4^x = 2^y$
  - b Copy and complete:
    $2^{11} = 2048$
    $2^{12} =$

9 **Investigation**
A cube is made from 1 cm × 1 cm × 1 cm cubes.

  - a The outside of a 3 × 3 × 3 cube is painted red.
    How many of the smaller cubes have 3 faces painted? How many of the smaller cubes have 2 faces ... 1 face ... 0 faces painted?
  - b Investigate a 4 × 4 × 4 cube.
  - c Predict the number of cubes with 2 faces painted in a 5 × 5 × 5 cube ... in a 52 × 52 × 52 cube ...
    Explain and justify your prediction.

Exercise commentary

The questions assess objectives on Framework Pages 57, 59, 109 and 133.

Problem solving
Questions 3 and 7 assess objectives on Framework Page 7.
Question 9 assesses Page 27.

Group work
Questions 3, 6, 7 and 9 are suitable for working in pairs.

Misconceptions
Students may have difficulty with negative powers. They may assume that a negative power produces a negative number:
$5^{-2} = ^-5^2 = ^-25$
Encourage students look for patterns in lists of descending powers. Emphasise that each answer is 10 times smaller than the previous one, i.e. previous answer ÷ 10. Encourage students to see the negative sign as indicating 'one over the positive power'.

Links
Algebraic expressions involving powers: Framework Page 115; Trial and improvement methods to solve equations: Page 133.

Homework

N2.1HW provides further practice at using index laws and trial and improvement methods to find square roots.

Answers

1 a 25 b 81 c 256 d 81 e 0.01 f 11 g 3 h 289 i 625 j 481
2 a i $2^2 \times 7^2$ ii $2^6 \times 3^3$ b i 24 ii 36
3 24, 25 4 a 2197 b $\frac{1}{25}$ c $\frac{1}{10}$ d 1 e 50 625 f 17 g $^-15$
5 a 3^6 b 4^5 c 5^2 d 7^3 e 36 f 6^9 g 448 h 13^3 i 576 j 4^{-2}
6 a i 4.47 ii 4.48 iii 31.62 b Exact answers: i 4.47 ii 4.48 iii 31.62
7 Morrisey is correct (for non-zero numbers).
8 a $x = 4$, $y = 8$ b 4096
9 a 8, 12, 6, 1 b 8, 24, 24, 8 c 36, 600; $12(n-2)$ for an n-sided shape.

Mental starter

Number ladders

Each student needs a number ladder with 10 spaces (**R5**).

Call out simple questions to give decimals to 2 dp between ¯10, and 10, for example, $96 \div 10$, $0.07 \div 0.1$.

Challenge students to put the numbers onto their ladder one by one in ascending order.

The first student to fill their ladder is the winner.

Useful resources

R5 – number ladders for mental starter

N2.2OHP – powers of 10

Introductory activity

This lesson continues work begun in Year 8 on powers of 10.

Check by asking questions that students can:

▸ **Multiply and divide by powers of 10:**
  ▸ 0.034×100, $565 \div 10$
▸ **Multiply and divide by 0.01 or $\frac{1}{10}$:**
  ▸ $\frac{1}{10}$ of £300, $8 \div 0.01$

Show **N2.2OHP**, and challenge students to fill in the missing powers of 10.
Emphasise that for negative powers,
$10^{-2} = \frac{1}{10^2} = \frac{1}{10 \times 10} = \frac{1}{100}$

Challenge students to write 3.7 in different ways using powers of 10.
▸ 0.37×10
▸ $370 \div 100$.

Discuss answers. Write the answers in a spider diagram.

Emphasise that:

▸ Multiplying by 0.001 = multiplying by $\frac{1}{1000}$ = dividing by 1000.

▸ Dividing by 0.001 = dividing by $\frac{1}{1000}$ = multiplying by 1000.
  Think – how many thousandths are there?

Challenge students to think how to multiply and divide a number by 10^2, 10^{-1}, 10^{-3}, etc. to get 3.7.
Encourage them to discuss their ideas in pairs.
Discuss methods used, encouraging examples to support any explanations. Add these answers to the diagram.

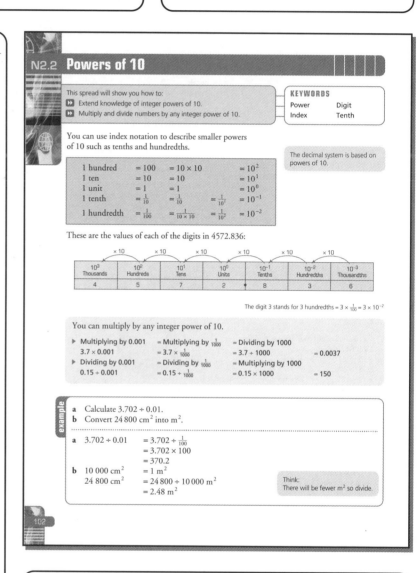

N2.2 **Powers of 10**

This spread will show you how to:
▸ Extend knowledge of integer powers of 10.
▸ Multiply and divide numbers by any integer power of 10.

KEYWORDS
Power   Digit
Index   Tenth

You can use index notation to describe smaller powers of 10 such as tenths and hundredths.

The decimal system is based on powers of 10.

1 hundred	$= 100$	$= 10 \times 10$	$= 10^2$
1 ten	$= 10$	$= 10$	$= 10^1$
1 unit	$= 1$	$= 1$	$= 10^0$
1 tenth	$= \frac{1}{10}$	$= \frac{1}{10}$	$= \frac{1}{10^1}$	$= 10^{-1}$
1 hundredth	$= \frac{1}{100}$	$= \frac{1}{10 \times 10}$	$= \frac{1}{10^2}$	$= 10^{-2}$

These are the values of each of the digits in 4572.836:

10^3 Thousands	10^2 Hundreds	10^1 Tens	10^0 Units	10^{-1} Tenths	10^{-2} Hundredths	10^{-3} Thousandths
4	5	7	2	8	3	6

The digit 3 stands for 3 hundredths $= 3 \times \frac{1}{100} = 3 \times 10^{-2}$

You can multiply by any integer power of 10.

▸ Multiplying by 0.001 = Multiplying by $\frac{1}{1000}$ = Dividing by 1000
  3.7×0.001 = $3.7 \times \frac{1}{1000}$ = $3.7 \div 1000$ = 0.0037
▸ Dividing by 0.001 = Dividing by $\frac{1}{1000}$ = Multiplying by 1000
  $0.15 \div 0.001$ = $0.15 \div \frac{1}{1000}$ = 0.15×1000 = 150

example

a   Calculate $3.702 \div 0.01$.
b   Convert 24 800 cm² into m².

a $3.702 \div 0.01$ $= 3.702 \div \frac{1}{100}$
                   $= 3.702 \times 100$
                   $= 370.2$

b   10 000 cm² $= 1$ m²
    24 800 cm² $= 24\,800 \div 10\,000$ m²
                $= 2.48$ m²

Think:
There will be fewer m² so divide.

102

Plenary

Challenge students to find the errors in these solutions:
▸ $5.72 \div 0.01 = 0.572$ ▸ $14.8 \div 10^3 = 0.148$
▸ $3.75 \times 10^{-2} = 375$

Encourage students to explain how they identified the error.
Challenge students to multiply or divide all these numbers to make 43: 0.43; 10^3; 10^{-1}; 0.01; $\frac{1}{10}$; 10^4; $\frac{1}{1000}$.

Discuss methods used.

Further activities

Challenge students to write a target number as many different ways as possible, using powers of 10.
For example
$15.2 = 1.52 \times 10$, $1520 \div 1000$, etc.
How many can they write in 5 minutes?

Differentiation

Core questions:
- Question 1 practises previous work on multiplying and dividing by powers of 10.
- Questions 2–7 focus on using powers of 10 written in index form.
- Questions 8 and 9 are more challenging questions involving powers of 10.

Extension tier: focuses on standard form.

Support tier: focuses on ordering decimals and multiplying and dividing by 10, 100, 1000.

Exercise N2.2

1 Calculate:
   a $46 \div 10$ b 3.8×100
   c $29.7 \div \frac{1}{10}$ d $0.16 \div 10$
   e $13.02 \times \frac{1}{10}$ f 0.27×0.1
   g $1.34 \div \frac{1}{100}$

2 Write down the value of these numbers:
   a 5×10^2 b 2.7×10^3
   c 7.62×10^2 d 1.04×10^5

3 Calculate:
   a 1.7×0.01 b 0.001×43
   c $10\,000 \times 1.2$ d $8 \div \frac{1}{1000}$
   e 9×0.001 f $23 \times \frac{1}{1000}$
   g $3.7 \div 0.001$ h $0.025 \div 0.01$
   i 0.07×0.01

4 The table shows metric conversions.

1 cm = 10 mm	1 cm² = 100 mm²
1 m = 100 cm	1 m² = 10 000 cm²
1 km = 1000 m	1 km² = 1 000 000 m²

Use the information to convert each of these measurements:
   a 0.32 km into mm
   b 2450 cm² into m²
   c $23\,500$ mm into km
   d 0.00045 km² into cm²

5 Write down the values of these numbers:
   a 34×10^{-2}
   b 124×10^{-3}
   c 267×10^{-5}
   d 0.024×10^3
   e 6.243×10^2
   f 8.4×10^{-3}

6 Nina is looking at microscopic organisms. The length of a micropod is 0.000517 cm and the length of a didipod is 0.001034 cm.
Use a calculator to work out the difference in length of the two organisms. Give your answer in millimetres.

7 **Puzzle**
Place these numbers in order from lowest to highest to spell something you might need to look at again.
   V 37.2×10^{-4}
   R 2.3×10^{-3}
   O $0.0023 \div 10^{-2}$
   I 4×0.001
   E $300 \div 10^5$
   N $0.0016 \div 0.001$
   I $110 \div 10^4$
   S 10.2×10^{-3}

8 Find the number that lies exactly halfway between each of these pairs of numbers:
   a 24×10^{-1} and 0.037×10^2
   b 3500×10^{-4} and 0.00069×10^3
   c $^-0.34 \times 10^2$ and 1400×10^{-2}
   d $^-274 \times 10^{-2}$ and 0.000115×10^4

9 Copy and complete these statements, giving your answers where appropriate as powers of 10:
   a $0.3 \times ? = 30$
   b $0.4 \times ? = 0.04$
   c $? \div 10^{-2} = 64$
   d $4.3 \times ? = 0.043$
   e $^-2.3 \div ? = ^-2300$
   f $^-0.013 \div ? = 1.3$

103

Exercise commentary

The questions assess objectives on Framework Pages 37, 39 and 83.

Problem solving
Question 6 assesses the objectives on Framework Page 21.

Group work
Questions 7 and 8 are suitable for working in pairs.

Misconceptions
Students may have difficulty with notation of negative powers of 10:
$34 \times 10^{-2} = 34 \times {}^-100$ or $(\frac{1}{340})^2$
Encourage students to rewrite in a more familiar form, e.g. $\frac{1}{100}$, and to write down an equivalent calculation, e.g. dividing by 100.
Encourage them to look at the change in the place value of the answers: How does it compare with the original?
Encourage them to think about the size of the multiplier/divider: Will the answer be larger or smaller?

Links
Index notation: Framework Pages 57–59; Use of standard form: Page 39.

Homework

N2.2HW is a multiplication and division game using powers of 10.

Answers

1 a 4.6 b 380 c 297 d 0.016 e 1.302 f 0.027 g 134
2 a 500 b 2700 c 762 d 104 000
3 a 0.017 b 0.043 c 12 000 d 8000 e 0.009 f 0.023 g 3700 h 2.5 i 0.0007
4 a 320 000 mm b 0.245 m² c 0.0235 km d 4 500 000 cm²
5 a 0.34 b 0.124 c 0.00267 d 24 e 624.3 f 0.0084
6 0.00517 mm 7 REVISION 8 a 3.05 b 0.52 c $^-10$ d $^-0.795$
9 a 10^2 b 10^{-1} c 0.64 d 10^{-2} e 10^{-3} f $^-10^{-2}$

103

Mental starter

Rounding bingo

Give students a selection of answers from a series of quick-fire mental questions, focusing on rounding:

Round [2.3423, 2756.8 ...] to the nearest [10, 100, 2 dp ...]. Each student chooses ten numbers from the answers and writes them in a two by five grid. Ask the questions. Students cross off each answer on their board until they have them all.

Discuss methods used and any incorrect answers.

Useful resources

R6 – number lines
N2.3OHP – doughnut example from Students' Book

Introductory activity

Check by asking questions that students understand:

▶ **Rounding and powers of 10:**
  ▶ to 1 dp is to the nearest 0.1.
▶ **How to round to 2 dp:**
  ▶ 3587.267 to the nearest 0.01.
▶ **How to use rounding in approximate answers:**
  ▶ Estimate the value of 293×5.1.

Challenge students to round 1.27873 to 1 dp, 2 dp and 3 dp.

Encourage students to show their answers on a number line (R6). Emphasise:

▶ Different ways of describing rounding to 3 dp: to the nearest thousandth, 0.001 or 10^{-3}.
▶ Looking at the next digit to decide to round up or down.
▶ The context of a rounded answer: to the nearest cm, mm ...

Discuss the doughnut example from the Students' Book, on N2.3OHP.

Challenge students to work in pairs to decide which is the best of the estimates given on the OHP. Encourage them to justify why the other eight values are not good estimates. Discuss strategies. Emphasise:

▶ Rounding the number at every stage of the calculation:
  $40 \times 5 \times 20 \times 50 \times 10 = 2$ tonnes
▶ Approximating based on the average load of a lorry: between one tonne and 10 tonnes.
▶ The number of kg in one tonne/g in one kg.

Emphasise that rounding at the end of a calculation is more accurate.

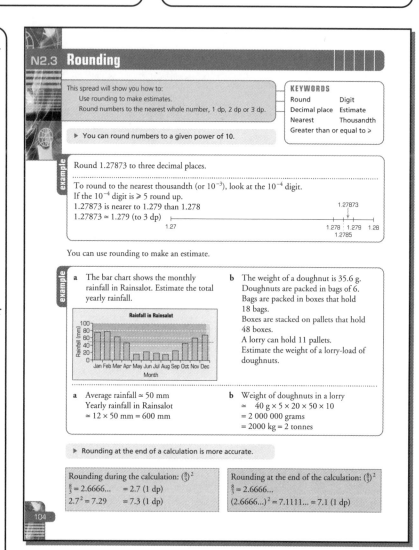

Plenary

Split the class into two groups:

Group 1 always rounds their answers after each part of a problem, but Group 2 only rounds at the end.

Challenge the groups to solve this problem:

▶ 17 boxes each weigh 4.89 kg. Find 28% of the total weight.

Discuss answers. Emphasise strategies and methods used, the accuracy of the answers, and the greater accuracy given by rounding at the end of the calculation.

Further activities

N2.3ICT provides practice at using number lines for rounding and estimation, including finding square roots.

Alternatively

Students could estimate how much water they drink, or crisps/fruit they eat each day/week/year and in a lifetime.
How long does it take them to eat their own body weight?

Differentiation

Core questions:
- ▶ Question 1 practises previous work on rounding.
- ▶ Questions 2–6 focus on rounding to given powers of 10, and using rounding to make estimates.
- ▶ Questions 7 and 8 extend to considering degrees of accuracy in problem solving.

Extension tier: focuses on upper and lower bounds.

Support tier: focuses on rounding to powers of 10, the nearest whole number and 1 or 2 dp.

Exercise N2.3

1 Round each of these numbers:
  a to the nearest ten
  b to the nearest whole number
  c to one decimal place
  d to two decimal places.
    i 43.181   ii 9.951
    iii 129.333   iv 12.0999

2 Use your calculator to work out these answers correct to 3 dp:
  a 13% of 2.4465 kg   b $\frac{5}{7}$ of 19 m
  c The weight of a biscuit if 14 biscuits weigh 250 g.

3 a Write down an approximate answer for each of these questions, clearly showing your method of approximation:
    i $\frac{24.51 \times 7.8}{2.1}$
    ii $2.7 + (115.3 - 12.78 \times 6.4)$
    iii $\{4.4^2 + (7.2 - 0.738)\}^2$
    iv $\frac{4.8 \times 3.7^2}{1.7}$
  b Use your calculator to work out the exact answers, where appropriate giving your answer to 3 dp.

4 A micropod has a length of 0.000517 cm. How many whole micropods would stretch across a line 3 mm long? Use your calculator.

5 a Identify the best estimate to the following calculations from the numbers in the box:

    | 6 | 7 | 8 |
    | 9 | 10 | 60 |

    i 63.23 ÷ 6.94
    ii 16.3 × 0.48
  b Estimate the answer to $\frac{6.56 + 23.7}{3.14}$
    Give your answer to the nearest whole number.

6 **Investigation**
  a When a toilet flushes it uses 9.24 litres of water.
    If a toilet is flushed 17 times a day, about how much water is used per day? Approximately how much water is used per week ... per month ... per year ... per lifetime of a person?
  b The volume of water in Lake Windermere is about 330 000 000 m³. Approximately how long would it take to flush the volume of the lake down the toilet?

    > 1 m³ = 1000 litres

7 a The Blakeburn shopping centre has a length of 700 m to the nearest 100 m, and a length of 650 m to the nearest 10 m. Write down a possible length of the Blakeburn shopping centre.
  b Two more shopping centres both have a length of 850 m to the nearest 10 m but have different lengths to the nearest 100 m. Write down a possible length of each of the shopping centres.

8 This diagram shows the football pitch of Greenburgh Utd:

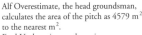

Alf Overestimate, the head groundsman, calculates the area of the pitch as 4579 m² to the nearest m².
Fred Underestimate, the assistant groundsman, calculates the area of the pitch as 4438 m² to the nearest m².
Explain how both groundsmen have arrived at their answers.

105

Exercise commentary

The questions assess objectives on Framework Pages 43, 45 and 103.

Problem solving
Questions 4, 6 and 7 assess objectives on Framework Page 21.

Group work
Questions 6–8 are suitable for working in pairs.

Misconceptions
Students may use the same degree of accuracy throughout the calculation when approximating:
$(4.4^2 + (7.2 - 0.738))^2 \sim [4^2 + (7-1)]^2$
$= 22^2 = 484$ (too complex)
or $22^2 \sim 20^2 = 400$ (inaccurate)
Encourage students to round each part to an appropriate degree of accuracy that makes the problem easier and more accurate.
Think of 4.4^2 as 4×5:
$(4.4^2 + (7.2 - 0.738))^2 \sim (20 + 6.5)^2$
$= 26.5^2 \sim 25^2 = 625$

Links
Measures: Framework Pages 229–231.

Homework

N2.3HW provides more complex problems involving rounding and rounding errors.

Answers

1 a i 40 ii 10 iii 130 iv 10   b i 43 ii 10 iii 129 iv 12
  c i 43.2 ii 10.0 iii 129.3 iv 12.1   d i 43.18 ii 9.95 iii 129.33 iv 12.10
2 a 0.318 kg   b 13.571 m   c 17.857 g   3 a i $(25 \times 8) \div 2 = 100$
    ii $3 + (115 - 15 \times 5) = 43$ iii $(20 + 5)^2 = 625$ iv $(5 \times 16) \div 2 = 40$
  b i 91.037   ii 36.208   iii 666.776   iv 38.654   4 580 micropods
5 a i 9 ii 8   b 10   6 a Estimates close to: 170, 1000, 4000, 48 000, 3 500 000 litres
  b About 6 000 000 years or 3.6×10^{10} flushes   7 a 650 m ≤ length < 655 m
  b 845 m ≤ length 1 < 850 m, 850 m ≤ length 2 < 855 m,
8 Different rounding estimates: 49.5 × 92.5, 48.5 × 91.5

Mental starter

Make 99

Roll three dice, or pick from number cards (**R1**) to generate three digits.

Challenge students to make up a number using these three digits.

For example, 8, 3, 1 can make 83.1

Repeat, and ask students to add their numbers together.

The aim is to add numbers to reach 99, to the nearest whole number. The first to reach 99 is the winner.

Useful resources

R1 – number cards or dice for the mental starter

Introductory activity

Refer to the mental starter.

Challenge students to:

▶ Add 24, ⁻15, 12 and ⁻13.

▶ Solve 47 + 273, 13.4 − 5.8

Discuss methods and strategies used to add and subtract numbers mentally.

Challenge students to discuss in pairs what methods they would use to add and subtract different pairs of these numbers: ⁻7.9, $4\frac{3}{5}$, 23.652, 12.47, $1\frac{7}{8}$

Discuss the different methods available for easier or harder problems.

Emphasise:

▶ Some sums can be done mentally, others need to be written.

▶ Before you start:

  ▶ Change numbers into the same form: decimals/fractions.

  ▶ Re-write questions involving negative numbers.

  ▶ Approximate each answer.

▶ It is important to decide appropriately which strategy to use, for example, partitioning is not always helpful with fractions.

Encourage students to work out some of the calculations and discuss their ideas.

Emphasise the different strategies for mental and written addition and subtraction:

▶ partitioning

▶ compensation

▶ counting up

▶ standard column method.

Discuss the examples in the Students' Book.

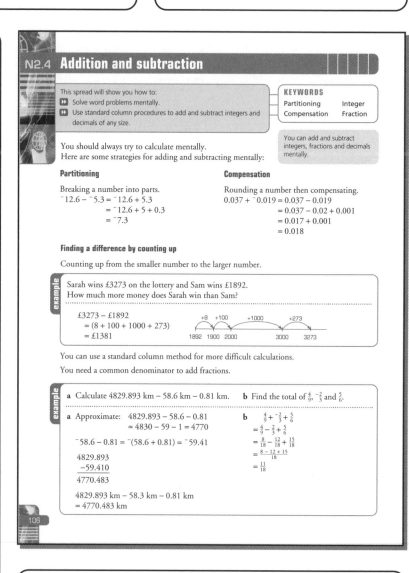

N2.4 Addition and subtraction

This spread will show you how to:
- Solve word problems mentally.
- Use standard column procedures to add and subtract integers and decimals of any size.

KEYWORDS
Partitioning · Integer
Compensation · Fraction

You can add and subtract integers, fractions and decimals mentally.

You should always try to calculate mentally.
Here are some strategies for adding and subtracting mentally:

Partitioning

Breaking a number into parts.
⁻12.6 − ⁻5.3 = ⁻12.6 + 5.3
= ⁻12.6 + 5 + 0.3
= ⁻7.3

Compensation

Rounding a number then compensating.
0.037 + ⁻0.019 = 0.037 − 0.019
= 0.037 − 0.02 + 0.001
= 0.017 + 0.001
= 0.018

Finding a difference by counting up

Counting up from the smaller number to the larger number.

example

Sarah wins £3273 on the lottery and Sam wins £1892.
How much more money does Sarah win than Sam?

£3273 − £1892
= (8 + 100 + 1000 + 273)
= £1381

+8 +100 +1000 +273
1892 1900 2000 3000 3273

You can use a standard column method for more difficult calculations.
You need a common denominator to add fractions.

example

a Calculate 4829.893 km − 58.6 km − 0.81 km. **b** Find the total of $\frac{4}{9}$, $\frac{-2}{3}$ and $\frac{5}{6}$.

a Approximate: 4829.893 − 58.6 − 0.81
≈ 4830 − 59 − 1 = 4770

⁻58.6 − 0.81 = ⁻(58.6 + 0.81) = ⁻59.41

$$\begin{array}{r} 4829.893 \\ -59.410 \\ \hline 4770.483 \end{array}$$

4829.893 km − 58.3 km − 0.81 km
= 4770.483 km

b $\frac{4}{9} + \frac{-2}{3} + \frac{5}{6}$
$= \frac{4}{9} - \frac{2}{3} + \frac{5}{6}$
$= \frac{8}{18} - \frac{12}{18} + \frac{15}{18}$
$= \frac{8 - 12 + 15}{18}$
$= \frac{11}{18}$

106

Plenary

Challenge students to use the five numbers from the introductory activity to make: ⁻12.607. [⁻7.9 + 12.47 + $4\frac{3}{5}$ + $1\frac{7}{8}$ − 23.652]

Discuss strategies. Encourage some students to discuss their methods with the class. Emphasise:

▶ Approximation is useful.

▶ Convert all numbers to decimals.

▶ Trial and improvement.

Further activities

Students can devise puzzles like those in questions 6 and 7 for a partner to solve.

Differentiation

Core questions:

▶ Question 1 practises mental addition and subtraction similar to Key Stage 3 mental tests.
▶ Questions 2–5 focus on adding and subtracting in context using a range of methods.
▶ Questions 6 and 7 extend to using mixed units and numbers in context.

Extension tier: focuses on adding and subtracting decimals and fractions.

Support tier: focuses on adding and subtracting decimals.

Exercise N2.4

1 Here are five questions you should be able to do in your head. Give yourself about 10 seconds for each question.
   a Find the sum of 1.4, 3.6, 2.6 and 4.4.
   b Write $\frac{28}{35}$ in its simplest form.
   c Vicky has £140. She buys a coat costing £69. How much money does she have left?
   d What is 3000 − 67?
   e Write three odd numbers that add up to 33.

2 Look at these number cards:

   a What is the total of all six cards?
   b Which three numbers have the lowest possible total?
   c Copy and complete this number sentence using one of the cards to make the lowest possible answer.

3 Calculate each of these, using a mental or written method as appropriate:
   a Two of the angles of a triangle are 46 degrees and 57 degrees. Calculate the size of the missing angle.
   b Three years ago Ralph was 1.36 m tall. Now he is 1.7 m tall. How much has Ralph grown?
   c Richie earns £342.60 a week. Chloe earns £401.87 a week. How much more money does Chloe earn each week than Richie?
   d Steve wins £4563 on the lottery. Sue wins £2791. How much more money does Steve win than Sue?

4 In a newspaper, there are three photographs on the same page.
   ▶ Photograph 1 uses $\frac{1}{3}$ of the page.
   ▶ Photograph 2 uses $\frac{1}{6}$ of the page.
   ▶ Photograph 3 uses $\frac{1}{8}$ of the page.
   What fraction of the page is not covered by photographs?

5 Calculate these using a mental or written method:
   a 12.17 + 3 + 1.04
   b 16.4 − 2.53 + ⁻1.8
   c $\frac{2}{7} + \frac{3}{5}$ d $2\frac{2}{3} − 1\frac{2}{5}$
   e 24.7 − ⁻92.6 + 53.53
   f 5.79 + 3.7 + 9 + 2.79
   g 1.8 − 3.17 − 0.93
   h 1.0562 + 24.92 + 6378
   i 4567.98 − 67.4 − 0.7
   j 5.18 km + ⁻0.0674 km
   k 8305 m − ⁻340.003 m + 0.0032 m
   l $\frac{2}{5} + \frac{3}{4} − \frac{1}{3}$ m $1\frac{1}{3} + \frac{-5}{6} − \frac{1}{4}$

6 **Puzzle**
   Two families buy tickets for the circus.
   The Greens family buy 2 adult tickets and 2 child tickets.
   They pay a total of £8.90.
   The Browns family buy 1 adult ticket and 3 child tickets.
   They pay a total of £8.35.
   What is the cost of a child ticket?

7 **Puzzle**
   Calculate the perimeter of this shape.
   Give your answer in metres.

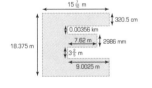

107

Exercise commentary

The questions assess objectives on Framework Pages 93, 99 and 105.

Problem solving

Question 6 assesses objectives on Framework Page 3.
Question 7 assesses objectives on Page 21.

Group work

Questions 2, 4, 6 and 7 are suitable for working in pairs.

Misconceptions

Students may not use the same units of measurement throughout.
Encourage students to change all measurements into the same unit before they start, and to approximate their answer first.
Drawing a diagram, if appropriate, with all the correct measurements in the same units may help.

Links

Measures: Framework Pages 229–231.

Homework

N2.4HW provides further practice at mental addition and subtraction.

Answers

1 a 12   b $\frac{4}{5}$ c £71   d 2933   e Example: 1 + 3 + 29
2 a 2   b ⁻5, ⁻3, ⁻2   c ⁻5 − ⁺7 = ⁻12
3 a 77°   b 0.34 m or 34 cm   c £59.27   d £1772
4 $\frac{3}{8}$
5 a 16.21   b 12.07   c $\frac{31}{35}$ d $1\frac{4}{15}$ e 170.83   f 21.28   g ⁻2.3
   h 6403.9762   i 4499.88   j 5.1126 km   k 8645.0062 m   l $\frac{49}{60}$ m $\frac{7}{12}$
6 £1.95   7 101.395 m

Mental starter

Challenge students to complete this calculation, picking numbers from the list: **Start number ÷ divider × multiplier**
Start numbers: 168, 240, 120, 270, 252, 210, 150, 128, 144, 280
Dividers: 2, 2, 3, 3, 4, 4, 5, 6, 8, 10
Multipliers: 2, 3, 4, 5,5, 6, 7,8, 9, 10
They can only use each number once.
This can be played in teams, the score being the correct answer.

Useful resources

R6 – number line for the exercise
Food packaging for Further activities

Introductory activity

Refer to the mental starter.
Check by asking questions that students can:

▶ **Multiply and divide by 0.1 and 0.01.**
▶ **Multiply and divide using factors:**
  ▶ $3 ÷ 0.02 = 3 ÷ 2 ÷ 0.01 = 150$
▶ **Multiply using partitioning:**
  ▶ $21 × 0.73 = 20 × 0.73 + 1 × 0.73$
    $= 15.33$

Challenge students to make up a calculation from these numbers:
$1\frac{7}{10}$, 170%, 1.7, £310, 268 km
Discuss strategies. Encourage students to discuss their working.
Emphasise:

▶ **Multiplying a fraction by an integer using partitioning:**
  $\frac{17}{10} × 310 = 17 × 310 × \frac{1}{10}$
▶ **Cancelling of common factors:**
  $\frac{17}{10} × 310 = 17 × 31$

Repeat with 170% of £310.
Emphasise:

▶ **The equivalence of fractions, decimals and percentages:**
  $170\% \rightarrow \frac{170}{100} \rightarrow 1.7$
▶ **Use of factors to simplify the calculation:**
  $310 = 31 × 10$

Discuss the second example in the Students' Book. Emphasise that finding a percentage or fraction of an amount is all about multiplying and dividing.

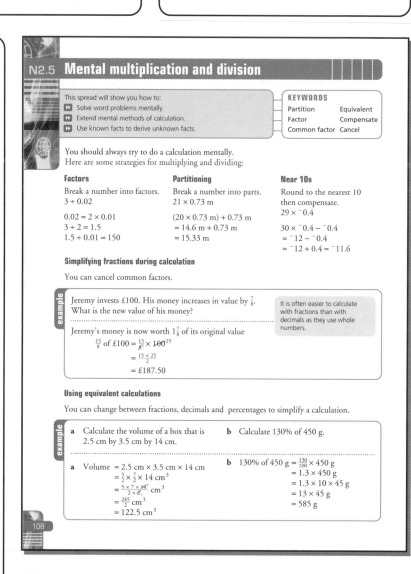

N2.5 Mental multiplication and division

This spread will show you how to:
▶ Solve word problems mentally.
▶ Extend mental methods of calculation.
▶ Use known facts to derive unknown facts.

KEYWORDS
Partition   Equivalent
Factor   Compensate
Common factor Cancel

You should always try to do a calculation mentally.
Here are some strategies for multiplying and dividing:

Factors	Partitioning	Near 10s
Break a number into factors.	Break a number into parts.	Round to the nearest 10 then compensate.
$3 ÷ 0.02$	$21 × 0.73$ m	$29 × {}^-0.4$
$0.02 = 2 × 0.01$	$(20 × 0.73$ m$) + 0.73$ m	$30 × {}^-0.4 - {}^-0.4$
$3 ÷ 2 = 1.5$	$= 14.6$ m $+ 0.73$ m	$= {}^-12 - {}^-0.4$
$1.5 ÷ 0.01 = 150$	$= 15.33$ m	$= {}^-12 + 0.4 = {}^-11.6$

Simplifying fractions during calculation

You can cancel common factors.

example
Jeremy invests £100. His money increases in value by $\frac{7}{8}$. What is the new value of his money?

It is often easier to calculate with fractions than with decimals as they use whole numbers.

Jeremy's money is now worth $1\frac{7}{8}$ of its original value
$$\frac{15}{8} \text{ of } £100 = \frac{15}{8} × 100^{25}$$
$$= \frac{15 × 25}{2}$$
$$= £187.50$$

Using equivalent calculations

You can change between fractions, decimals and percentages to simplify a calculation.

example
a Calculate the volume of a box that is 2.5 cm by 3.5 cm by 14 cm.
b Calculate 130% of 450 g.

a Volume $= 2.5$ cm $× 3.5$ cm $× 14$ cm
$= \frac{5}{2} × \frac{7}{2} × 14$ cm^3
$= \frac{5 × 7 × 14}{2 × 2}$ cm^3
$= \frac{245}{2}$ cm^3
$= 122.5$ cm^3

b 130% of 450 g $= \frac{130}{100} × 450$ g
$= 1.3 × 450$ g
$= 1.3 × 10 × 45$ g
$= 13 × 45$ g
$= 585$ g

108

Plenary

Challenge students in pairs to make up calculations that involve:
▶ Finding a fraction or percentage.
▶ Multiplication and division of fractions.
▶ Multiplying an integer by a decimal.
Encourage students to list the different mental strategies they would use. Emphasise the common points:
▶ They are all multiplications or divisions.
▶ The equivalence of fractions, decimals and percentages.

Further activities

Students could use the information on food packaging to estimate the weight of one biscuit in a packet, or weight of biscuits in a 48 packet box.

Differentiation

Core questions:
▶ Question 1 practises mental multiplication and division problems similar to Key Stage 3 mental tests.
▶ Questions 2–6 focus on multiplying and dividing in context using a range of methods.
▶ Questions 7 and 8 extend to more problem-solving contexts.

Extension tier: focuses on using mental skills in a range of contexts.

Support tier: focuses on mental strategies for multiplication and division.

Exercise N2.5

1 Here are seven questions you should be able to do in your head. Give yourself about 10 seconds for each question.
 a What is 400 divided by 10?
 b If $3k = 21$, what is the value of $7k$?
 c What is $1 \div 0.02$?
 d If $17 \times 380 = 6460$, how many 17s are there in 3230?
 e Write an approximate answer to the calculation $297.8 \div 4.98$.
 f What is $4^4 \div 16$?
 g Calculate the mean of these numbers: 0, 1, 3, 3, 4.

2 Calculate:
 a 19×11 b 0.9×6
 c $^-3 \times 15$ d $126 \div 8$
 e 5×1.7 f 23×29
 g $35 \div 0.1$ h 0.7×30
 i $^-47 \times 0.01$ j $224 \div 7$
 k $\frac{3}{7}$ of 105   l $232 \times \frac{5}{8}$
 m $^-21 \times 0.7$ n $^-42 \div 0.06$
 o $\frac{3}{5} \times ^-24$ p $^-8 \div ^-0.04$
 q $^-0.18 \div 0.3$ r $^-13 \times 4.1$
 s 5.4×1.5

3 a A shop sells flowers at £1.95 a bunch. Find the cost of 25 bunches of flowers.
 b A rectangle is 19 cm long and 11 cm wide. Calculate the area of the rectangle.

4 Here are six number cards:

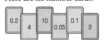

 a Which two cards when multiplied together give the lowest answer?
 b Which two cards, when one is divided by the other, can be used to make a quotient of 200?

5 Calculate:
 a The total weight of 19 pies each weighing 0.4 kg.
 b The total distance covered in 31 turns of a wheel if the circumference of the wheel is 0.92 m.
 c The value of $39x$ if $x = 1.8$.
 d The value of y when $x = 2.7$ if $y = 11x - 5$.
 e Parking costs 15p for every 20-minute period. How much will it cost to park a car from 8.15 am until 5.35 pm?
 f The entrance fee for a cinema is £3.45 per person. What is the total cost for a party of 19 people to visit the cinema?
 g Find the number of loaves of bread each weighing $\frac{4}{5}$ kg that can be made using 8 kg of bread mixture.

6 Calculate:
 a $\frac{2}{5}$ of 20.5   b 20% of £3.65
 c Increase 350 kg by 30%
 d Decrease 220m by 19%
 e $\frac{7}{20}$ of £375   f $\frac{2}{9} \times 189$
 g $\frac{11}{7} \times \frac{23}{19}$ h $\frac{12}{25} \div \frac{20}{21}$

7 **Puzzle**
Ben works out 39.7×0.083 on his calculator. His calculator shows an answer of 0.032951. Explain why this cannot be the right answer.

8 **Puzzle**
Find two numbers whose:
 a sum is 0.7 and whose product is 0.12
 b sum is $^-11.5$ and whose product is 28
 c difference is 28 and whose quotient is 8
 d difference is 6 and whose quotient is $^-0.5$.

109

Exercise commentary

The questions assess objectives on Framework Pages 89, 97, 99 and 101.

Problem solving
Question 5 assesses objectives on Framework Page 3.
Question 8 assesses objectives on page 7.

Group work
Questions 7 and 8 are suitable for working in pairs.

Misconceptions
Students may calculate a percentage of an amount rather than working out the percentage increase. Encourage them to read the question carefully:
▶ Highlight key words.
▶ Decide if the answer will be larger or smaller than the original.
▶ Use a number line (**R6**).
Students may have difficulties with place value. Encourage them to approximate to work out the order of the answer, and to remember rules for multiplying by numbers greater than/less than one.

Links
Measures: Framework Pages 229–231.

Homework

N2.5HW provides practice at multiplication and division in context, including using fractions, percentages and decimals.

Answers

1 a 40 b 49 c 50 d 190 e 60 f 16 g 2.2
2 a 209 b 5.4 c $^-45$ d 15.75 e 8.5 f 667 g 350 h 21 i $^-0.47$ j 32
  k 45 l 145 m $^-14.7$ n $^-700$ o $^-14\frac{2}{5}$ p 200 q $^-0.6$ r $^-53.3$ s 8.1
3 a £48.75 b 209 cm^2 4 a 0.05, 0.1 b 10, 0.05
5 a 7.6 kg b 28.52 m c 70.2 d 24.7 e £4.20 f £65.55 g 10
6 a 8.2 b £0.73 c 455 kg d 178.2 m e £131.25 f 42 g $1\frac{120}{133}$ h $\frac{63}{125}$
7 It should be about $40 \times 0.1 = 4$.
8 a 0.3, 0.4 b $^-3.5, ^-8$ c 4, 32 d $^-2, 4$ (or 2, $^-4$)

Mental starter

Matching pairs

Split students into two teams.

Place 14 cards (from **R34**) face down.

A player from Team 1 picks two cards.

If the calculations match, then they score a point and remove the cards. If they don't match, then turn them over and Team 2 has a turn.

Useful resources

R34 – matching cards for the mental starter

Introductory activity

Refer to the mental starter.

Emphasise that for any written calculation it is important to work out a mental approximation first.

Check by asking questions that students can:

▶ Convert fractions to decimals and vice versa:

  ▶ 36.2 as a fraction

▶ Use a written method of multiplication:

  ▶ 342 × 28

Challenge students to write down as many methods as possible to solve: 36.2 × 5.1

Collate results in a spider diagram.

Discuss and compare strategies and methods. Discuss the advantages of each method.

Emphasise:

▶ Answer should have the correct place value.

▶ Mental approximation first.

▶ Multiplying by 0.1 is equivalent to dividing by 10.

▶ Multiplying of numbers greater/smaller than 1.

Work through the first example in the Students' Book, emphasising that 36.2 = 362 ÷ 10 and 0.56 = 56 ÷ 100.

Discuss strategies and methods.

Emphasise the key steps:

▶ Approximate.

▶ Equivalent calculation.

▶ Standard method for integers.

▶ Calculate the answer.

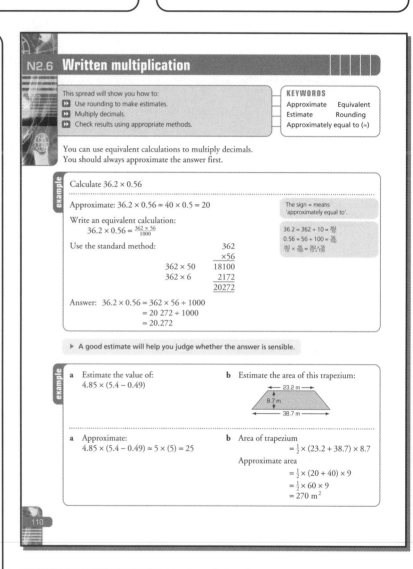

N2.6 **Written multiplication**

This spread will show you how to:
▶▶ Use rounding to make estimates.
▶▶ Multiply decimals.
▶▶ Check results using appropriate methods.

KEYWORDS
Approximate   Equivalent
Estimate   Rounding
Approximately equal to (≈)

You can use equivalent calculations to multiply decimals.
You should always approximate the answer first.

example

Calculate 36.2×0.56

Approximate: $36.2 \times 0.56 \approx 40 \times 0.5 = 20$

The sign ≈ means 'approximately equal to'.

Write an equivalent calculation:
$36.2 \times 0.56 = \frac{362 \times 56}{1000}$

$36.2 = 362 \div 10 = \frac{362}{10}$
$0.56 = 56 \div 100 = \frac{56}{100}$
$\frac{362}{10} \times \frac{56}{100} = \frac{362 \times 56}{10 \times 100}$

Use the standard method:

$$\begin{array}{r} 362 \\ \times 56 \\ \hline \end{array}$$

$362 \times 50 \quad 18100$
$362 \times 6 \quad \underline{2172}$
$\underline{20272}$

Answer: $36.2 \times 0.56 = 362 \times 56 \div 1000$
$= 20\ 272 \div 1000$
$= 20.272$

▶ A good estimate will help you judge whether the answer is sensible.

example

a Estimate the value of:
$4.85 \times (5.4 - 0.49)$

b Estimate the area of this trapezium:

23.2 m
8.7 m
38.7 m

a Approximate:
$4.85 \times (5.4 - 0.49) \approx 5 \times (5) = 25$

b Area of trapezium
$= \frac{1}{2} \times (23.2 + 38.7) \times 8.7$
Approximate area
$= \frac{1}{2} \times (20 + 40) \times 9$
$= \frac{1}{2} \times 60 \times 9$
$= 270 \text{ m}^2$

110

Plenary

Challenge students to find a number that is: Greater than one; greater than zero but less than one; less than zero.

Encourage students to describe the size of the product of any two numbers, and give examples. Emphasise:

▶ The size when multiplying a positive number by a number between zero and one.

▶ The sign when multiplying positive/negative numbers.

Differentiation

Core questions:

▸ Questions 1 and 2 practise long multiplication in problem-solving contexts.
▸ Questions 3–7 practise multiplication up to a three-digit by a two-digit number.
▸ Questions 8 and 9 extend to more demanding multiplications.

Extension tier: focuses on using written multiplication methods with decimals.

Support tier: focuses on written multiplication and division using whole numbers.

Exercise N2.6

1 **a** One tin of dog food weighs 830 g. Karl and Vicky place 59 tins into a box. What is the total weight of the 59 tins in kilograms?
   b What is the volume of a box measuring 12 cm in height, 7 cm in length and 5 cm in width?

2 **Puzzle**
   A number is a multiple of 22 and 37, and it has four digits. What is the largest number it could be?

3 Calculate:
   a 7×0.01 **b** 6×0.8
   c 19×7 **d** 13×15
   e 23×17 **f** 1.7×23
   g 0.17×23 **h** 29×28
   i 6.25×80 **j** 2.3×39
   k 3.5×120 **l** 72×60
   m 8.1×0.09

4 Gerald makes toy wooden aeroplanes. He sells the aeroplanes for £3.75 each. On Wednesday, Gerald sells 37 aeroplanes. How much money does he get for the 37 aeroplanes?

5 Calculate, using a mental or written method as appropriate:
   a 0.3×0.7 **b** 2.54×6
   c 8.57×9 **d** 14.3×2.4
   e 41.5×3.7 **f** 18.7×5.6
   g 29.8×7.4 **h** 69.2×0.67
   i 12.7×0.43 m
   j 53.8 km $\times 0.57$ km
   k 39.2 kg $\times 0.98$
   l 34% of 29.6 tonnes
   m 13% of 17.8m

6 **a** What is the cost of 64.2 m of wood at £0.87 per metre?
   b What is the cost of 31.6 kg of gravel at £0.67 per kilogram?

7 **a** Kitchen worktops costs £212 per square metre. How much would it cost to cover this area of worktop?

   b Horace decides to build a rectangular path in his garden. His path will be 0.82 m wide and 12.6 m long. What is the area of the path?

8 **Puzzle**
   Answer each of the multiplications and find the appropriate letter.
   The letters will reveal the answer to the question 'How do you stop moles digging holes in your garden?'

   a 4.6×3.8 48.6   = I
   b 2.7×18 115.94   = T
   c 23.6×0.78 0.4704   = V
   d 387×4.6 38.896   = H
   e 187×0.62 106.68   = O
   f 34.7×0.8 0.09728   = L
   g 73×2.65 18.408   = D
   h 29.4×3.8 27.76   = H
   i 88.4×0.44 17.48   = H
   j 381×0.28 111.72   = S
   k 0.56×0.84 2.4548   = E
   l 3.23×0.76 1780.2   = E
   m 0.256×0.38 193.45   = E

9 **Challenge**
   a Calculate these using a written method:
   i 6.2×2.35
   ii 3.75×2.62
   iii 13.9×7.62
   iv 12.3×6.942
   v $3.42 \times 45.2 \times 17.8$
   b Make up a decimal multiplication of your own. Check it using a calculator.

Exercise commentary

The questions assess objectives on Framework Pages 43, 89, 97, 103 and 105.

Problem solving

Questions 1 and 7 assess objectives on Framework Page 21.
Question 2 assesses objectives on Page 7.

Group work

Questions 2 and 7 are suitable for working in pairs.

Misconceptions

Students may use a written method for all problems. Encourage them to first use a mental method.
Students may have difficulty finding the correct equivalent calculation:
$0.56 \times 0.84 = \frac{(56 \times 84)}{100}$
Encourage students to approximate, and to write two decimals as fractions that can be multiplied together.

Links

Measures: Framework Pages 229–231;
Using the laws of arithmetic: Page 85.

Homework

N2.6HW is an investigation into the product of parts of the number 19.

Answers

1 **a** 48.97 kg   **b** 420 cm³   **2** 9768
3 **a** 0.07   **b** 4.8   **c** 133   **d** 195   **e** 391   **f** 39.1   **g** 3.91   **h** 812
   i 500   **j** 89.7   **k** 420   **l** 4320   **m** 0.729   **4** £138.75
5 **a** 0.21   **b** 15.24   **c** 77.13   **d** 34.32   **e** 153.55   **f** 104.72   **g** 220.52
   h 46.364   **i** 5.461 m   **j** 30.666 km²   **k** 38.416 kg   **l** 10.064 tonnes
   m 2.314 m   **6 a** £55.85   **b** £21.17   **7 a** £195.04   **b** 10.332 m²
8 **a** 17.48   **b** 48.6   **c** 18.408   **d** 1780.2   **e** 115.94   **f** 27.76   **g** 193.45   **h** 111.72
   i 38.896   **j** 106.68   **k** 0.4704   **l** 2.4548   **m** 0.09728; HIDE THE SHOVEL
9 **a i** 14.57   **ii** 9.825   **iii** 105.918   **iv** 85.3866   **v** 2751.5952

Mental starter

Ask the students a series of quick-fire mental questions, focusing on multiplication and division:

17×19 [323]; If one dozen is 12, how many in 21 dozen? [252]; How many 12s in 540? [45]; 34×0.04 [1.36]; 58 multiplied by what is 3.48? [0.06]; How many times does 18 divide into 432? [24]

Students can answer by various methods:

holding up cards, all answering together, writing answers down.

Useful resources

N2.7OHP – Students' Book example
Reference books or Internet access

Introductory activity

Refer to the mental starter.

Check by asking questions that students can:

▸ Divide mentally two- and three-digit by two-digit numbers:
  ▸ $148 \div 6$; $58 \div 14$

▸ Use a written method to divide a three-digit by a two-digit whole number:
  ▸ $623 \div 25$

▸ Multiply mentally decimal numbers less than one to 1 or 2 dp by small whole numbers:
  ▸ 0.7×4; 0.06×3

Challenge students in pairs to work out:
$723 \div 5.8$; $72.3 \div 5.8$; $72.3 \div 58$; $723 \div 58$
Discuss methods.
Emphasise that:

▸ It is important to mentally approximate first.

▸ Some problems appear harder because the divisor is not an integer.

▸ One calculation can be used to work out the others using powers of 10.

Work through the example in the Students' Book, on N2.7OHP.
Encourage students to approximate first.
Discuss equivalent calculations to achieve an integer divisor.
Solve the problem using the standard method as appropriate.

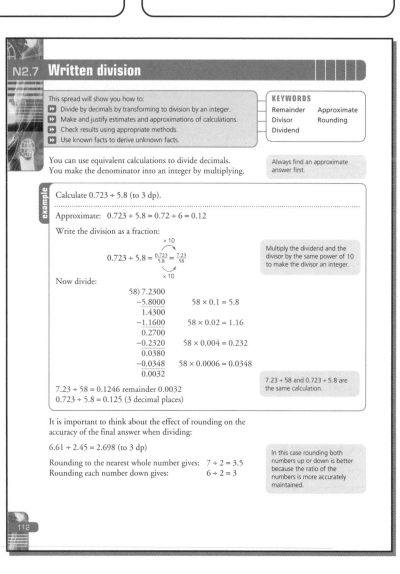

N2.7 **Written division**

This spread will show you how to:
▸▸ Divide by decimals by transforming to division by an integer.
▸▸ Make and justify estimates and approximations of calculations.
▸▸ Check results using appropriate methods.
▸▸ Use known facts to derive unknown facts.

KEYWORDS
Remainder   Approximate
Divisor   Rounding
Dividend

You can use equivalent calculations to divide decimals. You make the denominator into an integer by multiplying.

Always find an approximate answer first.

example

Calculate $0.723 \div 5.8$ (to 3 dp).

Approximate: $0.723 \div 5.8 \approx 0.72 \div 6 = 0.12$

Write the division as a fraction:

$$0.723 \div 5.8 = \frac{0.723}{5.8} = \frac{7.23}{58}$$

Multiply the dividend and the divisor by the same power of 10 to make the divisor an integer.

Now divide:

```
58) 7.2300
   -5.8000        58 × 0.1 = 5.8
    1.4300
   -1.1600        58 × 0.02 = 1.16
    0.2700
   -0.2320        58 × 0.004 = 0.232
    0.0380
   -0.0348        58 × 0.0006 = 0.0348
    0.0032
```

$7.23 \div 58 = 0.1246$ remainder 0.0032
$0.723 \div 5.8 = 0.125$ (3 decimal places)

7.23 ÷ 58 and 0.723 ÷ 5.8 are the same calculation.

It is important to think about the effect of rounding on the accuracy of the final answer when dividing:

$6.61 \div 2.45 = 2.698$ (to 3 dp)

Rounding to the nearest whole number gives: $7 \div 2 = 3.5$
Rounding each number down gives: $6 \div 2 = 3$

In this case rounding both numbers up or down is better because the ratio of the numbers is more accurately maintained.

112

Plenary

Encourage students to work out:
$48 \div 48$, 24, 16, 8, 2, 1, 0.5, 0.1, 0.01 etc.
Discuss whether answers will be larger or smaller.
Look at dividing by negative numbers:
$48 \div {}^-24$, $^-8$, $^-2$, $^-1$, $^-0.5$, $^-0.1$, $^-0.01$ etc.
Challenge students to work out $48 \div 0$.
Discuss answers and strategies.
Emphasise that dividing a number by zero has no proper meaning.

Further activities

Students could find figures for populations and areas of countries, from books or the Internet, and calculate the population density for each country (number of people per square km).

Differentiation

Core questions:

▶ Question 1 practises long multiplication and division.
▶ Questions 2–5 practise division up to any three-digit by two-digit number including word problems in context.
▶ Question 6 extends to more open problem solving.

Extension tier: focuses on dividing decimals.

Support tier: focuses on long division using simple numbers.

Exercise N2.7

1 Calculate, giving your answer to 1 dp where appropriate:
  a 0.6×11 **b** 0.09×15
  c 0.07×20 **d** 3.2×9
  e $71.4 \div 0.1$ **f** $899 \div 29$
  g $589 \div 34$ **h** $167.5 \div 19$
  i $115 \div 2.5$ **j** $288 \div 6.4$
  k $141.4 \div 43$ **l** $51 \div 2.6$

2 **a** At Cheapo Supermarket, tins are stacked in layers inside cupboards. The height of a tin is 14 cm. The height of a cupboard is 1.34 m. How many layers of tins can be kept in the cupboard?
  b Glyn has to put sheets of manuscript into folders. Each folder can hold exactly 24 pieces of manuscript. Glyn has 500 sheets of manuscript. How many folders can be completely filled with sheets of manuscript?
  c At Gro-well Garden Centre, shrubs cost £23 each. Mr Titchmarsh has £300 to spend on shrubs. How many shrubs can he buy?

3 Calculate these using a written method, giving your answer to 2 dp where appropriate:
  a $129 \div 0.6$ **b** $406.8 \div 0.9$
  c $236.4 \div 0.08$ **d** $0.056 \div 0.0037$
  e $0.724 \div 8.4$ **f** $4.29 \div 0.056$
  g $12.8 \div 0.65$ **h** $0.387 \div 7.2$
  i $\frac{3}{5} \div \frac{11}{25}$ **j** $\frac{14}{15} \div \frac{9}{7}$

4 **a** Sheila has to shovel sand into bags. Each bag can hold 0.8 kg of sand. If Sheila has 140 kg sand, how many bags will she need?
  b A piece of fabric is 135.3 m long. A machine cuts the fabric into strips of length 0.06 m. How many strips can be cut out of a 135.3 m piece of fabric?

5 **a** Angus is driving along a motorway at a speed of 1.2 km per minute. He has to travel another 324.6 km at this speed before he leaves the motorway. How long will it take Angus to travel 324.6 km at 1.2 km per minute?
  b Harry buys his biodegradable washing-up liquid in bulk. He is not sure how much his container can hold, but he can fill it for a cost of £9.72. The washing-up liquid costs £1.35 a litre. How much liquid can Harry's container hold?

6 **Investigation**
  Here are the lengths of some creatures:

Creature	Length
Blue whale	26.2 m
Polar bear	2.45 m
Human male	1.79 m
Rusty spotted cat	39 cm
Pygmy jerboa	0.036 m
Bumblebee bat	0.029 m
Scorpion	0.013 m
Dwarf pygmy goby fish	0.0086 m
Micro-moth	2 mm

  a How many scorpions would fit along the length of a polar bear?
  b How many times bigger than a pygmy jerboa is a human male?
  c What percentage of the length of a blue whale is a polar bear?
  d Which creature is just over 200 times the length of another creature?
  e Make up some more statements of your own using the table of information.

Exercise commentary

The questions assess objectives on Framework Pages 89, 97, 101, 103 and 107.

Problem solving

Question 6 assesses objectives on Framework Page 21. The whole exercise assesses objectives on Page 31.

Group work

Questions 2, 4 and 5 are suitable for working in pairs.

Misconceptions

Students may adjust the answer as if it were multiplication:
$0.724 \div 8.4 = 7.24 \div 84$ (multiply by 10) $= 0.086 = 0.0086$ (divide by 10). Encourage approximating first. Encourage students to write the two decimals as a fraction, and compare with equivalent fractions: you can multiply the top and bottom of a fraction by a number and the value remains the same.

Links

Measures: Framework Pages 229–231; Using the laws of arithmetic: Page 85.

Homework

N2.7HW is an investigation into inequalities and arithmetic operations.

Answers

1 **a** 6.6   **b** 1.35   **c** 1.4   **d** 28.8   **e** 714   **f** 31   **g** 17.3   **h** 8.8
  i 46   **j** 45   **k** 3.3   **l** 19.6
2 **a** 9   **b** 20   **c** 13
3 **a** 215   **b** 452   **c** 2955   **d** 15.14   **e** 0.09   **f** 76.61
  g 19.69   **h** 0.05   **i** $1\frac{4}{11}$ **j** $\frac{98}{135}$
4 **a** 175   **b** 2255   5 **a** 4 h 30 min 30 s   **b** 7.2 litres
6 **a** 188   **b** 49.7   **c** 9.4%
  d Human male (208 times bigger than dwarf pygmy goby fish)

Mental starter

Hit the target

Roll three dice, or pick from number cards to generate a three-digit target number.

Challenge students to use these numbers, plus operations, to make up the target number: 4, 5, 8, 15, 20, 40.

Students can use each number only once, and have to get as close to the target as possible. They can score points for how close their number is to the target.

Useful resources

Class set of **scientific calculators**
Class set of **non-scientific calculators**
N2.8OHP – calculations and answers

Introductory activity

Refer to the mental starter.

Remind students that this lesson is about using the order of operations, especially square roots and powers.

Check by asking questions that students know:

▸ **The order of operations:**
  ▸ $13 + 3 \times 6^2 \div (4 + 5)$
▸ **How to enter calculations on a calculator:**
  ▸ Use your calculator to work out the previous problem.

Challenge students in pairs to use two different types of calculator (scientific and non-scientific) **to work out the calculations on N2.8OHP and match them to the correct answer.**

Encourage them to write down exactly which buttons they pressed to work out the answers.

Discuss methods used.

Emphasise:
▸ Order of operations
▸ Need for jottings with a simple calculator
▸ Need for mental approximations
▸ Extra hidden brackets needed for a division.

Discuss the differences between the calculators.

Work through the second and third examples in the Students' Book.

Emphasise:
▸ Hidden brackets in calculations
▸ The order of buttons when multiplying by a bracket
▸ Use of nested brackets, for example: $120 - [4^2 \times (3 - (4 - 6))]$.

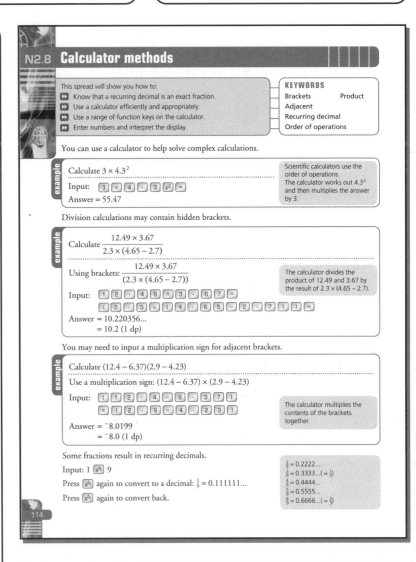

Plenary

Review the key points:
▸ Use the order of operations in more complex calculations.
▸ Carry out calculations using the function keys of a calculator.

Challenge students to produce a poster of one of the calculations, or of their own problem, illustrating the buttons used on both types of calculator.

Discuss the posters and ask students to check that each other's calculations are correct.

Further activities

Challenge more able students to design a poster showing an algebraic formula for a complex calculation into which numbers can be substituted.

Differentiation

Core questions:
- ▶ Question 1 practises approximating and then using a calculator to find the exact answer.
- ▶ Questions 2–4 practise entering more complex calculations into a calculator.
- ▶ Questions 5–7 extend to an substituting values into formulae.

Extension tier: focuses on recurring decimals and reciprocals.

Support tier: focuses on mental and calculator methods for calculations involving indices and hidden brackets.

Exercise N2.8

1 a Write down an approximate answer for each of these questions, clearly showing your method of approximation.
   i 29^2 ii $\sqrt{70}$
   iii 6.8^2 iv $\sqrt{523.9}$
   v $\frac{4}{9} + \frac{3}{7} + \frac{17}{21}$ vi $2\frac{5}{6} + 3\frac{4}{7} - \frac{9}{14}$

   b Use your calculator to work out the exact answers, where appropriate giving your answer to two decimal places or leaving your answer as a fraction.

2 Solve these calculations using a mental, written or calculator method. Where appropriate, give your answer to 2 dp.
   a $(19.1 - 1.9)(19.1 + 1.9)$
   b $\dfrac{(3.7 - 6)^2 + 2.8}{\sqrt{(2.5^2 + 7 \times 3.4)}}$
   c $\dfrac{44.87 \times 72.1}{2.04 \times (7.1 - 3.8)}$
   d $\dfrac{7 \times \sqrt{(7.3^2 + 8^2)}}{3.5^2 - 1.7}$
   e $[(4.3)^2 - 3(8.1 - 0.076)]^2$
   f $7.3 + (4.8 - \sqrt{(11^2 - 6.4^2)})$.

3 a Find 5% of 15% of 2440 m.
   b Calculate $\frac{3}{8}$ of $\frac{2}{5}$ of £23.
   c An antique vase increases in value by 13% per year. Its original value is £150. Calculate the value of the vase after 5 years.

4 **Puzzle**
   Four consecutive whole numbers have a product of 863 040.
   What are the numbers?

5 **Investigation**
   Charlie makes concrete blocks. To work out the volume of water (in litres) he needs to make a concrete block, he uses this rule:

   > Volume of water = (length of block in metres)^2 + 6 (length of block in metres)

   a Calculate the volume of water in litres needed to make a concrete block of length 4.86 m.
   b Calculate the length of block that can be made using 100 litres of water. Give your answer to two decimal places.

6 Use your calculator to evaluate each of these formulae, giving your answers to 1 dp as appropriate:
   a Find the area (A) of a trapezium if $A = \frac{1}{2}(a + b)h$ when $a = 2.4$ m, $b = 3.87$ m and $h = 2.7$ m.
   b Find the circumference (C) of a circle if $C = \pi d$, when $d = 34.7$ cm and $\pi = 3.14$ (2 dp).
   c Find the area (A) of an annulus if $A = \pi(r_1^2 - r_2^2)$, when $r_1 = 18\frac{1}{2}$ cm and $r_2 = 11\frac{2}{5}$ cm. (Use $\pi = \frac{22}{7}$)
   d Find the area (A) of a triangle if $A = \sqrt{(s(s - a)(s - b)(s - c))}$, when $a = 6.4$ cm, $b = 4.2$ cm, $c = 8.9$ cm and $s = \frac{1}{2}(a + b + c)$.
   e Find the value of b if $b = \frac{3p^3(p - 5)}{4p}$ when $p = 3.8$.

7 **Puzzle**
   a By substituting values of your own choice, check to see which of these formulae are the same (use $\pi = 3.14$):

   $$V = \pi r^2 h \qquad h = \frac{\pi}{r V}$$
   $$r = \sqrt{\left(\frac{V}{\pi h}\right)} \qquad V = \frac{\pi}{r^2 h}$$
   b Explain and justify your answers.

Exercise commentary

The questions assess objectives on Framework Pages 109 and 139.

Problem solving
Question 5 assesses objectives on Framework Page 21.
The exercise assesses objectives on Page 31.

Group work
All questions are suitable for working in pairs, with students verifying their answers on calculators.

Misconceptions
Students may not see the hidden brackets in a calculation, in division or when multiplying brackets.
Encourage students to approximate first, and then write the calculation as the numerator divided by the denominator, using brackets.

Links
Rounding: Framework Page 43; Powers and roots, Page 57; Using the laws of arithmetic: Page 85.

Homework

N2.8HW is an investigation into using the number 8 in calculations. It extends to making loop cards.

Answers

1 a i $30^2 = 900$ ii $\sqrt{70} \approx \sqrt{64} = 8$ iii $7^2 = 49$ iv $\sqrt{529} = 23$ v $\frac{1}{2} + \frac{1}{2} + \frac{3}{4} = 1\frac{3}{4}$
   vi $3 + 3\frac{1}{2} - \frac{1}{2} = 6$ b i 841   ii 8.37   iii 46.24   iv 22.89   v $1\frac{43}{63}$ vi $5\frac{16}{21}$

2 a 361.2   b 1.48   c 480.56   d 7.19   e 31.16   f 3.15

3 a 18.3 m   b £3.45   c £276.37

4 29, 30, 31, 32   5 a 52.78 litres   b 7.44 m

6 a 8.5 m^2 b 109.0 cm   c 667.2 cm^2 d 12.4 cm^2 e ⁻3.42

7 b $V = \pi r^2 h$ and $r = \sqrt{\left(\frac{V}{\pi h}\right)}$, and $h = \frac{\pi}{r^2 V}$ and $V = \frac{\pi}{r^2 h}$

Summary

The key objectives for this unit are:
▸ Make and justify estimates and approximations of calculations. (103)
▸ Use standard column procedures to add and subtract integers and decimals of any size. (105)
▸ Multiply and divide by decimals, dividing by transforming to division by an integer. (105–107)
▸ Give solutions to an appropriate degree of accuracy. (31)

Check out commentary

1 Students sometimes fail to choose the correct mathematical operation when solving a problem. Emphasise the importance of deciding whether a question is to be solved using a multiplication or a division calculation. Encourage students to re-read the question, highlight key words, use the context of the question to check if an answer is reasonable, etc.

2 Students often round 3.86 and 1.29 to the nearest whole number, producing a very inaccurate approximation. Encourage students to be flexible when rounding, looking for opportunities that simplify the result while maintaining a fair degree of accuracy. For example, rounding 3.89 and 1.29 to 1 dp, produces a much closer approximation and an easy mental calculation.

3 Students may attempt to add these measurements using a column method, but fail to line up the numbers correctly. Encourage them to estimate the answer and emphasise the use of standard column methods for addition.

4 Students may attempt to calculate 22% of £58.40 using a mixed mental/written method. Emphasise the multiplicative nature of percentage calculations and encourage students to represent it as 0.22×58.4, which they can then work out using an appropriate written method. For part **b**, encourage students to estimate first, in order to check that their answer is sensible.

Plenary activity

Discuss how to calculate 4.73×6.2.
Discuss what other calculations can be solved using this fact, for example 47.3×6.2.
Repeat for a division problem such as $2.78 \div 6.3$
Emphasise the use of estimates to check the size of answer.

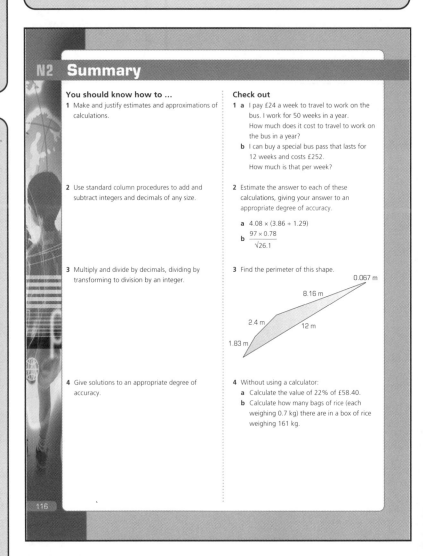

N2 Summary

You should know how to ...

1 Make and justify estimates and approximations of calculations.

2 Use standard column procedures to add and subtract integers and decimals of any size.

3 Multiply and divide by decimals, dividing by transforming to division by an integer.

4 Give solutions to an appropriate degree of accuracy.

Check out

1 **a** I pay £24 a week to travel to work on the bus. I work for 50 weeks in a year. How much does it cost to travel to work on the bus in a year?
   b I can buy a special bus pass that lasts for 12 weeks and costs £252. How much is that per week?

2 Estimate the answer to each of these calculations, giving your answer to an appropriate degree of accuracy.
   a $4.08 \times (3.86 \div 1.29)$
   b $\dfrac{97 \times 0.78}{\sqrt{26.1}}$

3 Find the perimeter of this shape.
   0.067 m
   8.16 m
   2.4 m
   12 m
   1.83 m

4 Without using a calculator:
   a Calculate the value of 22% of £58.40.
   b Calculate how many bags of rice (each weighing 0.7 kg) there are in a box of rice weighing 161 kg.

116

Development

Addition, subtraction, multiplication and division are used throughout Mathematics. Further practice in context is found in **P1**.

Links

Addition, subtraction, multiplication and division are used throughout Mathematics and in other subject areas such as Science and Geography.

Revision

Students should work through D3, D4, D5 and D6 in the 5–7 Revision Book.

Mental starters

Objectives covered in this unit:
▶ Add, subtract, multiply and divide negative numbers.
▶ Find products of small integer powers.
▶ Know and use squares, cubes, roots and index notation.
▶ Know or derive quickly the prime factorisation of numbers to 30 and factor pairs of a number.
▶ Find highest common factors and lowest common multiples.
▶ Recall multiplication and division facts.
▶ Multiply a 2-digit number by a 1-digit number.
▶ Substitute values into expressions.
▶ Use metric units and units of time.
▶ Discuss and interpret graphs.

Resources needed

* means class set needed
Essential:
A4.9OHP – distance–time graph
R8 – grid in four quadrants
R9 – grid in one quadrant
Calculators*   Graph paper*
Useful:
A4.1OHP – factor trees
A4.2OHP – Venn diagrams
A4.3OHP – index cards
A4.8OHP – real-life graph
A4.1F – dividing by primes
A4.5F – parallel lines
A4.6F – gradient and intercept
A4.9F – melting ice
A4.7ICT* – graphs of functions

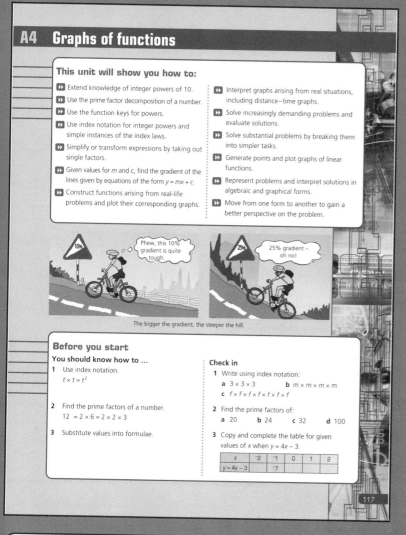

A4 Graphs of functions

This unit will show you how to:

▶▶ Extend knowledge of integer powers of 10.
▶▶ Use the prime factor decomposition of a number.
▶▶ Use the function keys for powers.
▶▶ Use index notation for integer powers and simple instances of the index laws.
▶▶ Simplify or transform expressions by taking out single factors.
▶▶ Given values for m and c, find the gradient of the lines given by equations of the form $y = mx + c$.
▶▶ Construct functions arising from real-life problems and plot their corresponding graphs.

▶▶ Interpret graphs arising from real situations, including distance–time graphs.
▶▶ Solve increasingly demanding problems and evaluate solutions.
▶▶ Solve substantial problems by breaking them into simpler tasks.
▶▶ Generate points and plot graphs of linear functions.
▶▶ Represent problems and interpret solutions in algebraic and graphical forms.
▶▶ Move from one form to another to gain a better perspective on the problem.

Phew, this 10% gradient is quite tough.

25% gradient – oh no!

The bigger the gradient, the steeper the hill.

Before you start

You should know how to ...

1 Use index notation.
$t \times t = t^2$

2 Find the prime factors of a number.
$12 = 2 \times 6 = 2 \times 2 \times 3$

3 Substitute values into formulae.

Check in

1 Write using index notation:
   a $3 \times 3 \times 3$ **b** $m \times m \times m \times m$
   c $f \times f \times f \times f \times f \times f \times f$

2 Find the prime factors of:
   a 20   **b** 24   **c** 32   **d** 100

3 Copy and complete the table for given values of x when $y = 4x - 3$.

x	-2	-1	0	1	2
$y = 4x - 3$		-7			

117

Unit commentary

Aim of the unit

This unit starts by considering factors, multiples and primes and develops to using index notation and the index laws. It then develops graphical work, focusing on how to find the gradient. Students then apply this to real-life graphs.

Introduction

Discuss students' understanding of the term 'gradient'. Refer to examples from everyday life to emphasise that a greater gradient means a steeper hill. Use the pictures in the Students' book to discuss how to measure a gradient.

Framework references

This unit focuses on:
Teaching objectives pages: 37, 55–59, 109, 115–117, 165–167, 173–175.
Problem solving pages: 7, 9, 27, 31.

Check in activity

Factor and prime bingo

Students choose 9 numbers between 1 and 30 and write them in a 3 × 3 grid. Call out questions based on factors and primes:
▶ I am a factor of 24.   ▶ I am a multiple of 5.
▶ I am a 3 squared.
▶ I am a prime number between 9 and 14.
Students cross off one number that satisfies the condition.
Continue until one student has crossed off all their numbers.

Differentiation

Support tier

Focuses on squares, cubes and primes, HCFs and LCMs and then goes on to straight line graphs and real-life graphs.

Extension tier

Focuses on simplifying and factorising algebraic expressions, then graph work on gradients, curves and inequalities.

Mental starter

Factor pairs

Ask students for factor pairs of 22.

Emphasise that there are two different pairs: 1×22 and 2×11.

Ask for factor pairs of other numbers such as 70, 28, 45 etc.

Encourage students to work systematically to find all the pairs.

Ask students for the factor pairs of 36, 49, 19, 13 etc.

Emphasise that a square number has a repeated factor and a prime number has only two factors: 1 and itself.

Useful resources

A4.1OHP – factor trees for 30, 48 and 84
A4.1F – dividing by primes

Introductory activity

Refer to the mental starter.

Discuss definitions of factor, square and prime. Encourage students to list the first 10 square numbers and the prime numbers to 30.

Emphasise that 2 is the only even prime number and discuss why.

Discuss whether 1 is a prime number.

Encourage students to refer back to the definition to see why it isn't.

Discuss how to write the number 6 as a product of prime factors.

You may need to recap the meaning of the term 'product'.

Emphasise that 2 and 3 are prime so $6 = 2 \times 3$ as a product of primes.

Discuss how to write 12 as a product of primes.

Emphasise that you need to break down one of the factors into its prime factors: $3 \times 4 = 3 \times 2 \times 2$

Discuss how to write this using index notation: 3×2^2.

Discuss how to find prime factors for larger numbers such as 48 or 84. These are on **A4.1OHP**.

Encourage students to work systematically, breaking down factors one at a time.

Discuss an efficient way of recording working.

Emphasise the use of a factor tree as in the Students' Book.

With a good group you could go on to discuss finding the HCF of two numbers (say 48 and 84).

Emphasise that you find the common factors and multiply them.

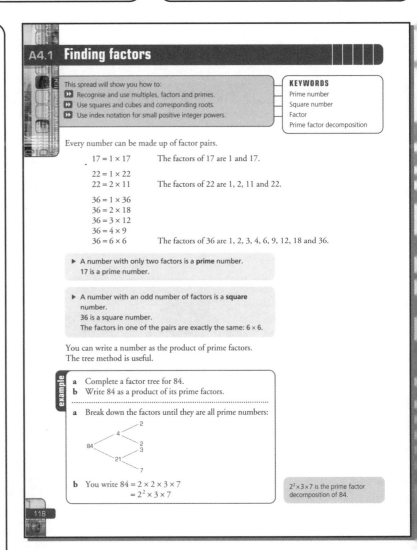

A4.1 Finding factors

This spread will show you how to:
▶▶ Recognise and use multiples, factors and primes.
▶▶ Use squares and cubes and corresponding roots.
▶▶ Use index notation for small positive integer powers.

KEYWORDS
Prime number
Square number
Factor
Prime factor decomposition

Every number can be made up of factor pairs.

$17 = 1 \times 17$ The factors of 17 are 1 and 17.

$22 = 1 \times 22$
$22 = 2 \times 11$ The factors of 22 are 1, 2, 11 and 22.

$36 = 1 \times 36$
$36 = 2 \times 18$
$36 = 3 \times 12$
$36 = 4 \times 9$
$36 = 6 \times 6$ The factors of 36 are 1, 2, 3, 4, 6, 9, 12, 18 and 36.

▶ A number with only two factors is a **prime** number.
17 is a prime number.

▶ A number with an odd number of factors is a **square** number.
36 is a square number.
The factors in one of the pairs are exactly the same: 6×6.

You can write a number as the product of prime factors.
The tree method is useful.

example

a   Complete a factor tree for 84.
b   Write 84 as a product of its prime factors.
....
a   Break down the factors until they are all prime numbers:

b   You write $84 = 2 \times 2 \times 3 \times 7$
               $= 2^2 \times 3 \times 7$

$2^2 \times 3 \times 7$ is the prime factor decomposition of 84.

118

Plenary

Challenge students to find a number with exactly seven factors.

Further activities

A4.1F demonstrates an alternative method for finding prime factors, using division by primes.

Differentiation

Core questions:

▸ Questions 1–3 focus on finding factors.

▸ Questions 4–8 focus on prime factors and using index notation.

▸ Question 9 is a challenging question for able students.

Extension tier: focuses on using the laws of indices.

Support tier: focuses on finding factors and multiples.

Exercise A4.1

1 In a productagon, the number in the square is the product of the numbers in the circles on either side.
Copy and complete these productagons.

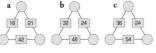

2 Find all the factor pairs of each of these numbers.
a 18 **b** 15 **c** 28
d 80 **e** 36

3 a Find all the factors of 42 and of 70. Write the factors in separate lists.
b List the common factors.
c Write down the highest common factor of 42 and 70.

4 Complete prime factor trees for each of these numbers. The first one is started for you.

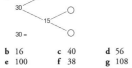

b 16 **c** 40 **d** 56
e 100 **f** 38 **g** 108

5 7^3 means $7 \times 7 \times 7 = 343$
Write down the actual value of each of these:
a 6^2 **b** 8^2 **c** 12^2
d 30^2 **e** 3^3 **f** 1^3
g 5^3 **h** 9^3

6 $\sqrt{60}$ lies somewhere between 7 ($\sqrt{49}$) and 8 ($\sqrt{64}$).
Write down the whole numbers that each of these square roots lie between.
a $\sqrt{30}$ **b** $\sqrt{10}$
c $\sqrt{75}$ **d** $\sqrt{42}$
e $\sqrt{110}$

7 **Mix and match**
The prime factors in group A match a number in group B.
Match each pair together.

8 The number 48 has prime factors $2^4 \times 3$ (which is $2^2 \times 3 \times 2^2$).
a Find four more numbers that include $2^2 \times 3$ as prime factors.
b What is the largest number less than 100 that includes the prime factors $2^2 \times 3$?

9 **Investigation**
You can write 13 as the difference of two consecutive squares:
$7^2 - 6^2 = 49 - 36 = 13$.
What other numbers less than 30 can be written as a difference of two consecutive squares?

119

Exercise commentary

The questions assess objectives on Framework Pages 55–57.

Problem solving

Questions 1, 8 and 9 assess objectives on Framework Pages 7–9.

Group work

Questions 1–3 may be done together as a class activity. Questions 8 and 9 are suitable for paired work.

Misconceptions

Students can usually complete factor trees successfully, but they do not realise what the tree shows.

Emphasise that the prime factors are at the ends of the branches.

Students may find index notation confusing and have difficulty working out 2×3^2.

Encourage them to use the order of operations: work out $3^2 = 9$ then $2 \times 9 = 18$.

For question 9, students will find it easier if the numbers 1 to 30 are set out in a table.

Links

Index notation in algebra: Framework Page 115.

Homework

A4.1HW focuses on finding and identifying factors.

Revision

Students should work through N1 in the 5–7 Revision Book.

Answers

1 **a** 3, 6, 7 **b** 4, 8, 6 **c** 4, 9, 6
2 **a** $1 \times 18, 2 \times 9, 3 \times 6$ **b** $1 \times 15, 3 \times 5$ **c** $1 \times 28, 2 \times 14, 4 \times 7$
   d $1 \times 80, 2 \times 40, 4 \times 20, 8 \times 10$ **e** $1 \times 36, 2 \times 18, 3 \times 12, 4 \times 9, 6 \times 6$
3 **a** 1, 2, 3, 6, 7, 14, 21, 42; 1, 2, 5, 7, 10, 14, 35, 70 **b** 1, 2, 7, 14 **c** 14
4 **a** $2 \times 3 \times 5$ **b** $2 \times 2 \times 2 \times 2$ **c** $2 \times 2 \times 2 \times 5$ **d** $2 \times 2 \times 2 \times 7$
   e $2 \times 2 \times 5 \times 5$ **f** 2×19 **g** $2 \times 2 \times 3 \times 3 \times 3$
5 **a** 36 **b** 64 **c** 144 **d** 900 **e** 27 **f** 1 **g** 125 **h** 729 6 **a** 5, 6 **b** 2, 3
   c 8, 9 **d** 6, 7 **e** 10, 11 7 $2^2 \times 3 \times 5 = 60, 2 \times 5 \times 7 = 70, 3^2 \times 5 = 45, 5^2 \times 7 = 175,$
$2^2 \times 3^2 = 36, 2^4 \times 3^2 = 144$ 8 **a** 12, 36, 60, 72 **b** 96 9 **a** $6^2 - 5^2 = 11, 5^2 - 4^2 = 9$ etc.

119

Mental starter

Common factors

Give students a pair of numbers, such as 18 and 30.

Ask them for a factor that is common to both numbers.

Encourage them to give all the common factors.

Discuss which is the largest.

Repeat with other simple pairs, such as 24 and 20, 32 and 12.

Useful resources

A4.1OHP – prime factor trees for 48 and 84

A4.2OHP – Venn diagrams

Introductory activity

Refer to the mental starter.

Discuss the definition of the highest common factor.

Discuss how to find the HCF of two numbers, such as 48 and 84.

Encourage students to think of systematic ways of working.

Emphasise that using a factor tree is efficient as it is a good way to ensure they have listed all the factors. (**A4.1OHP** shows the factor trees of 48 and 84.)

Discuss how to find the highest common factor from factor trees.

It is useful to start simply, with say 18 and 30 from the mental starter.

Emphasise that you find all the prime factors that are common to both trees, and multiply them to find the HCF.

Discuss when it is useful to find the HCF: when factorising algebraic expressions.

Discuss an example of finding the HCF of two expressions: $12x$ and $15x^2$.

Emphasise that the same principle of listing the factors applies.

Discuss what is meant by a multiple.

Emphasise that it is the number multiplied by a factor.

Discuss how to find the multiples of 6: they are the 6 times table.

Discuss how to find the lowest common multiple of 6 and 9: it is the lowest number in both times tables, 18.

Discuss how to find the LCM of 48 and 84 from the factor trees.

Emphasise that you use all the factors of 48 and any other new factors of 84.

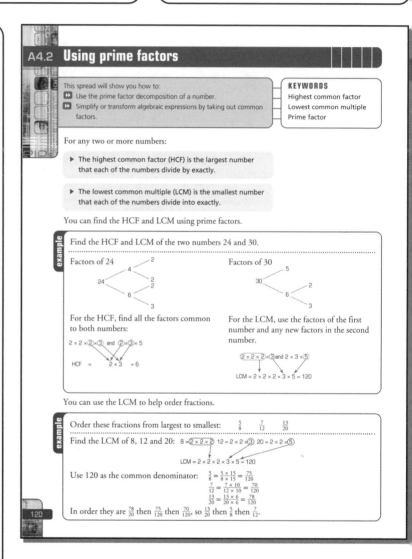

A4.2 Using prime factors

This spread will show you how to:
- Use the prime factor decomposition of a number.
- Simplify or transform algebraic expressions by taking out common factors.

KEYWORDS
Highest common factor
Lowest common multiple
Prime factor

For any two or more numbers:

▶ The highest common factor (HCF) is the largest number that each of the numbers divide by exactly.

▶ The lowest common multiple (LCM) is the smallest number that each of the numbers divide into exactly.

You can find the HCF and LCM using prime factors.

example

Find the HCF and LCM of the two numbers 24 and 30.

Factors of 24

Factors of 30

For the HCF, find all the factors common to both numbers:

$2 \times 2 \times 2 \times 3$ and $2 \times 3 \times 5$

HCF $= 2 \times 3 = 6$

For the LCM, use the factors of the first number and any new factors in the second number.

$2 \times 2 \times 2 \times 3$ and $2 \times 3 \times 5$

LCM $= 2 \times 2 \times 2 \times 3 \times 5 = 120$

You can use the LCM to help order fractions.

example

Order these fractions from largest to smallest: $\frac{5}{8}$ $\frac{7}{12}$ $\frac{13}{20}$

Find the LCM of 8, 12 and 20: $8 = 2 \times 2 \times 2$ $12 = 2 \times 2 \times 3$ $20 = 2 \times 2 \times 5$

LCM $= 2 \times 2 \times 2 \times 3 \times 5 = 120$

Use 120 as the common denominator: $\frac{5}{8} = \frac{5 \times 15}{8 \times 15} = \frac{75}{120}$

$\frac{7}{12} = \frac{7 \times 10}{12 \times 10} = \frac{70}{120}$

$\frac{13}{20} = \frac{13 \times 6}{20 \times 6} = \frac{78}{120}$

In order they are $\frac{78}{20}$ then $\frac{75}{120}$ then $\frac{70}{120}$, so $\frac{13}{20}$ then $\frac{5}{8}$ then $\frac{7}{12}$.

Plenary

Discuss approaches to question 4.

Encourage students to list the factors of each term and then find the LCM as in question 3.

Emphasise that once students are confident they do not need to list all the factors on paper but will need to continue to do so in their heads.

Further activities

Less confident students will need more practice finding the LCM and HCF of pairs of smaller numbers such as 9 and 15, and 18 and 12.
A Venn diagram may help (A4.2OHP).

Differentiation

Core questions:
▸ Questions 1–3 focus on finding the HCF and LCM.
▸ Questions 3–6 focus on finding the HCF of algebraic expressions.
▸ Question 7 extends to factorising more challenging algebraic expressions.

Extension tier: focuses on fractional and negative indices, and reciprocals.

Support tier focuses on prime factorisation.

Exercise A4.2

1 a Copy and complete these factor trees for 70 and 112:

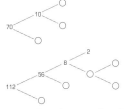

b Write each number as a product of prime factors.
c Use the prime factors to work out the HCF and LCM.

2 a Find the prime factors of these pairs of numbers:
   i 45 and 81   **ii** 54 and 126
   iii 80 and 104
b Find the HCF.
c Find the LCM.

3 Find the LCM of the denominators of these fractions and write down which of the fractions in each pair is larger.
  a $\frac{5}{9}$ and $\frac{8}{15}$ **b** $\frac{7}{12}$ and $\frac{12}{21}$
  c $\frac{3}{8}$ and $\frac{5}{14}$ **d** $\frac{11}{28}$ and $\frac{16}{35}$

4 Find the HCF of each term in these expressions.
Use the HCF to factorise the expressions.
The first one is started for you.
  a $12x + 15y = 2 \times 2 \times 3 \times x + 3 \times 5 \times y$
              $= 3(2 \times 2 \times x \quad + \qquad)$
              $= 3(\qquad + \qquad)$
  b $20r - 16p$ **c** $28a + 21b$
  d $18d - 45e$ **e** $36f + 24g$
  f $49x + 21y - 14z$

5 The HCF of each pair of terms is written in the cloud.

Match each pair with its HCF.

  a $3x^2$ and $6x$
  b $12x$ and $4x^3$
  c $5x^3$ and $10x^2$
  d $9x^3$ and $6x^2$
  e $20x$ and 8

6 Find the HCF for each pair of terms.
The first one is done for you.

  a $3x^2y$ and $6xy^2$
     $3x^2y = 3 \times x \times x \times y$
     $6xy^2 = 2 \times 3 \times x \times y \times y$
     $HCF = 3 \times x \times y = 3xy$

  b $12xy^3$ and $4x^3y$
  c $5x^3y^2$ and $10x^2y^3$
  d $9x^3y^3$ and $6x^2y$
  e $20xy^4$ and $8x^3y^2$

7 Factorise these expressions.
The first one is started for you.

  a $3x^2y - 12xy = 3xy(x - \quad)$

  b $4x - 6xy$
  c $4y^2 + 8y$
  d $15xy - 10y^2$
  e $14x^2y + 10xy$
  f $6xy^2 + 9x^2y$

Exercise commentary

The questions assess objectives on Framework Pages 55 and 117.

Problem solving
Questions 4–7 assess objectives on Framework Page 27.

Group work
Questions 3–6 are appropriate for paired work.

Misconceptions
Students may struggle to find the LCM from factor trees.
Encourage the use of a Venn diagram instead (A4.2OHP) – the terms in the overlap multiply to the HCF and all the factors multiply to the LCM.

Links
Index notation: Framework Pages 57–59 and 115. Ordering fractions: Page 65.

Homework

A4.2HW provides practice in finding HFC and LCM and factorising algebraic expressions.

Revision

Students should work through N6 in the 5–7 Revision Book.

Answers

1 b $2 \times 5 \times 7$, $2 \times 2 \times 2 \times 2 \times 7$ **c** HCF = 14, LCM = 560
2 a i $3 \times 3 \times 5$, $3 \times 3 \times 3 \times 3$ **ii** $2 \times 3 \times 3 \times 3$, $2 \times 3 \times 3 \times 7$
    iii $2 \times 2 \times 2 \times 2 \times 5$, $2 \times 2 \times 2 \times 13$ **b i** 9 **ii** 18 **iii** 8
   c i 405 **ii** 378 **iii** 1040   **3 a** 45, $\frac{5}{9}$ **b** 84, $\frac{7}{12}$ **c** 56, $\frac{3}{8}$ **d** 140, $\frac{16}{35}$
4 a $3(4x + 5y)$ **b** $4(5r - 4p)$ **c** $7(4a + 3b)$ **d** $9(2d - 5e)$ **e** $12(3f + 2g)$
  f $7(7x + 3y - 2z)$ **5 a** $3x$ **b** $4x$ **c** $5x^2$ **d** $3x^2$ **e** 4
6 b $4xy$ **c** $5x^2y^2$ **d** $3x^2y$ **e** $4xy^2$ **7 a** $3xy(x - 4)$ **b** $2x(2 - 3y)$
  c $4y(y + 2)$ **d** $5y(3x - 2y)$ **e** $2xy(7x + 5)$ **f** $3xy(2y + 3x)$

A4.3 Index notation

Mental starter

Multiply!

Practise multiplying two-digit numbers by a single digit mentally:

$43 \times 6 = 40 \times 6 + 3 \times 6$
$= 240 \quad + 18$
$= 258$

Encourage students to explain their own methods.

Useful resources

A4.3OHP – index cards

Introductory activity

Use **A4.3OHP** or write these expressions on the board:

$3^4, 4^3, 4^2, 3^5$

Show each expression in turn and ask for the value.

Emphasise that 4^3 means $4 \times 4 \times 4$ and so on.

Discuss how to input indices in a calculator.

Discuss the value of $3^4 \times 3^5$.

Encourage students to suggest ways in which you can write the expression more simply.

Emphasise that you can combine the terms because they use the same base:

$3^4 \quad \times \quad 3^5$
$= 3 \times 3 \times 3 \times 3 \times 3 \times 3 \times 3 \times 3 \times 3$
$= 3^9$

Encourage students to make the link that $4 + 5 = 9$.

Emphasise this by asking students how to simplify $4^3 \times 4^2$:

$2 + 3 = 5$ so $4^3 \times 4^2 = 4^5$.

Encourage students to generalise:

$x^a \times x^b = x^{a+b}$

Discuss how to simplify $3^4 \times 4^3$.

Emphasise that this cannot be simplified as it means:

$3 \times 3 \times 3 \times 3 \times 4 \times 4 \times 4$.

Discuss how to divide using indices:

$4^3 \div 4^2 = \frac{4 \times 4 \times 4}{4 \times 4} = 4$

Emphasise that 4 means 4^1 and encourage students to generalise as for multiplication. Repeat with $3^5 \div 3^4$.

Emphasise that $x^a \div x^b = x^{a-b}$

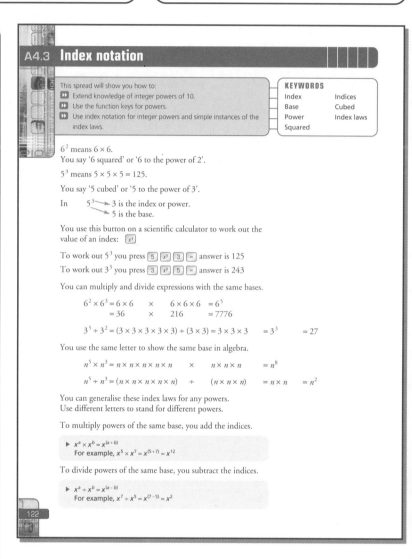

A4.3 Index notation

This spread will show you how to:
- Extend knowledge of integer powers of 10.
- Use the function keys for powers.
- Use index notation for integer powers and simple instances of the index laws.

KEYWORDS
Index   Indices
Base   Cubed
Power   Index laws
Squared

6^2 means 6×6.
You say '6 squared' or '6 to the power of 2'.

5^3 means $5 \times 5 \times 5 = 125$.
You say '5 cubed' or '5 to the power of 3'.

In 5^3 → 3 is the index or power.
→ 5 is the base.

You use this button on a scientific calculator to work out the value of an index: x^y

To work out 5^3 you press 5 x^y 3 = answer is 125
To work out 3^5 you press 3 x^y 5 = answer is 243

You can multiply and divide expressions with the same bases.

$6^2 \times 6^3 = 6 \times 6 \quad \times \quad 6 \times 6 \times 6 \quad = 6^5$
$\quad\quad\quad = 36 \quad \times \quad 216 \quad\quad = 7776$

$3^5 \div 3^2 = (3 \times 3 \times 3 \times 3 \times 3) \div (3 \times 3) = 3 \times 3 \times 3 \quad = 3^3 \quad = 27$

You use the same letter to show the same base in algebra.

$n^5 \times n^3 = n \times n \times n \times n \times n \quad \times \quad n \times n \times n \quad = n^8$
$n^5 \div n^3 = (n \times n \times n \times n \times n) \quad \div \quad (n \times n \times n) \quad = n \times n \quad = n^2$

You can generalise these index laws for any powers.
Use different letters to stand for different powers.

To multiply powers of the same base, you add the indices.

▶ $x^a \times x^b = x^{(a+b)}$
For example, $x^5 \times x^7 = x^{(5+7)} = x^{12}$

To divide powers of the same base, you subtract the indices.

▶ $x^a \div x^b = x^{(a-b)}$
For example, $x^7 \div x^5 = x^{(7-5)} = x^2$

122

Plenary

Discuss question 6.

Ask questions such as:

▶ Which statements are always true? Why?
▶ Which are never true?
▶ Which are correct algebra statements but not always true? How do you know?
▶ Which can be true but are not algebraically correct?

Further activities

Students could complete the tables in question 3 for other bases, such as 3 and 5. They could write equations like the ones in question 2 for a partner to solve.

Differentiation

Core questions:

▶ Questions 1–3 focus on using a calculator to work out the value of indices.

▶ Questions 4–6 focus on simplifying expressions involving indices.

▶ Question 7 is a challenging question for able students.

Extension tier: focuses on simplifying and constructing algebraic expressions.

Support tier: focuses on squares, cubes and roots.

Exercise A4.3

1 Use the x^y button on your calculator to work out each of these:

a 6^4 b 3^7
c 4^5 d 2^9
e 5^5 f 9^3
g 8^6 h 15^3
i 7^5

2 Use your calculator to work out the value of x in these equations:

a $4096 = 4^x$ b $729 = 3^x$
c $6561 = 9^x$ d $117\,649 = x^6$
e $1024 = x^{10}$ f $65\,536 = x^8$
g $x = 6^7$ h $390\,625 = x^8$

3 Copy and complete these tables. Use your calculator if necessary.

a

Index form	Value
10^4	
10^3	1000
10^2	
10^1	
10^0	
10^{-1}	
10^{-2}	

b

Index form	Value
2^4	
2^3	8
2^2	
2^1	
2^0	
2^{-1}	
2^{-2}	

Hint: to input ⁻3 press [3] [+/-]

4 Write each of these expressions as a power with one base.
The first one is done for you.

a $3^2 \times 3^4 = 3 \times 3 \times 3 \times 3 \times 3 \times 3 = 3^6$
b $4^3 \times 4^2$ c $5^6 \times 5^2$
d $6^5 \times 6^3$ e $7^4 \div 7^2$
f $9^3 \div 9^2$ g $10^5 \div 10^2$
h $2^7 \div 2^3$

5 Write each of these expressions as a single power in the form y^n:

a $y^3 \times y^2$ b $y^5 \times y^2$ c $y^7 \times y^3$
d $y^9 \times y^4$ e $y^3 \div y^2$ f $y^3 \div y$
g $y^6 \div y^6$ h $y^2 \div y^3$ i $y^3 \div y^5$

6 **Challenge**
Copy the table. Decide which statements are always true, sometimes true or never true and put them in the correct columns in your table.

Always	Sometimes	Never

a $7^x = 1$ b $x^5 \div x^3 = x^2$
c $x^2 + x^2 = x^4$ d $x^2 \times x^3 = x^6$
e $x^0 = 10$ f $x^2 < x$
g $2^x = x^2$ $(x \neq 2)$

For each statement that is sometimes true, give a value for x to show that it is true.

7 **Challenge**
a Write $y \times y \times y \times y$ in its simplest form.
b What is $x^y + y^x$ when $x = 2$ and $y = 3$?
c If $2^x + 3 = 4$, what is x?
d If $x^x = 27$, what is x?

123

Exercise commentary

The questions assess objectives on Framework Pages 37, 57, 59 and 115.

Problem solving

Questions 5–7 assess objectives on Framework Page 27.

Group work

Questions 3 and 6 are particularly appropriate for paired discussion.
It is useful to discuss students' strategies in question 2 as a class.

Misconceptions

Students may find the negative powers confusing in question 3.
Encourage them to use the patterns in the tables to see what is happening.
It is useful to think about 2^3 as $1 \times 2 \times 2 \times 2$ and so $2^{-3} = 1 \div (2 \times 2 \times 2)$.
Students often multiply the powers instead of adding: $4^2 \times 4^3 \rightarrow 4^6$. Use question 4 to check that they do not make this error.
Encourage them to list all the numbers and count to emphasise that you add the numbers.

Links

Using a calculator: Framework Page 109.
Finding roots: Page 57.

Homework

A4.3HW gives more practice in calculations involving indices.

Revision

Students should work through N9 in the 5–7 Revision Book.

Answers

1 a 1296 b 2187 c 1024 d 512 e 3125 f 729 g 262 144
  h 3375 i 16 807

2 a 6 b 6 c 4 d 7 e 2 f 4 g 279 936 h 5

3 a 10 000, 1000, 100, 10, 1, 0.1, 0.01 b 16, 8, 4, 2, 1, 0.5, 0.25

4 b 4^6 c 5^8 d 6^8 e 7^2 f 9^1 g 10^3 h 2^4

5 a y^5 b y^7 c y^{10} d y^5 e y^1 f y^2 g y^0 h y^{-1} i y^{-2}

6 a Sometimes: $x = 0$ b Always c Sometimes: $x = 1$ d Sometimes: $x = 1$
  e Never f Sometimes: $x = \frac{1}{2}$ g Never   7 a y^4 b 17 c 0 d 3

123

Mental starter

Who am I?

Describe a number between 1 and 100.

Students have to guess which number you are.

Use words such as factor, multiple, prime, square, cube.

For example:

▶ I am a square number and a cube number. [64]

▶ I am an even/odd square with five factors. [16/81]

Useful resources

Calculators

Introductory activity

Refer to the mental starter.

Discuss students' strategies for finding the numbers.

Emphasise the strategy of listing the numbers and working systematically.

Encourage students to list all the square numbers to 100.

Discuss how to write them as powers of 2.

Discuss any patterns that students notice.

Emphasise that they are all even and that the last digit makes a recurring pattern:

2, 4, 8, 6, 2, 4, 8, 6, ...

Repeat for the cube numbers until students can see a pattern in the last digit: they may need to go up to 3^8.

Discuss the example from the Students' Book – is $2^n + 3^m$ always even, always odd or can't you tell? [n, m integers $\geqslant 1$]

Emphasise that by understanding the nature of each term you can see what happens when you add them:

Even + odd = odd so the result will always be odd.

Emphasise that the approach is enough to prove that $2^n + 3^m$ is always odd.

Discuss whether 7^n is always odd.

Emphasise that you can list the powers of 7 until you can see a pattern.

Encourage students to suggest how the pattern helps answer the question.

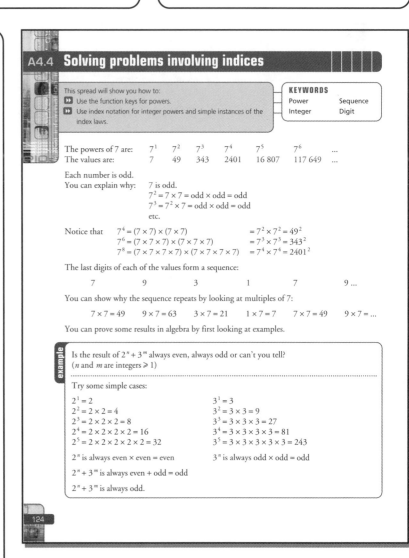

Plenary

Discuss question 5.

Encourage students to discuss strategies.

Emphasise the strategy of listing enough terms to understand the pattern of the last digits.

Discuss how understanding the pattern can help.

Further activities

Fractional powers

Encourage students to investigate the power of $\frac{1}{2}$.

They can use a calculator to find the power of $\frac{1}{2}$ of all the numbers up to 100, writing down those that give whole number answers. Encourage them to consider what the numbers have in common.

Differentiation

Core questions:

▶ Questions 1 and 2 focus on working out the value of indices.
▶ Questions 3–8 focus on using patterns in powers.
▶ Questions 9 and 10 are challenging questions for able students.

Extension tier: focuses on expanding and factorising algebraic expressions.

Support tier: focuses on solving problems involving squares and cubes.

Exercise A4.4

1 Choose one of the signs >, < or = to make each of these statements true.
   a $8^5 \_\_ 8^4$ b $4^3 \_\_ 3^4$
   c $2^4 \_\_ 4^2$ d $5^3 \_\_ 3^5$
   e $4^3 \_\_ 2^6$ f $8^3 \_\_ 2^7$
   g $2^3 \times 5^3 \_\_ 10^3$ h $(0.5)^2 \_\_ (0.5)^3$

2 Work out the value of n in each of these equations.
   a $3^3 + 3^2 = 3^n$ b $5^4 \div 5^2 = 5^n$
   c $9^6 \div 9^2 = 9^n$ d $8^3 \times 8^2 = 8^n$
   e $5^4 \times 5^3 \div 5^2 = 5^n$ f $4^6 \div 4^n = 4^3$

3 a Calculate the values of the terms of this sequence:
   $4^1 \quad 4^2 \quad 4^3 \quad 4^4 \quad 4^5 \quad 4^6$
   b What digit does 4^{12} end in?
   c What digit does 4^{13} end in?
   d Will 4^n ever be an odd number? Explain your answer.

4 You are told that the last digit for the value of 5^x is 7.
   Could this be a true statement? Explain your answer.

5 a Match each number in the box to its equivalent index form without using a calculator.

   b Use a calculator to work out the values for a, b, c, d and e.

6 Look at these numbers:

   a Which is the largest?
   b Which is equal to 4^3?
   c Which two add up to 10^2?

7 Which of these are square numbers?

8 Copy and complete these statements:
   a If $2^8 = 256$ then $2^9 = \_\_\_$
   b If $2^{15} = 32\ 768$ then $2^{14} = \_\_\_$
   c If $64 = 8^n = 4^p = 2^q$ then $n = \_\_\_, p = \_\_\_, q = \_\_\_$
   d If $\sqrt{144} = (144)^{\frac{1}{2}} = 12$ then $(81)^{\frac{1}{2}} = \_\_\_$

9 Triples
   The numbers in the cloud are in triples.

   For example: $\frac{16}{2} = 8 = 2^3$.
   Find five more triples.

10 You are told that $x^2 - y^2 = (x + y) \times (x - y)$
   a Check the formula is true when $x = 7$ and $y = 5$ (so $7^2 - 5^2$).
   b Use the formula to work out the values of $17^2 - 13^2$ and $56^2 - 44^2$. Check your answers using a calculator.

Exercise commentary

The questions assess objectives on Framework Pages 57, 59, 109 and 115.

Problem solving

Questions 3 and 4 assess objectives on Framework Pages 7 and 31.
Questions 8 and 10 assess Page 27.

Group work

Questions 3 to 7 are particularly appropriate for paired discussion.

Misconceptions

In question 2, students tend to multiply or divide the powers rather than adding or subtracting.
Encourage them to work from first principles to remind themselves of the laws of indices.
Students tend to find generalisations difficult to draw for questions 3–5.
Encourage them to list the multiples and to look at the last digit in each case.
In questions 8 and 9, students will need to know that the power of $\frac{1}{2}$ is equivalent to the square root – they may investigate this using a calculator.

Links

Solving equations: Framework Pages 123–125.

Homework

A4.4HW focuses on using patterns to solve problems involving indices.

Revision

Students should work through A1 in the 5–7 Revision Book.

Answers

1 a >   b <   c =   d <   e =   f >   g =   h >
2 a 1   b 2   c 4   d 5   e 5   f 3
3 a 4, 16, 64, 256, 1024, 4096   b 6   c 4   d No, it will end in 4 or 6.
4 No, it will end in 5.
5 a $3^a = 2187$, $4^b = 262\ 144$, $5^c = 78\ 125$, $6^d = 7776$, $10^e = 1\ 000\ 000$
   b $a = 7$, $b = 9$, $c = 7$, $d = 5$, $e = 6$ **6** a 4^4 b 2^6 c $2^6, 6^2$
7 $2^4, 2^6$ **8** a 512   b 16 384   c $n = 2, p = 4, q = 6$ d 9
9 $\sqrt{16} = (16)^{\frac{1}{2}} = 2^2$, $1^{16} = 1 = 16^0$, $2^4 = 4^2 = 16^1$, $16^2 = 4^4 = 2^8$, $\frac{1}{4} = (16)^{-1} = \frac{1}{16}$
10 a $7^2 - 5^2 = 24 = 12 \times 2$ b 120, 1200

Mental starter

Express it!
Give students simple expressions such as:
$$y = 2x - 1 \qquad y = 3x + 4 \qquad y = 3 - 2x \qquad y = 1 - 3x$$
Ask them for the value of y given a value of x.
Give different values of x including negative values.
Discuss methods and ways of keeping track of results.

Useful resources

R8 – coordinate grid
A4.5F – parallel lines
Graph paper

Introductory activity

Refer to the mental starter.
Discuss how to draw the graph for the function $y = 3 - 2x$.
Emphasise that you work out pairs of value that satisfy the function, then plot them on a grid.
Encourage students to use a table of values and to work systematically.
Discuss what students would expect the graph to look like and why.
Draw the graph together on an OHP of **R8**.
Discuss whether the graph matches with students' expectations.
Emphasise that it is a straight line because the y values go down in twos.
Discuss why the function is downward sloping – because the y values decrease each time the x value increases.

Discuss the gradient and the intercept of the graph and how you can find them from the equation.

Encourage students to sketch the graph of $y = 4x - 3$ on a new copy of **R8**.
Discuss what they would expect it to look like and why first.
Discuss students' methods. They may have used a range of methods:
▶ Using a table of values.
▶ Choosing two values – encourage them to use at least three!
▶ Using the gradient and intercept.

Discuss how to recognise that a function will produce a straight line.
Emphasise that you need at least three points to specify the line – the third acts as a check.

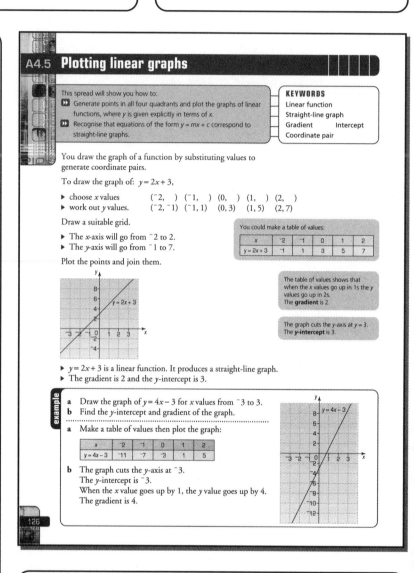

A4.5 Plotting linear graphs

This spread will show you how to:
▶▶ Generate points in all four quadrants and plot the graphs of linear functions, where y is given explicitly in terms of x.
▶▶ Recognise that equations of the form $y = mx + c$ correspond to straight-line graphs.

KEYWORDS
Linear function
Straight-line graph
Gradient   Intercept
Coordinate pair

You draw the graph of a function by substituting values to generate coordinate pairs.

To draw the graph of: $y = 2x + 3$,

▶ choose x values   (⁻2,) (⁻1,) (0,) (1,) (2,)
▶ work out y values.   (⁻2, ⁻1) (⁻1, 1) (0, 3) (1, 5) (2, 7)

Draw a suitable grid.

▶ The x-axis will go from ⁻2 to 2.
▶ The y-axis will go from ⁻1 to 7.

Plot the points and join them.

You could make a table of values:

x	⁻2	⁻1	0	1	2
$y = 2x + 3$	⁻1	1	3	5	7

The table of values shows that when the x values go up in 1s the y values go up in 2s.
The **gradient** is 2.

The graph cuts the y-axis at $y = 3$.
The **y-intercept** is 3.

▶ $y = 2x + 3$ is a linear function. It produces a straight-line graph.
▶ The gradient is 2 and the y-intercept is 3.

example

a Draw the graph of $y = 4x - 3$ for x values from ⁻3 to 3.
b Find the y-intercept and gradient of the graph.

a Make a table of values then plot the graph:

x	⁻2	⁻1	0	1	2
$y = 4x - 3$	⁻11	⁻7	⁻3	1	5

b The graph cuts the y-axis at ⁻3.
The y-intercept is ⁻3.
When the x value goes up by 1, the y value goes up by 4.
The gradient is 4.

Plenary

Discuss question 2.
Encourage students to explain their approach to drawing the graphs.
Discuss what the point of intersection means.
Emphasise that the equations have an equal value at that point so $2x + 1 = 3x - 2$.
Discuss question 3, focusing on the lines with the largest and smallest gradients.

Further activities

A4.5F contains an activity about recognising parallel lines and understanding how the equation of the line specifies the y-intercept. It is recommended after successful completion of question 3.

Differentiation

Core questions:
▶ Question 1 focuses on plotting points to produce straight lines.
▶ Question 2 focuses on plotting graphs from equations.
▶ Question 3 encourages students to understand how the gradient is specified by the equation of the line.

Extension tier: focuses on expanding double brackets.

Support tier: focuses on plotting graphs of simple linear functions.

Exercise A4.5

1 Copy the coordinate grid.
  a Plot the points:
   (3, 9) (⁻1, ⁻5), (⁻5, ⁻7) (4, 10)
   (⁻2, ⁻8) (⁻2, ⁻1) (2, 4) (1, 5)

  The points lie on two different lines.

  b Draw the two straight lines.
  c For each line, write the coordinate pair when $x = 0$, (0, ?).
  d For each line, write the coordinate pair when $y = 7$, (?, 7).
  e Label the steeper line A.

2 a Copy and complete these tables of values for the linear functions $y = 2x + 1$ and $y = 3x - 2$.
  b Plot the points on a coordinate grid.
  c Write down the coordinates of the point where the two lines intersect.

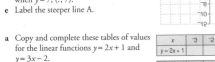

3 Match
  a Match the description of the graph to its equation. Use the graph to help you.

  The y-coordinate:
   ▶ is always double the x-coordinate
   ▶ is always equal to the x-coordinate
   ▶ is always a quarter of the x-coordinate
   ▶ is always four times the x-coordinate
   ▶ is always half of the x-coordinate

  $y = 4x$
  $y = \frac{1}{2}x$
  $y = x$
  $y = 2x$
  $y = \frac{1}{4}x$

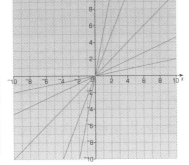

  b Each line goes through (0, 0). Explain how you know this from the equation of each graph.
  c Which line is the steepest (largest gradient)? Which has the smallest gradient?
  d Explain how you find the gradient from the equation.
  e Does the line $y = 7x$ have a large or small gradient?

127

Exercise commentary

The questions assess objectives on Framework Pages 165 and 167.

Problem solving
The exercise assesses objectives on Framework Page 27.

Group work
Question 3 is suitable for paired work.

Misconceptions
Students commonly mix up the gradient and the intercept, particularly with downward sloping lines.
A useful strategy is to encourage students to always plot the point where $x = 0$ which is the y-intercept.
It is suggested that students gain confidence in plotting points from an equation and having an understanding of each of the parts before they start to sketch the graph using the gradient and intercept.

Links
Solving equations: Framework Pages 123–125.

Homework

A4.5HW gives more practice in plotting linear graphs and begins to investigate parallel lines.

Revision

Students should work through A2 in the 5–7 Revision Book.

Answers

1 a,b,e grid with lines $y = 2x + 3$ and $y = 3x - 2$ drawn. $y = 3x - 2$ is labelled A. **c** (0, 3), (0, ⁻2) **d** (2, 7), (3, 7)
2 a $y = $ ⁻5, ⁻3, ⁻1, 1, 3, 5, 7; $y = $ ⁻11, ⁻8, ⁻5, ⁻2, 1, 4, 7
  b points plotted on a grid **c** (3, 7)
3 a $y = 2x$, $y = x$, $y = \frac{1}{4}x$, $y = 4x$, $y = \frac{1}{2}x$
  b None of the equations has a number term.
  c $y = 4x$, $y = \frac{1}{4}x$ **d** It's the number in front of x. **e** Large

127

Mental starter

Give students two numbers and ask for the difference:
⁻1 and 5   ⁻3 and 4   5 and ⁻2 etc.
Move on to include direction. Ask students to work out:
⁻1 + 3   ⁻3 − 4   3 − 2   ⁻2 + 5   1 − 6 etc.
Encourage students to explain reasoning using a number line.
Move on to multiplying and dividing with negatives:
⁻2 × 3   ⁻4 ÷ 2   9 ÷ ⁻3   ⁻12 ÷ ⁻4
Discuss rules and strategies.

Useful resources

R8 – coordinate grid
A4.6F – gradient and intercept

Introductory activity

On an OHP of R8, ask volunteers to sketch graphs with a gradient of 2.
Students should explain why the gradient is 2 and what the intercept is.
Encourage a volunteer to sketch a graph with a gradient of 2 and an intercept of ⁻3.

Discuss what the graphs have in common – they are all parallel.
Emphasise that this is because they all have the same gradient or slope.

Discuss how to work out the gradient of one of the graphs.
Emphasise that you work out the change in y for an increase of one in x.
Link to the idea of gradient when going downhill or uphill – for every one along, how far do you go up or down?
Emphasise the formula:
$$\text{Gradient} = \frac{\text{Change in } y}{1 \text{ unit increase in } x}$$

and that even more generally:
$$\text{Gradient} = \frac{\text{Change in } y}{\text{Change in } x}$$

Draw two lines on a clean OHP of R8.
Discuss how to find the gradient of each line.
Emphasise that you count across one on the x-axis and see how much y increases or decreases by.

Emphasise that downward sloping lines have a negative gradient.
For each line, discuss the intercept and hence the equation.

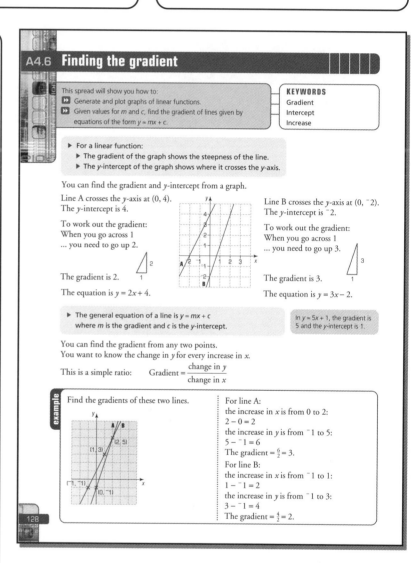

A4.6 **Finding the gradient**

This spread will show you how to:
- Generate and plot graphs of linear functions.
- Given values for m and c, find the gradient of lines given by equations of the form $y = mx + c$.

KEYWORDS
Gradient
Intercept
Increase

▶ For a linear function:
  ▶ The gradient of the graph shows the steepness of the line.
  ▶ The y-intercept of the graph shows where it crosses the y-axis.

You can find the gradient and y-intercept from a graph.

Line A crosses the y-axis at (0, 4).
The y-intercept is 4.

To work out the gradient:
When you go across 1
... you need to go up 2.

The gradient is 2.

The equation is $y = 2x + 4$.

Line B crosses the y-axis at (0, ⁻2).
The y-intercept is ⁻2.

To work out the gradient:
When you go across 1
... you need to go up 3.

The gradient is 3.

The equation is $y = 3x − 2$.

▶ The general equation of a line is $y = mx + c$
  where m is the gradient and c is the y-intercept.

In $y = 5x + 1$, the gradient is 5 and the y-intercept is 1.

You can find the gradient from any two points.
You want to know the change in y for every increase in x.

This is a simple ratio: $\text{Gradient} = \dfrac{\text{change in } y}{\text{change in } x}$

example

Find the gradients of these two lines.

For line A:
the increase in x is from 0 to 2:
$2 − 0 = 2$
the increase in y is from ⁻1 to 5:
$5 − ⁻1 = 6$
The gradient $= \frac{6}{2} = 3$.

For line B:
the increase in x is from ⁻1 to 1:
$1 − ⁻1 = 2$
the increase in y is from ⁻1 to 3:
$3 − ⁻1 = 4$
The gradient $= \frac{4}{2} = 2$.

128

Plenary

Give students equations of three graphs:
$y = 5x − 3$ $y = 1 − 3x$ $y = x + 3$
Encourage students to describe what each graph will look like, relative to each other.
Encourage students to sketch each graph using the gradient and intercept.

Further activities

A4.6F is a structured activity, where students identify the equations of lines on a grid by considering their gradient and y-intercept.

Differentiation

Core questions:
▸ Question 1 focuses on recognising a straight line graph from an equation.
▸ Question 2 focuses on working out gradients and intercepts from equations.
▸ Questions 3 and 4 focus on calculating gradients from graphs.

Extension tier: focuses on finding gradients of parallel and perpendicualr lines.
Support tier: focuses on comparing features of graphs and equations.

Exercise A4.6

1 Match each of these graphs with the correct gradient, y-intercept and equation.

  i gradient = 2, y-intercept = $^-3$ **A** $y = 2x + 3$
  ii gradient = 3, y-intercept = 2   **B** $y = 3x + 2$
  iii gradient = 2, y-intercept = 3   **C** $y = 2x - 3$
  iv gradient = 3, y-intercept = $^-2$ **D** $y = 3x - 2$

  a   **b** 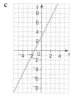   **c**    **d**

2 For each of these equations:
  i $y = 2x + 6$ **ii** $y = 3x - 4$
  iii $y = 4x + 1$ **iv** $y = \frac{1}{2}x - 2$
  a Write down the gradient and y-intercept.
  b Sketch the graph on a coordinate grid with x from $^-3$ to 3 and y from $^-10$ to 10.

3 Work out the gradient of each of these graphs.
  Show all your working clearly.

  a   **b**   **c**    **d**

4 Here are the equations of four graphs:
  i $y = x + 3$ **ii** $y = 3x$
  iii $y = 3x - 2$ **iv** $y = 2 - 3x$
  a A graph has a gradient of 3 and a y-intercept of $^-2$.
    Which equation matches this description?
  b Write similar descriptions for the other three graphs.

129

Exercise commentary

The questions assess objectives on Framework Pages 165 and 167.

Problem solving
The exercise assesses objectives on Framework Page 27.

Group work
Question 1 is suitable for students to work orally in pairs before discussion as a whole class, focusing on the gradient and intercept.

Misconceptions
Students commonly mix up the gradient and the intercept, particularly with downward sloping lines.
A useful strategy is to encourage students to always plot the point where $x = 0$ which is the y-intercept.
Encourage students to explain to each other what the graph will look like before sketching it in question 2.

Links
Solving equations: Framework Pages 123–125.

Homework

A4.6HW gives more practice in identifying gradient and y-intercept from the equation of a line and relating this to its graph.

Revision

Students should work through A3 in the 5–7 Revision Book.

Answers

1 a iv, D   **b** i, C   **c** iii, A   **d** ii, B
2 a i 2, 6   **ii** 3, $^-4$ **iii** 4, 1   **iv** $\frac{1}{2}$, $^-2$
  b Appropriate sketches of graphs
3 a 2   **b** 1   **c** 3   **d** 4
4 a iii   **b i** gradient of 1 and y-intercept of 3
    ii gradient of 3 and y-intercept of 0
    iv gradient of 2 and y-intercept of $^-3$.

Mental starter

It's implicit

Give students three equations:

$y + 3x = 1$ $\quad$ $2y + x = 9$ $\quad$ $3y - x - 4 = 0$

Give a value of x and ask students to find the value of y for each equation.

Repeat for other values of x.

Give a value of y and ask students to give the value of x.

Repeat for other y values.

Useful resources

R8 – coordinate grid

Introductory activity

Refer to the mental starter.

Discuss methods for finding the other value.

Emphasise that you substitute the known value to form an equation then solve the equation to find the unknown.

Discuss the difference between equations of the form $y = mx + c$ and $ax + by + c = 0$.

Emphasise that the former gives y explicitly and the latter implicitly.

Discuss how to draw the graph of the function $y + 3x = 1$.

Emphasise that you can make a table of values in the same way as for explicit functions.

Discuss how to find the gradient and y-intercept from the equation.

Emphasise that you need to rearrange it to the form $y = mx + c$.

Discuss the steps involved for each function.

Emphasise that rearranging the equation is similar to solving it – you do the same thing to both sides at each stage, keeping the y term on the left.

It may be useful to work through the first few examples in question 1 if students are finding the work difficult.

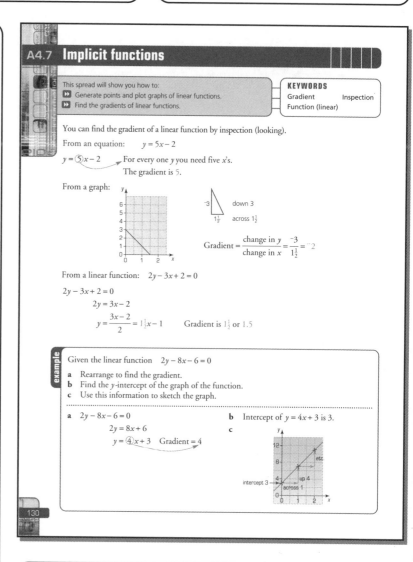

Plenary

Discuss question 2.

Encourage students to explain their strategies.

Emphasise that they can find two points on the line and see which equation the pairs satisfy as an alternative to rearranging the equation.

Further activities

In **A4.7ICT** students plot graphs of functions, including using the gradient and intercept.

Alternatively

Students could draw some of the graphs in question 1 by finding where the graphs cross the axes, by substituting $y = 0$ and $x = 0$ into the implicit function.

Differentiation

Core questions:

▸ Question 1 focuses on rearranging expressions to make y the subject.
▸ Questions 2 and 3 focus on finding gradients and intercepts from implicit equations.
▸ Question 4 involves finding the equation of a line joining two points.

Extension tier: focuses on plotting and transforming quadratic and cubic graphs.
Support tier: focuses on matching equations to their straight-line graphs.

Exercise A4.7

1 Rearrange these implicit functions to make y the subject of the equation:
  a $y - 2x = 3$ **b** $y - 3x + 2 = 0$ **c** $y + 3x - 4 = 0$
  d $\frac{y}{3} - x = 0$ **e** $\frac{y}{5} - 2x = 0$ **f** $\frac{y}{2} + 6x = 0$
  g $2y - 4x = 6$ **h** $2y + 3x = 12$ **i** $2y - 5x - 3 = 0$

2 Match each implicit function with a linear equation and a graph.

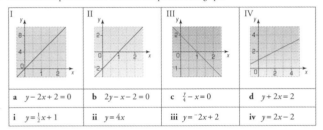

a $y - 2x + 2 = 0$	**b** $2y - x - 2 = 0$	**c** $\frac{y}{4} - x = 0$	**d** $y + 2x = 2$
i $y = \frac{1}{2}x + 1$	**ii** $y = 4x$	**iii** $y = {}^-2x + 2$	**iv** $y = 2x - 2$

3 **i** Match each of these implicit functions with their gradient and intercept.

  a $y - 3x + 2 = 0$
  b $y - 4x = 5$
  c $\frac{y}{4} - x = 0$
  d $y + 3x - 2 = 0$

	Gradient	Intercept
i	4	0
ii	3	$^-2$
iii	$^-3$	2
iv	4	5

  ii On a grid with x from $^-4$ to 4, and y from $^-15$ to 15, sketch each of the functions above.

4 **Challenge**
  Here is a kite ABCD on a grid.
  a Match the correct line to these three equations.
  ▸ line through A and B
  ▸ line through C and B
  ▸ line through D and C
  ▸ line through D and A
  ▸ line through D and B
  ▸ line through C and A

$y = 0$
$y + 2x = 4$
$y + x + 2 = 0$

  b Work out the equations of the remaining three lines.

131

Exercise commentary

The questions assess objectives on Framework Pages 165 and 167.

Problem solving
The exercise assesses objectives on Framework Page 27.

Group work
Questions 2 and 3 are suitable for paired work.

Misconceptions
Many students find transforming equations difficult and confusing.
It is important that they think of the method as if they are solving an equation so they work systematically.
Students will often multiply or divide inappropriately, failing to do so to each and every term.
Encourage students to rearrange the equation so that the y term is on the left before multiplying or dividing each term.

Links
Solving equations: Framework Pages 123–125. Transforming expressions: Page 117.

Homework

A4.7HW focuses on drawing graphs and identifying equations of graphs given implicitly.

Revision

Students should work through A4 in the 5–7 Revision Book.

Answers

1 **a** $y = 2x + 3$ **b** $y = 3x + 2$ **c** $y = 4 - 3x$ **d** $y = 3x$ **e** $y = 10x$
  f $y = {}^-12x$ **g** $y = 2x + 3$ **h** $y = 6 - \frac{3}{2}x$ **i** $y = \frac{5}{2}x + \frac{3}{2}$
2 **a** iv, II **b** i, IV **c** ii, I **d** iii, III
3 **i a** ii **b** iv **c** i **d** iii   **ii** Sketches as appropriate
4 **a** $y = 0$, line through D and B; $y + 2x = 4$, line through A and B;
    $y + x + 2 = 0$, line through D and C;
  b $y = x - 2$, line through C and B; $y = 2x + 4$, line through D and A;
    $x = 0$, line through C and A

131

Mental starter

How far?

Practise distance–time problems.

I am travelling at 40 km per hour.

▶ How far do I travel in 1 hour/2 hours/5 hours, etc?
▶ How long will it take to travel 120 km? 100 km? 14 km?

Repeat for other speeds.

Useful resources

R9 – coordinate grid (one quadrant)
A4.8OHP – graph from the Students' Book example

Introductory activity

Refer to the mental starter.

Encourage students to give the formula for the average speed.

Emphasise that it must be the average speed over a given distance.

Discuss how to rearrange the formula to find the distance or the time.

Encourage students to discuss ways of remembering the formulae and the units used.

Emphasise that you can show a journey on a distance–time graph.

Discuss real-life graphs that students use in other subjects.

Emphasise that the slope of the graph at any stage shows the rate of change of one variable given a change in the other.

Discuss the graph from the Students' Book example (shown on **A4.8OHP**).

Discuss what the axes show and hence what the slopes mean – the change in the amount of fuel over time.

Ask questions based on the graph:

▶ How much fuel did the car have to start with? At the end of the race?
▶ When did it refuel? How can you tell?
▶ When was it travelling at the fastest rate? How can you tell?

Emphasise that the fuel goes down at a constant rate because the car is travelling at more or less a constant speed.

Discuss how the graph would look if the fuel changed at a variable rate.

Emphasise that the graph would be curved.

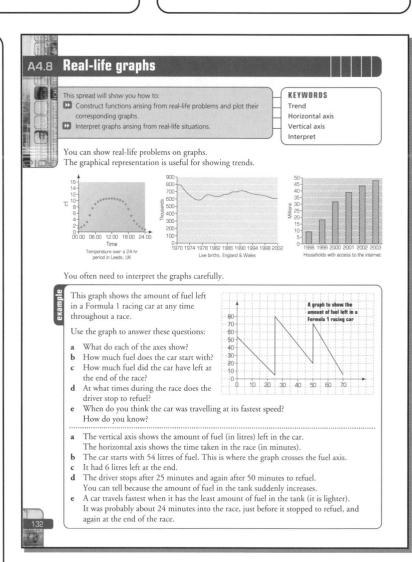

A4.8 Real-life graphs

This spread will show you how to:
▶ Construct functions arising from real-life problems and plot their corresponding graphs.
▶ Interpret graphs arising from real-life situations.

KEYWORDS
Trend
Horizontal axis
Vertical axis
Interpret

You can show real-life problems on graphs.
The graphical representation is useful for showing trends.

Temperature over a 24-hr period in Leeds, UK

Live births, England & Wales

Households with access to the internet

You often need to interpret the graphs carefully.

example

This graph shows the amount of fuel left in a Formula 1 racing car at any time throughout a race.

Use the graph to answer these questions:

a What do each of the axes show?
b How much fuel does the car start with?
c How much fuel did the car have left at the end of the race?
d At what times during the race does the driver stop to refuel?
e When do you think the car was travelling at its fastest speed? How do you know?

A graph to show the amount of fuel left in a Formula 1 racing car

a The vertical axis shows the amount of fuel (in litres) left in the car.
  The horizontal axis shows the time taken in the race (in minutes).
b The car starts with 54 litres of fuel. This is where the graph crosses the fuel axis.
c It had 6 litres left at the end.
d The driver stops after 25 minutes and again after 50 minutes to refuel.
  You can tell because the amount of fuel in the tank suddenly increases.
e A car travels fastest when it has the least amount of fuel in the tank (it is lighter).
  It was probably about 24 minutes into the race, just before it stopped to refuel, and again at the end of the race.

132

Plenary

Discuss question 2.

Plot the points on an OHP of **R9**.

Encourage students to describe how the curve grows, in as much detail as possible.

Emphasise that the weight must be estimated from the curve if it has not been recorded exactly.

Further activities

Students could research data on average rainfall, or car ownership and plot graphs to show these.

Differentiation

Core questions:
▶ Question 1 focuses on reading a curved graph.
▶ Questions 2 and 3 focus on drawing and interpreting real-life curved graphs.
▶ Question 4 involves extrapolating from a curved graph.

Extension tier: focuses on solving inequalities.

Support tier: focuses on interpreting and sketching graphs of real-life situations.

Exercise A4.8

1 The graph shows the height of a sunflower grown from seed.
The main sunflower opened after 12 weeks.
 a Describe how the plant has grown in the 12 weeks.
 b How tall did the sunflower grow?
 c How tall was the sunflower after 7 weeks? How tall was the sunflower after 9 weeks?
 d Estimate how many cm per day the plant grew in the period from 7 weeks to 9 weeks.

2 The table shows the weight of a baby during his first year.

Age	birth	1 month	2	3	4	5	6	7	8	9	10	11	12
Weight/kg	3.2	3.5	4.2	5.1	4.9	6.2	7.3	8.5	9.8	10.5	11	11.4	11.8

 a Plot this information on a copy of the graph and join the points smoothly.
 b Estimate how old the baby was when he weighed 6 kg.
 c When the baby was 3 months old he had a virus. How is this shown in the graph?
 d A healthy baby should grow to about 3 times their birth weight after a year. Do you think this baby was healthy?

3 This graph shows the relationship between the area of a square and the length of each side.
 a What is the area of a square of side length 4 cm?
 b The area of a square is 30 cm². Estimate the length of each side.
 c The length of a side of a square is 2.6 cm. Estimate its area to the nearest 1 cm².

4 Koi carp grow to be large fish. Here are the lengths of a koi measured during its first 8 years of life.

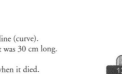

Age (x)	6 months	1 yr	2 yrs	4 yrs	5 yrs	7 yrs	8 yrs
Length (y)	4 cm	5 cm	8 cm	17 cm	23 cm	38 cm	47 cm

 a Plot these points on a grid and join them up with a smooth line (curve).
 b Estimate from your graph how old the fish would be when it was 30 cm long.
 c Estimate how long the fish was when it was 3 years old.
 d The fish lived to be 10 years old. Estimate how long it was when it died.

133

Exercise commentary

The questions assess objectives on Framework Pages 173 and 175.

Problem solving
The exercise assesses objectives on Framework Page 27.

Group work
All questions are suitable for paired discussion.

Misconceptions
In questions 2 and 4, students need to join the points with a smooth curve which can be quite a difficult skill to master. Encourage students to work lightly in pencil to join the points freehand. Students often make mistakes when reading from graphs. Encourage them to estimate answers before using the graph, for example they should know the range within which the answer lies.

Links
Students will use real-life graphs in other subject areas such as Geography and Science.

Homework

A4.8HW focuses on interpreting and plotting real-life graphs.

Revision

Students should work through N7 in the 5–7 Revision Book.

Answers

1 a The increase in height was slow, then quicker, then slower again.
 b 2 m c About 0.8 m, 2.5 m d About 12 cm per day
2 a Appropriate graph b About 4.8 months or 4 months 3 weeks
 c The graph goes down instead of up.
 d No, this baby is larger than average (3.7 times birth weight).
3 a 16 cm² b 5.5 cm c 7 cm²
4 a Appropriate graph b 6 years c 12 cm d About 70 cm

Mental starter

Give students three speeds, three times and three distances:

▶ 45 km/h   80 km/h   15 km/h
▶ 2 h   6 h   1.5 h
▶ 180 km   90 km   300 km

Ask questions based on these measures:
I travel at 45 km/h for 6 h. How far do I go?
Which distance would take me 2 h at what speed?

Useful resources

A4.9OHP – distance–time graph from the Students' Book
A4.9F – melting ice problem
Graph paper for Further activities

Introductory activity

Refer to the mental starter.
Emphasise that you can show a journey on a distance–time graph.
Discuss how different a journey of 300 km in 2 h and 300 km in 6 h would look on a graph.
Emphasise that the faster you travel the steeper the line.

Discuss the distance–time graph from the Students' Book example, shown on **A4.9OHP**.
Emphasise that the downward slope means that the train is travelling towards London, not backwards!
Discuss the solution to each part of the question.
Develop part **d** to consider how to find the average speed for this part of the journey.
Encourage students to use the formula:
Average speed = $\frac{\text{Distance}}{\text{Time}}$

Encourage students to think carefully about which units to use.
Emphasise that they can work it out in minutes then convert to hours.
Discuss how to do this.
Discuss which students find easier – working in minutes then converting or working in hours throughout.

Discuss the average speed for other parts of the journey and then for the journey as a whole.

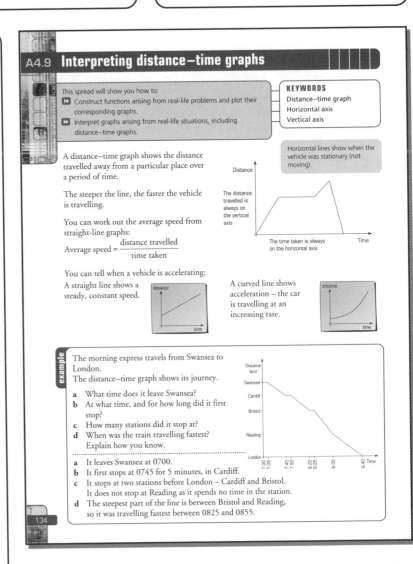

A4.9 Interpreting distance–time graphs

This spread will show you how to:
▶▶ Construct functions arising from real-life problems and plot their corresponding graphs.
▶▶ Interpret graphs arising from real-life situations, including distance–time graphs.

KEYWORDS
Distance–time graph
Horizontal axis
Vertical axis

A distance–time graph shows the distance travelled away from a particular place over a period of time.

The steeper the line, the faster the vehicle is travelling.

You can work out the average speed from straight-line graphs:
Average speed = $\frac{\text{distance travelled}}{\text{time taken}}$

You can tell when a vehicle is accelerating:
A straight line shows a steady, constant speed.

A curved line shows acceleration – the car is travelling at an increasing rate.

Horizontal lines show when the vehicle was stationary (not moving).

The distance travelled is always on the vertical axis

The time taken is always on the horizontal axis

example

The morning express travels from Swansea to London.
The distance–time graph shows its journey.

a What time does it leave Swansea?
b At what time, and for how long did it first stop?
c How many stations did it stop at?
d When was the train travelling fastest? Explain how you know.
....
a It leaves Swansea at 0700.
b It first stops at 0745 for 5 minutes, in Cardiff.
c It stops at two stations before London – Cardiff and Bristol. It does not stop at Reading as it spends no time in the station.
d The steepest part of the line is between Bristol and Reading, so it was travelling fastest between 0825 and 0855.

134

Plenary

Discuss question 3.
Emphasise that the upward slope shows the distance away from sea level and that the downward slope shows the funicular coming back down, but that the speed is always positive.

Further activities

In **A4.9F** students plot a time–mass graph to show how the mass of a block of ice decreases on a hot day, and consider how the air temperature affects the melting rate.

Differentiation

Core questions:
▶ Question 1 focuses on reading a simple distance–time graph.
▶ Question 2 focuses on a graph with variable speed.
▶ Question 3 involves finding the speed of a part of the journey.

Extension tier: focuses on representing inequalities graphically.

Support tier: focuses on interpreting and drawing distance–time graphs.

Exercise A4.9

1 Karen travels from Manchester to Nottingham by car.
The distance–time graph shows different stages in her journey.
She left Manchester at 16.15 hrs.
Match each of these statements to a stage in the journey.
  i She stops at a motorway service station for a break.
  ii She drives quickly on the motorway for 5 minutes.
  iii She drives on the motorway at a constant speed for 1 hour.
  iv She drives quickly on the motorway for 20 minutes.
  v She drives at a slower speed for 40 minutes.
  vi She hits busy traffic on the motorway and drives slowly for 30 minutes.

2 This distance–time graph shows the flight from Earth to the Moon of Apollo 11 in 1969.
It was from this flight that Neil Armstrong and Ed 'Buzz' Aldrin became the first men to step on the moon.
  a Approximately how far is the Moon from the Earth?
  b For how long did Apollo 11 orbit the Moon?
  c How far was it from Earth after 3 days?
  d When were they 100 000 miles from Earth?
  e How far did they travel in day 1? How far in day 2? Can you explain the difference?

3 A funicular railway is often found on the coast, taking passengers up (and down) the side of a cliff.
  a How long does it stop at Midstation?
  b How high is Midstation?
  c What is the speed of the railway in m/s?
  d Describe the journey from sea level to cliff top.

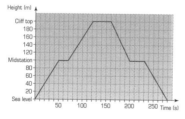

135

Exercise commentary

The questions assess objectives on Framework Pages 173 and 175.

Problem solving
The exercise assesses objectives on Framework Page 27.

Group work
Students would benefit from discussing questions in pairs.

Misconceptions
Students find the downward slopes in a distance–time graph difficult to understand.
Emphasise that the graphs show the distance travelled away from a fixed point and have little relation to negative gradients.
Generally students need to understand the two scales on the graph – one showing time which always increases and one showing distance travelled away from a given place.

Links
Measures: Framework Pages 229–231.

Homework

A4.9HW focuses on interpreting a distance–time graph and calculating average speeds.

Revision

Students should work through N8 in the 5–7 Revision Book.

Answers

1 i *d* **ii** *c* **iii** *a* **iv** *e* **v** *f* **vi** *b*
2 a About 230 000 **b** Just over 8 days **c** About 230 000 **d** 17 July
  e 100 000 miles, about 70 000 miles. Booster rockets dropped off after Day 1, so less power.
3 a 20 s **b** 100 m **c** 2 m/s
  d The railway progresses at constant speed for 50 s up to Midstation where it stops for 20 s. It then takes another 50 s to reach the cliff top. It waits for 40 s, then comes down at the same speed, waiting for 30 s at Midstation.

Summary

The key objectives for this unit are:
▶ Given values for m and c, find the gradient of lines given in the form $y = mx + c$. (165–167)
▶ Construct functions arising from real-life situations and plot their corresponding graphs. (173–175)
▶ Interpret graphs arising from real situations. (173–175)

Check out commentary

1 Students may mix up the gradient and the intercept, writing the equation as $y = cx + m$.
Encourage them to check their equation using a point on the line, in particular using the intercept is a useful way of emphasising which one the intercept is.

2 Students need to choose a suitable scale to use.
Emphasise the strategy of considering the range needed on each axis and choosing the scale accordingly.
Encourage students to always plot time on the x-axis.
They need to read the values carefully as they are not in a regular sequence.
This may confuse some students, especially when they need to join the points which make no obvious pattern.
Encourage students to join the points straight after plotting them to help avoid this difficulty.

3 Students often misread graphs for various reasons, commonly not reading the value from the graph itself but from a near gridline.
Encourage students to think about the range of answers so that they can check whether their answer is sensible.

Plenary activity

Ask students to plot the graphs of $y = 3x - 2$ and $y = x - 3$ on the same axes.
They should work in pairs. One student describes what the graph will look like. Their partner then must draw the graph from the instructions.

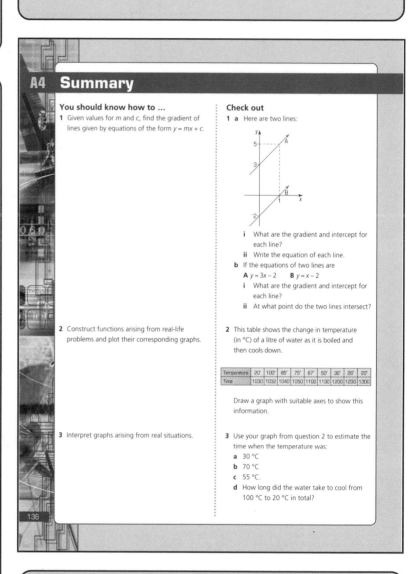

Development

This is the last algebra unit before students take the Key Stage 3 tests and is the main place in which graph work is developed. Students will revisit some of the graph work in **A5** and build on the ideas in GCSE courses.

Links

Students will use real-life graphs in other subject areas such as science. Factors are useful in solving number problems mentally.

Revision

This unit is covered in N2, N3, A5 and A6 in the 5–7 Revision Book.

Mental starters

Objectives covered in this unit:
▶ Simplify fractions by cancelling.
▶ Convert between fractions, decimals and percentages and between improper fractions and mixed numbers.
▶ Know or derive complements of 0.1, 1, 10.
▶ Solve simple problems involving probabilities.
▶ Apply mental skills to solve simple problems.

Resources needed

* means class set needed
Essential:
R6 – number lines
Coins*
Dice*

Useful:
D2.1OHP – probability examples
D2.4OHP – experimental probability
R1 – digit cards
Graph paper
D2.4ICT* – calculating probabilities

D2 Probability

This unit will show you how to:
▶▶ Use the vocabulary of probability in interpreting results involving uncertainty and prediction.
▶▶ Identify all the mutually exclusive outcomes of an experiment.
▶▶ Know that the sum of probabilities of all mutually exclusive outcomes is 1 and use this when solving problems.
▶▶ Estimate probabilities from experimental data.
▶▶ Use efficient methods to add, subtract and multiply fractions.
▶▶ Solve increasingly demanding problems in probability and evaluate solutions.
▶▶ Present a concise, reasoned argument using diagrams and related explanatory text.

There is a 50 : 50 chance of going the right way.

Before you start
You should know how to ...
1 Understand and use the probability scale from 0 to 1.

2 Identify all the possible outcomes of a single event.

3 Convert between fractions, decimals and percentages.

Check in
1 Mark these events on a probability scale:
  a getting a head on a throw of a coin
  b getting a 7 on a throw of a dice.

2 The letters of the word

CROCODILE

are placed in a bag.
List the possible outcomes when you choose a letter at random.

3 Change to percentages:
  a $\frac{3}{4}$ b 0.4   c $\frac{7}{20}$ d 0.35

Unit commentary

Aim of the unit
This unit revises understanding of probability in preparation of the Key Stage 3 test. It aims to deepen students' understanding of theoretical and experimental probability and the relationship between them. The unit uses fractions, decimals and percentages to represent and calculate probabilities. There is an emphasis on accurate use of language and constructing reasoned arguments.

Introduction
Encourage students to think of practical examples where probabilities can be found. For example, a goalkeeper has a 50% chance of diving the right way when saving a penalty. Emphasise that this unit covers the skills and knowledge needed for the Key Stage 3 tests but understanding the main ideas of probability is also very important.

Framework references
This unit focuses on:
Teaching objectives pages:
277, 279, 281, 283.
Problem solving pages: 23, 31.

Check in activity

Challenge students to calculate the theoretical probability of throwing a 4 using a normal dice. What is the theoretical probability of a even number?
Encourage students to express these probabilities as fractions, decimals and percentages.

Differentiation

Support tier
Focuses on expressing and calculating probabilities and the relationship between theoretical and experimental probability.

Extension tier
Focuses on consolidating probability techniques, extending to expected frequency and relative frequency.

Mental starter

Use a set of **R1** digit cards. Challenge students to answer questions on probabilities on cards picked from the set, for example:
What is the probability of getting an even number; a number less than six; what is an event with a probability of $\frac{3}{5}$?
Encourage students to give their answers as fractions, decimals and percentages.
Remove two of the cards and ask further questions on the new set.

Useful resources

R1 – digit cards
R6 – number lines
D2.1OHP – Students' Book example

Introductory activity

Refer to the mental starter.
Remind students that probability:
▸ Can be expressed as a fraction, decimal or percentage.
▸ Is always between 0 (impossible) and 1 (certain).

Discuss the first three diagrams in the Students' Book. Use three lines from **R6** (number lines) marked from 0 to 1 in fractions (top line), decimals (middle line) and percentages (bottom line). Challenge students to give you the probability for each example in each of the three forms. Remind students to use a calculator to find decimal equivalents for the card example.

Emphasise use of the formula for theoretical probability, making sure that all outcomes are equally likely. Challenge students to describe an example where all outcomes are not equally likely, for example, a biased spinner or trick dice. Emphasise that the formula cannot be used in these cases.

Discuss the example in the Students' Book, on **D2.1OHP**. Challenge students to complete the sample space diagram for the two dice. Discuss answers. Encourage students to spot all the outcomes that lead to a score of 5.
Emphasise the use of notation:
▸ Probability of scoring a 5 can be written as p(5).

Challenge students to work out other probabilities from the sample space, for example:
p(7), p(less than 10), p(1).

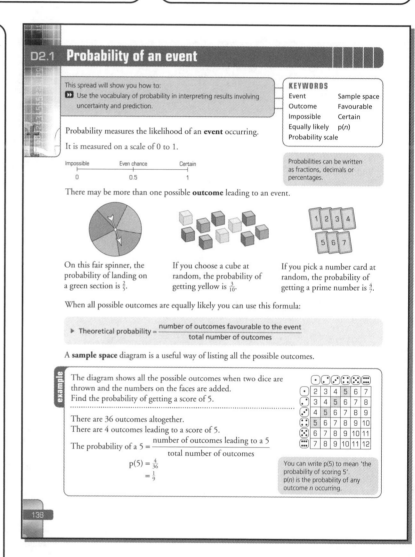

D2.1 Probability of an event

This spread will show you how to:
▸ Use the vocabulary of probability in interpreting results involving uncertainty and prediction.

KEYWORDS
Event   Sample space
Outcome   Favourable
Impossible   Certain
Equally likely p(n)
Probability scale

Probability measures the likelihood of an **event** occurring.
It is measured on a scale of 0 to 1.

Impossible   Even chance   Certain
0   0.5   1

Probabilities can be written as fractions, decimals or percentages.

There may be more than one possible **outcome** leading to an event.

On this fair spinner, the probability of landing on a green section is $\frac{2}{5}$.

If you choose a cube at random, the probability of getting yellow is $\frac{3}{10}$.

If you pick a number card at random, the probability of getting a prime number is $\frac{4}{7}$.

When all possible outcomes are equally likely you can use this formula:

▸ Theoretical probability = $\dfrac{\text{number of outcomes favourable to the event}}{\text{total number of outcomes}}$

A **sample space** diagram is a useful way of listing all the possible outcomes.

The diagram shows all the possible outcomes when two dice are thrown and the numbers on the faces are added.
Find the probability of getting a score of 5.

	1	2	3	4	5	6
1	2	3	4	5	6	7
2	3	4	5	6	7	8
3	4	5	6	7	8	9
4	5	6	7	8	9	10
5	6	7	8	9	10	11
6	7	8	9	10	11	12

There are 36 outcomes altogether.
There are 4 outcomes leading to a score of 5.
The probability of a 5 = $\dfrac{\text{number of outcomes leading to a 5}}{\text{total number of outcomes}}$

$p(5) = \frac{4}{36}$
$\quad\;\; = \frac{1}{9}$

You can write p(5) to mean 'the probability of scoring 5'. p(n) is the probability of any outcome n occurring.

138

Plenary

Discuss answers to question 2. Encourage students to discuss correct use of the formula for theoretical probability.
Discuss answers to question 6. Challenge students to answer more questions on the diagram, such as the probability that the answer will be more than 10, etc. Emphasise the amount of information that can be gained from seeing clearly all the outcomes in the sample space. Challenge students to convert their answers to fractions, decimals and percentages.

Further activities

Challenge students to draw up sample space diagrams for the first examples on page 138. For example, a sample space diagram for all the colours on the spinner. Encourage students to challenge each other with their own questions, such as the probability that the same colour occurs twice in two spins of the spinner.

Differentiation

Core questions:
- Questions 1 and 2 focus on basic ideas of probability.
- Questions 3–5 focus on finding probabilities using the formula and justifying decisions.
- Questions 6 and 7 extend to further probability in context, and sample space diagrams.

Extension tier: focuses on calculating theoretical probability of mutually exclusive events, and expected frequency.
Support tier: focuses on theoretical probability.

Exercise D2.1

1 James has 36 blue and yellow counters. When he chooses a counter at random, it is equally likely that he will pick either a blue or a yellow counter. How many counters of each colour are there? Explain your answer.

2 Mandy puts three red cubes, two green cubes and five blue cubes into a bag. She asks Javid to pick a cube without looking. Javid says:

> There are three different colours, so the probability of the cube being green is $\frac{1}{3}$.

a Explain why Javid is wrong.
b Work out the correct probability of Javid picking a green cube.
c Mark the probability of picking each colour on a probability scale.

3 Draw accurate diagrams of circular spinners, like the one on page 138, which meet these conditions:
a A spinner with 10 equal sections; the probability of the pointer landing on a black section is 30%.
b A spinner with 12 equal sections coloured red, blue or green; there is an equal probability of the pointer landing on each colour.
c A spinner with 6 equal sections; the probability of getting black, yellow or orange is $\frac{1}{2}$, $\frac{1}{6}$ and $\frac{1}{3}$ respectively.

4 Tickets numbered 1 to 25 are placed in a bag. One ticket is chosen at random. Find the probability that the number chosen will be:
a an even number
b less than 6
c a prime number.
Write each of your answers as a fraction, a decimal and a percentage.

5 Ben has two bags of marbles.
Bag A has 3 green and 2 red marbles.
Bag B has 5 green and 4 red marbles.
Ben is going to pick a marble at random from either bag A or bag B.
Which bag should Ben choose if he wants a green marble? Explain your reasoning.

6 Karen has number cards marked 2, 4, 6. Jenna has cards marked 3, 5, 7. They each pick one of their cards at random, and the numbers on the two cards are multiplied together.
a Draw a sample space diagram to show all the possible answers.
b Use your diagram to find the probability that the answer will be less than 20.

7 A washing machine has four different washing temperatures: 30 °C, 40 °C, 60 °C and 90 °C.
It has five different washing programs: A, B, C, D and E.
One combination of temperature and washing program can be written as (30, A).
a Write down all of the combinations in the same way.
Jasmine selects a wash temperature and program at random.
Her new jumper is in the wash, and will be safe provided that:
- the wash temperature is **lower** than 60 °C, and
- the washing program is **not** E.
On your list of combinations, circle the favourable outcomes for the event 'Jasmine's jumper gets washed safely'.
b Find the probability that Jasmine's jumper gets washed safely.

Exercise commentary

The questions assess objectives on Framework Page 277–281.

Problem solving
Questions 1 and 5 assess objectives on Framework Page 31.
Question 7 assesses Page 23.

Group work
Questions 1, 2 and 5 are suitable for discussion in pairs.

Misconceptions
Students often find the formula for theoretical probability difficult to use. Encourage students to first list all the outcomes of the event, and write this total in the denominator, and then pick the outcomes that they are looking for and write this total in the numerator.
Students may also have difficulty converting between fractions, decimals and percentages.
Encourage the use of a calculator for difficult fraction to decimal conversions, and thinking about percentages as 'parts per 100' or a fraction over 100.

Links
Problem solving: Framework Page 23.

Homework

D2.1HW focuses on identifying events and outcomes.

Revision

Students should work through D1 in the 5–7 Revision Book.

Answers

1 18 blue, 18 yellow   2 a There are different numbers of each colour, so the colours are not equally likely.   b $\frac{1}{5}$ c Red at $\frac{3}{10}$, Green at $\frac{1}{5}$, Blue at $\frac{1}{2}$
3 Spinners with: a 3 black sections, 7 of any other colour
  b 4 red, 4 blue, 4 green sections   c 3 black, 1 yellow, 2 orange sections
4 a $\frac{12}{25}$, 0.48, 48%   b $\frac{1}{5}$, 0.2, 20%   c $\frac{9}{25}$, 0.36, 36%
5 Bag A, as the probability is $\frac{3}{5}$ (60%) compared with $\frac{5}{9}$ (56%).
6 a Sample space diagram: 6, 10, 14; 12, 20, 28; 18, 30, 42   b $\frac{5}{9}$
7 a Favourable outcomes: (30, A), (30, B), (30, C), (30, D), (40, A), (40, B), (40, C), (40, D)   b $\frac{2}{5}$

Mental starter

Get to one!

Call out a series of decimal numbers between 0 and 1. For each number, challenge students to give the number that would add to make 1. For example, call out 0.3. The correct answer is 0.7. Extend numbers to more decimal places. Challenge students to continue with fractions such as $\frac{1}{3}, \frac{1}{5}, \frac{3}{8}, \frac{21}{48}$. Extend to include percentages.

Useful resources

Coins

Dice

Introductory activity

Challenge students in pairs to record the outcome of a series of coin tosses (heads/tails). Discuss answers. Emphasise that **heads** and **tails** are mutually exclusive outcomes, as they cannot both happen at the same time.

Challenge students to roll dice a number of times, recording the score and whether the outcome is even or odd. Discuss answers. Challenge students to identify the mutually exclusive outcomes, and the outcomes that are not mutually exclusive. Emphasise that the outcome could be, for example, both four and an even number. These are not mutually exclusive. Challenge students to calculate and add together the theoretical probabilities of each score occurring on the dice. Emphasise that the sum of the probabilities of all mutually exclusive outcomes is 1.

Discuss the first example in the Students' Book. Challenge students to find the probability of getting the bell. Emphasise that the total probability of the outcomes has to equal one, so you can do a subtraction to find the missing probability.

Discuss the second example in the Students' Book. Challenge students to find the missing probability. Discuss answers. Emphasise that there are four mutually exclusive outcomes. Emphasise that if you know the probability of an event, then you can estimate how many times it is likely to occur within a set of trials. Emphasise that in an experiment of 30 calls, you would expect to find the phone switched off in 0.4 of those 30 calls (12 times).

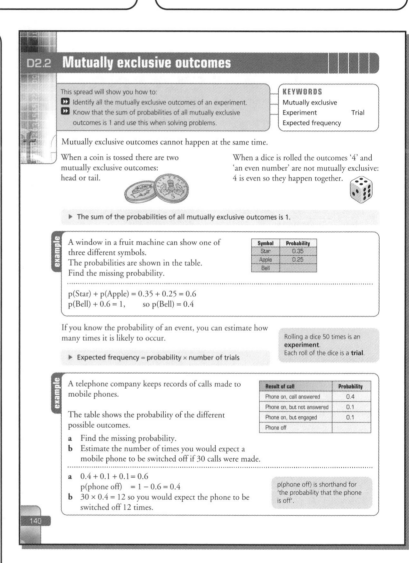

D2.2 Mutually exclusive outcomes

This spread will show you how to:
- Identify all the mutually exclusive outcomes of an experiment.
- Know that the sum of probabilities of all mutually exclusive outcomes is 1 and use this when solving problems.

KEYWORDS
Mutually exclusive
Experiment   Trial
Expected frequency

Mutually exclusive outcomes cannot happen at the same time.

When a coin is tossed there are two mutually exclusive outcomes: head or tail.

When a dice is rolled the outcomes '4' and 'an even number' are not mutually exclusive: 4 is even so they happen together.

▶ The sum of the probabilities of all mutually exclusive outcomes is 1.

example
A window in a fruit machine can show one of three different symbols.
The probabilities are shown in the table.
Find the missing probability.

Symbol	Probability
Star	0.35
Apple	0.25
Bell	

p(Star) + p(Apple) = 0.35 + 0.25 = 0.6
p(Bell) + 0.6 = 1,   so p(Bell) = 0.4

If you know the probability of an event, you can estimate how many times it is likely to occur.

Rolling a dice 50 times is an **experiment**. Each roll of the dice is a **trial**.

▶ Expected frequency = probability × number of trials

example
A telephone company keeps records of calls made to mobile phones.

The table shows the probability of the different possible outcomes.

a Find the missing probability.
b Estimate the number of times you would expect a mobile phone to be switched off if 30 calls were made.

Result of call	Probability
Phone on, call answered	0.4
Phone on, but not answered	0.1
Phone on, but engaged	0.1
Phone off	

a 0.4 + 0.1 + 0.1 = 0.6
p(phone off) = 1 − 0.6 = 0.4
b 30 × 0.4 = 12 so you would expect the phone to be switched off 12 times.

p(phone off) is shorthand for 'the probability that the phone is off'.

140

Plenary

Discuss answers to question 4. Emphasise that the three options given cover all of the possibilities, and that they are mutually exclusive. Challenge students to use this fact to find the answer to the first part of the question, and to solve this problem:

▶ If Grant check the machine 20 times in one week, how often would he expect to find the machine out of the office?

Discuss answers. Emphasise that the expected frequency is the probability times the number of trials, so the answer is $0.4 \times 20 = 8$.

Further activities

Challenge students to make up questions on expected frequency using the correct data from question 5. Encourage them to use examples that have a mixture of fractions, decimals and percentages.

Differentiation

Core questions:

▶ Questions 1–3 focus on the sum of all probabilities and the probability of events not occurring.
▶ Questions 4 and 5 focus on the sum of mutually exclusive probabilities.
▶ Questions 6 and 7 extend to finding expected frequencies from probabilities.

Extension tier: focuses on using tree diagrams to calculate probabilities of two or more events.

Support tier: focuses on finding complementary probabilities.

Exercise D2.2

1 The table shows the probability of three players winning a competition.

Player	Geraint	Sally	Zia
Probability of winning	$\frac{1}{2}$	20%	0.3

Work out the probability of each player **not** winning.

2 Sam makes a spinner with three sections marked A, B and C.
Sam says: 'There is an evens chance of the pointer landing on A. The probability of getting B is 30%, and the probability of getting C is a quarter.'
Explain why Sam must be wrong.

3 The table shows the probability of four players winning a game.

Player	Karis	Fiona	Laura	Gill
p(winning)	20%	35%	30%	15%

Find the probability of each player **not** winning the game.

4 Grant works in an office at an engineering company. He uses a machine that is shared with another office. The table shows probabilities for the status of the machine.

Machine status	Probability
In office: being used	0.22
In office: not being used	
Out of office	0.4

a Find the probability that the machine is in the office, but not being used.
b The probability of another piece of equipment being out of the office is 0.37.
Find the probability that it is in the office.

5 Four different five-sided spinners are all marked with letters A, B, C, D and E. The table shows the probability of getting each result for each spinner.

Result	A	B	C	D	E
Spinner 1	0.3	0.2	0.1	0.1	0.3
Spinner 2	$\frac{1}{5}$	0.2	20%	0.1	$\frac{1}{10}$
Spinner 3	28%	36%	27%	5%	5%
Spinner 4	$\frac{1}{4}$	$\frac{1}{8}$	$\frac{1}{4}$	$\frac{1}{8}$	$\frac{1}{4}$

The results for two of the spinners are wrong.
Find out which spinners have incorrect results. Explain your answers.

6 Jake takes a book from a shelf at random. The table shows the probability of getting different types of book.

Subject	Hardback	Paperback
Fiction	0.1	0.3
Sport	0.2	0
Computers	0.1	0.15
Animals	0.05	0.1

What is the probability that the book chosen will be:
a a paperback
b a book about computers.
There are 60 books on the shelf altogether.
c How many of them are books about animals?

7 There are four possible results in a fairground game. The table shows the probability of each result.

Result	Probability
Top prize	$\frac{1}{20}$
Consolation prize	$\frac{1}{10}$
Your money back	?
Lose	$\frac{3}{5}$

a What is the probability of getting your money back?
b What is the most likely result?
c What is the probability of not winning the top prize?
d What results would you expect if you played the game 100 times?

141

Exercise commentary

The questions assess objectives on Framework Page 279.

Problem solving

Question 2 assesses objectives on Framework Page 31.
Questions 4–7 assess objectives on Framework Page 23.

Group work

Questions 1 and 5 are suitable for discussion in pairs.

Misconceptions

Students may have difficulty converting between fractions, decimal and percentages or adding and subtracting different forms. Encourage them to convert everything into the same form before they do any calculation, and revise the relevant procedures from N1.

Links

Problem solving: Framework Page 23.

Homework

D2.2HW gives practice in identifying mutually exclusive outcomes and calculating probabilities.

Revision

Students should work through D2 in the 5–7 Revision Book.

Answers

1 $\frac{1}{2}$, 80%, 0.7
2 The probabilities add up to more than one.
3 80%, 65%, 70%, 85%
4 a 0.38 **b** 0.63
5 Spinners 2 (total probability = 1.1) and 3 (total probability = 101%)
6 a 0.55 **b** 0.25 **c** 9
7 a $\frac{1}{4}$ **b** Lose **c** $\frac{19}{20}$ **d** 5 top prizes, 10 consolation prizes, money back 25 times, lose 60 times

Mental starter

Write the numbers 1 to 10 horizontally across the board and the decimals 0.1 to 0.5 vertically below them.

Challenge students to make the decimals by creating fractions with the integers, using each once only. For example, use 1 and 10 to make $\frac{1}{10} = 0.1$. Cross off 1, 10 and 0.1 from the lists.

Discuss solutions, or nearest approximations, for all five decimal numbers. Repeat with different target decimals, for example, 0.6 to 1.4 in steps of 0.2.

Useful resources

R6 – number lines
Graph paper for Further activities

Introductory activity

Refer to the mental starter.

Emphasise that there are common fractions whose equivalents should be known. Use **R6** – number lines, to show quarters, fifths, and tenths from 0 to 1. Challenge students to give decimal and percentage equivalents for each fraction, and write them on the number lines. Emphasise that there are an unlimited number of fractions in between the values on the lines.

Encourage students to convert $\frac{3}{5}$ to a decimal and percentage. Discuss methods and strategies.

Discuss the first example in the Students' Book. Challenge students to express p(vowel) as a fraction, decimal and percentage. Then encourage them to find p(not vowel) and express that as a fraction, decimal and percentage. Emphasise that each probability is the same value, given in different forms.

Discuss the second example in the Students' Book. Encourage students to discuss their method for solving the problem before they start. Discuss strategies. Emphasise that they need to use the fact that the sum of all mutually exclusive outcomes is 1.

Discuss methods for adding the fractions. Emphasise that problems often involve adding and subtracting fractions.

Discuss the third example in the Students' Book. Remind students that you estimate the number of successes by multiplying the probability of success by the number of trials. Discuss strategies for multiplying fractions.

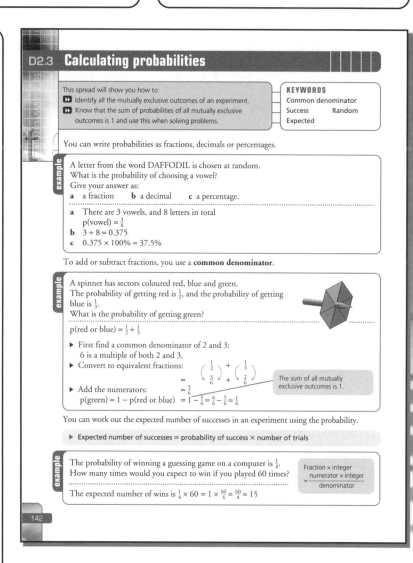

Plenary

Discuss answers to question 1. Use another copy of **R6** with three lines marked as fractions, decimals and percentages.

Challenge students to mark on each line the position of each probability and label it correctly. Discuss strategies for cancelling down fractions and for converting from a fraction to a percentage.

Discuss methods and strategies for question 6. Emphasise use of the formula for finding expected frequencies and the strategies for multiplying fractions.

Further activities

Challenge students to draw a line graph (on graph paper) for question 6, showing the expected number of successes (vertical axis) against the number of trials (horizontal axis). Encourage them to draw a separate line for each letter, and show data from 0 to 100 trials.

Differentiation

Core questions:
- ▶ Questions 1 and 2 focus on probabilities from equally likely outcomes.
- ▶ Questions 3–5 focus on finding the probability of events not occurring and of one of a pair of exclusive events occurring.
- ▶ Question 6 extends to finding expected frequencies.

Extension tier: focuses on expected frequency and making inferences from relative frequency.

Support tier: focuses on using sample space diagrams to calculate probabilities.

Exercise D2.3

1 A bag contains these numbers of coloured counters.

Colour	Pink	Blue	Yellow	Green	Orange
Number	4	6	9	12	5

A counter is chosen at random from the bag. Find the probability of the counter being:

a pink   b blue
c yellow   d green
e orange   f not blue.

Give each answer as:

i a fraction in its lowest terms
ii a percentage.

2 A bag of mixed sweets contains four different flavours.

Flavour	Lemon	Orange	Sherbet	Mint
Number of sweets	11	12	8	9

Alan likes all the flavours except lemon.
Beth only likes orange and mint.
Claire likes everything except orange.
Each person chooses a sweet from the bag at random.

a Find the probability of each person getting a sweet they like.
Give your answers as fractions in their lowest terms.
b Change each answer to a percentage.
c Mark each of the probabilities on a probability scale.

3 The probability of getting a winning ticket in six different lotteries is shown in the table.
Copy and complete the table.

Lottery	1	2	3	4	5	6
Probability of winning	½	⅓	⅜	⅝	13/17	9/125
Probability of not winning						

4 Roger picks a coloured cube at random from a bag.
The probability of getting a blue cube is $\frac{3}{25}$.
The probability of getting a yellow cube is $\frac{8}{25}$.
What is the probability of:
a **not** getting a blue cube
b getting a blue **or** a yellow cube?

5 When two ordinary dice are rolled and the scores are added, the probability of a total of 7 is $\frac{1}{6}$ and the probability of a total of 2 is $\frac{1}{36}$.
What is the probability of:
a not getting a total of 7
b not getting a total of 2
c getting a total of 2 **or** 7?

6 Jessica writes each letter of her name on a card.

She chooses a card at random, notes the letter, and then puts it back in the pack.
a How many times would you expect her to get a letter S if she repeated the experiment 50 times?
b How many vowels would you expect Jessica to get in 40 trials?
c How many times would you expect her to get a J or a C in 60 trials?

Exercise commentary

The questions assess objectives on Framework Pages 279 and 281.

Problem solving

Questions 2–6 assess objectives on Framework Page 23.

Group work

This exercise is suitable for group discussion after students have attempted each question on their own.

Misconceptions

Many students add or subtract the numerators of fractions as well as the denominators.

Encourage students to mark their answers on a number line (**R6**) and discuss what is obviously wrong with their answers and where they would expect the answer to be.

Links

Problem solving: Framework Page 23.

Homework

D2.3HW focuses on calculating probabilities using addition, multiplication and cancelling fractions.

Revision

Students should work through N4 in the 5–7 Revision Book.

Answers

1 a i $\frac{1}{9}$ ii 11.1%   b i $\frac{1}{6}$ ii 16.7%
   c i $\frac{1}{4}$ ii 25%   d i $\frac{1}{3}$ ii 33.3%
   e i $\frac{5}{36}$ ii 13.9%   f i $\frac{5}{6}$ ii 83.3%
2 a Alan $\frac{29}{40}$, Beth $\frac{21}{40}$, Claire $\frac{7}{10}$ b 72.5%, 52.5%, 70%
   c Probability scale with answers marked.
3 $\frac{1}{2}, \frac{2}{3}, \frac{3}{5}, \frac{5}{8}, \frac{13}{17}, \frac{116}{125}$ 4 a $\frac{22}{25}$ b $\frac{11}{25}$
5 a $\frac{5}{6}$ b $\frac{35}{36}$ c $\frac{7}{36}$ 6 a 14   b 17   c 17

D2.4 Experimental probability

Mental starter

Challenge the class to find the theoretical probability of a fair coin being heads [$\frac{1}{2}$]. Spin a fair coin and encourage students to record the result. Challenge them to find the experimental probability of it being a head [0 or 1].

Continue to spin the coin, adding up results as you go. Challenge students to find the experimental probability after each spin, and state their answer as a fraction, decimal and percentage.

Useful resources

D2.4OHP – examples from Students' Book
Coins

Introductory activity

Refer to the mental starter.

Emphasise that the theoretical probability of the outcome was known before the experiment. Challenge students to think of other situations where the theoretical probability is known beforehand. [Dice rolls, pack of cards, known balls in a bag.] Emphasise that in real life most probabilities are found from experimental trials. Discuss the formula for finding experimental probability.

Discuss the first example in the Students' Book, shown on **D2.4OHP.**

Challenge students to find the experimental probability of the counter landing on a line after the first set of 20 trials [$\frac{10}{20} = 0.5$] and for the last set of trials [$\frac{18}{20} = 0.9$]. Discuss answers. Emphasise that the complete set of 200 trials 'evens out' these individual results and gives a more reliable estimate.

Discuss the second example in the Students' Book, also on **D2.4OHP.**

Challenge students to find the experimental probability for each student. Discuss answers. Emphasise that all students found estimates that were more than 0.17 (the theoretical value). Discuss the combined result for the experimental probability. Emphasise that this is also much more than the theoretical value. Challenge students to discuss what this means for the dice. Emphasise that the dice are biased because the experimental value of the probability is significantly different to the theoretical value.

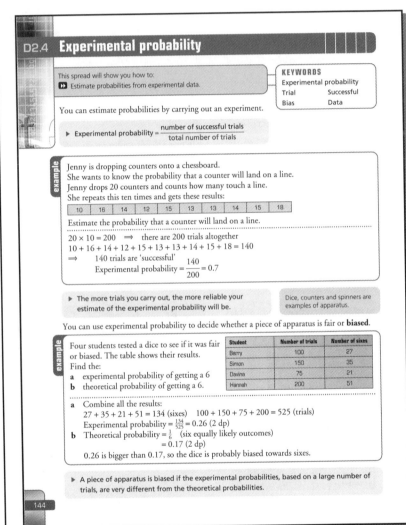

Plenary

Discuss answers to question 1. Emphasise that 1a is a question on theoretical probability that can be known beforehand. Emphasise that 1b is false, as this is only what you would expect given the theoretical value and is not certain. Emphasise that if you rolled the dice more times, you would expect results nearer the theoretical values. Emphasise that 1c is false, as each trial is independent of the trials before it.

Further activities

In **D2.4ICT**, students calculate frequencies and probabilities from experimental data using a spreadsheet.

Alternatively

Challenge students to calculate the experimental probability after each set of trials in the first example on page 144, for example, after 20 trials, 40 trials, up to the full data set. Challenge students to describe the trend of the probability values.

Differentiation

Core questions:

▶ Question 1 focuses on fundamental ideas of probability.

▶ Questions 2 and 3 focus on increasing numbers of trials and relative sample sizes.

▶ Questions 4 and 5 extend to combining data sets to produce 'best estimates' of experimental probabilities.

Extension tier: focuses on making inferences from relative frequency graphs.

Support tier: focuses on calculating and interpreting experimental probability.

Exercise D2.4

1 State whether these statements are true or false. Explain your answers.
   a If you roll a fair dice, the probability of getting a 6 is $\frac{1}{6}$.
   b If you roll a fair dice six times, you are certain to get a 6.
   c If you get three heads in a row when you toss a fair coin, you are more likely to get a tail next time.

2 Sam tests a dice to see whether it is fair. The table shows his results.

Score	1	2	3	4	5	6
Frequency	17	22	13	14	23	31

   a Estimate the probability of each score.
   b Do you think that the dice is fair? Explain your answer.

Sam's friends help him collect more results:

Score	1	2	3	4	5	6
Frequency	170	159	164	148	185	174

   c Estimate the probability of each score, based on the complete set of results.
   d Do you now think that the dice is fair? Explain your reasoning.

3 The table shows the number of children living in the first 20 houses in a street.

Number of children	Number of houses
0	5
1	6
2	7
3	2

   a Estimate the probability that the number of children living in a randomly chosen house in the street is at least two.
   b How reliable would your answer to part **a** be if there were:
      i 25 houses in the street altogether
      ii 200 houses altogether?
      Explain your reasoning.

4 A spinner is tested by four students to see if it is biased. Their results are shown in the table.

Student	Number of trials	Colour				
		Red	Blue	Green	Yellow	Black
Jolomi	200	43	41	22	19	75
Theo	25	8	7	0	2	8
Carol	100	24	22	18	10	26
Alice	75	15	23	6	8	23
Totals						

   a Which student's data should give the best estimates for experimental probability? Explain your answer.
   b The four students decided to collect all of their data together.
      Copy the table, and fill in the totals.
   c From the evidence in the table, do you think that the spinner is biased? Explain your answer.
   d Use the data to estimate the probability of the spinner landing on black.

5 Mike puts 25 coloured cubes in a bag. He asks five friends to estimate how many cubes of each colour there are. Each person picks a cube at random, records the colour, and puts it back in the bag.
   They repeat this 200 times. Here are their results:

Name	Black	White	Pink	Brown
Patrick	48	83	49	20
Sandra	36	86	53	25
Claire	29	88	55	28
Jon	43	76	59	22
Maria	40	83	59	18

   a Use Patrick's data to estimate the number of cubes of each colour.
   b Combine all the students' data and use this to work out another estimate of the number of cubes of each colour.
   c Which result should be more reliable, part **a** or part **b**? Explain your answer.

145

Exercise commentary

The questions assess objectives on Framework Pages 277 and 283.

Problem solving

The exercise assesses objectives on Framework Page 31.

Group work

All questions are suitable for discussion in pairs or in a group. Logical arguments for questions 1 and 2 can be developed in groups for the plenary.

Misconceptions

Students may have difficulty with question 1c, and assume that the probability must even itself out over a number of trials. Emphasise that the coin has no 'memory' of previous results, and the outcome is independent every time. Emphasise that the greater reliability of more trials is due to random results being evened out, not the apparatus deliberately correcting itself.

Links

Problem solving: Framework Page 23.

Homework

D2.4HW requires students to explain how to carry out an experiment to estimate an experimental probability.

Revision

Students should work through N5 in the 5–7 Revision Book.

Answers

1 a True b False c False
2 a 0.14, 0.18, 0.11, 0.12, 0.19, 0.26 b The dice may be biased in favour of 6, but more trials are needed to be sure. c 0.17, 0.16, 0.16, 0.14, 0.19, 0.18 d The dice appears to be fair.
3 a 0.45 b i Very reliable ii Much less reliable
4 a Jolomi, as he carried out most trials. b 400, 90, 93, 36, 39, 132
   c Yes d 0.33   5 a 6 black, 10 white, 6 pink, 3 brown
   b 5 black, 10 white, 7 pink, 3 brown c Part **b**, as there were more trials.

Summary

The key objectives for this unit are:

▶ Know that the sum of probabilities of all mutually exclusive outcomes is 1 and use this when solving problems. (279–281)
▶ Present a concise, reasoned argument using diagrams and related explanatory text. (31)

Plenary activity

Discuss this problem.

An arcade game shows one of four possible symbols:

	Probability
Cherry	$\frac{1}{4}$
Orange	?
Pear	$\frac{1}{2}$
Jackpot	$\frac{1}{16}$

What is the probability of an orange? Discuss how much the game should cost and how much the jackpot should be for the game to make a profit.

Check out commentary

1 Students should recognise that the three outcomes – red, green and orange – are mutually exclusive. This means all the probabilities add to 1.

2 Students should draw sample space diagrams or list the outcomes for each game in order to calculate the probabilities.
Emphasise the importance of working systematically.
Remind students to relate the probabilities they have found back to the original question and to decide which game they have most chance of winning.

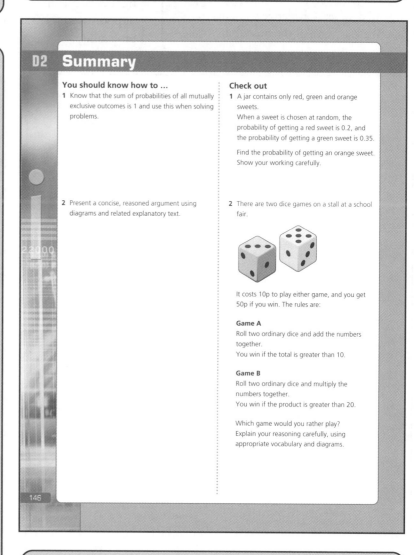

D2 Summary

You should know how to ...

1 Know that the sum of probabilities of all mutually exclusive outcomes is 1 and use this when solving problems.

2 Present a concise, reasoned argument using diagrams and related explanatory text.

Check out

1 A jar contains only red, green and orange sweets.
When a sweet is chosen at random, the probability of getting a red sweet is 0.2, and the probability of getting a green sweet is 0.35.

Find the probability of getting an orange sweet. Show your working carefully.

2 There are two dice games on a stall at a school fair.

It costs 10p to play either game, and you get 50p if you win. The rules are:

Game A
Roll two ordinary dice and add the numbers together.
You win if the total is greater than 10.

Game B
Roll two ordinary dice and multiply the numbers together.
You win if the product is greater than 20.

Which game would you rather play? Explain your reasoning carefully, using appropriate vocabulary and diagrams.

Development

The probability work in this unit is developed further in **D4**.

Links

This work uses the equivalence of fractions, decimals and percentages.
Experimental probability links to data projects, as well as work in other subject areas such as Science, Geography and History.

Revision

This unit is covered in D7, D8 and D9 in the 5–7 Revision Book.

Mental starters

Objectives covered in this unit:
▸ Visualise, describe and sketch 2-D and 3-D shapes.
▸ Visualise symmetries of 2-D and 3-D shapes.
▸ Estimate bearings.
▸ Use metric units for calculations.
▸ Use metric units for estimation.
▸ Convert between metric units.
▸ Multiply and divide integers.
▸ Discuss and interpret graphs.

Resources needed

* means class set needed
Essential:
R8* – grid in all four quadrants
R16 – 3-D shapes
Set of solids
Multilink cubes
Squared paper
Rulers*
A3 paper
Cut-out triangle and parallelogram (R14, R15)
String

Useful:
S3.2OHP – describing transformations
S3.5OHP – enlargements
S3.6OHP – a map
R14 – triangles
R15 – quadrilaterals
R35 – diagrams for Exercise S3.1
S3.3ICT* – combinations of transformations

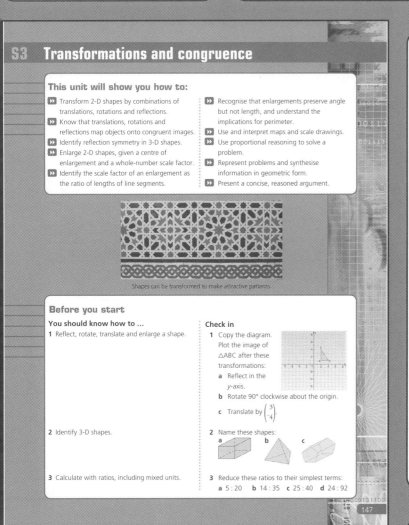

S3 Transformations and congruence

This unit will show you how to:

▸▸ Transform 2-D shapes by combinations of translations, rotations and reflections.
▸▸ Know that translations, rotations and reflections map objects onto congruent images.
▸▸ Identify reflection symmetry in 3-D shapes.
▸▸ Enlarge 2-D shapes, given a centre of enlargement and a whole-number scale factor.
▸▸ Identify the scale factor of an enlargement as the ratio of lengths of line segments.

▸▸ Recognise that enlargements preserve angle but not length, and understand the implications for perimeter.
▸▸ Use and interpret maps and scale drawings.
▸▸ Use proportional reasoning to solve a problem.
▸▸ Represent problems and synthesise information in geometric form.
▸▸ Present a concise, reasoned argument.

Shapes can be transformed to make attractive patterns.

Before you start

You should know how to ...
1 Reflect, rotate, translate and enlarge a shape.

2 Identify 3-D shapes.

3 Calculate with ratios, including mixed units.

Check in
1 Copy the diagram. Plot the image of △ABC after these transformations:
 a Reflect in the y-axis.
 b Rotate 90° clockwise about the origin.
 c Translate by $\begin{pmatrix} 3 \\ -4 \end{pmatrix}$.

2 Name these shapes:
 a   b   c

3 Reduce these ratios to their simplest terms:
 a 5:20 b 14:35 c 25:40 d 24:92

147

Unit commentary

Aim of the unit
The unit aims to develop students' understanding of transformations, including enlargements. The unit develops the ideas of congruence and similarity and students go on to use proportional reasoning in interpreting maps and scales. There is a section on planes of symmetry of 3-D shapes.

Introduction
Discuss what students understand by the term 'transformation'.
Encourage them to give examples of how a shape can be transformed.
An example of moving around bedroom furniture can be useful as it is often within students' experience.

Framework references
This unit focuses on:
Teaching objectives pages:
79–81, 203–207, 209, 213–217.
Problem solving pages:
15, 27, 29, 31.

Differentiation

Support tier
Focuses on bearings, combinations of transformations, and enlargements leading to scale drawings and ratio.

Extension tier
Focuses on transformations, extending to enlargement by fractional scale factors, congruence, similarity, and scale and proportion.

Check in activity

Who am I?
Students work in pairs and take turns.
One student describes a 3-D shape from a box of solids using geometric terms.
Encourage use of faces, edges, vertices and views.
The other student sketches the shape (or picks it out of the box of solids) and names it.

Mental starter

What's my line?
Give students three or four coordinates from a straight line, such as:
$y = 3$ $\qquad$ $x = {}^-2$ $\qquad$ $y = x$
Students plot the points on an **R8** coordinate grid, then name the line.

Useful resources

R8 – coordinate grid
R35 – diagrams for exercise
Squared paper
Cut-out triangle (R14)
Cut-out parallelogram for plenary (**R15**)

Introductory activity

Refer to the mental starter.
Discuss the equation of a line that is parallel to the x-axis or the y-axis, and of the line $y = x$.
Emphasise that on the line $y = x$, x-coordinate = y-coordinate.

Place a cut-out of a triangle on an OHP of a coordinate grid (R8).
Encourage students to write down the coordinates of the vertices.
Move the triangle using a translation.
Discuss how to describe the move.
Encourage use of technical language: translation.
Emphasise that it has exactly the same orientation but has moved a distance parallel to each axis.
Discuss how to write down the precise movement.
Emphasise the convention: go across then up.

Repeat for a reflection – flip over the original triangle.
Discuss how to describe the move.
Emphasise that you need to give a line of reflection, or mirror line.

Repeat for a rotation – turn the original triangle.
Emphasise that you need to give a centre, and an angle and direction.

Encourage students to write down the coordinates of the vertices following a given transformation.
Discuss answers, using the triangle and grid as a visual aid.

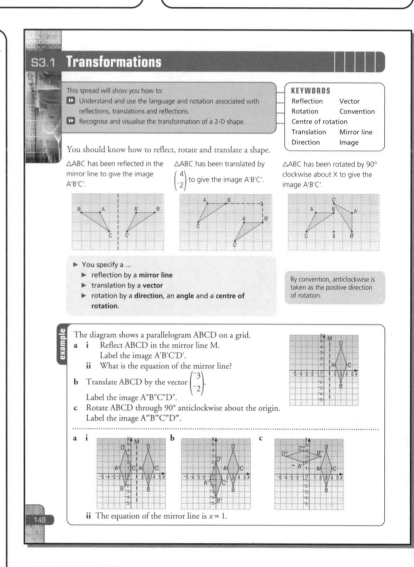

Plenary

Place a cut-out parallelogram on the coordinate grid.
Coordinates: (2, 0) (5, 0) (4, 2) (1, 2).
Challenge students to give the coordinates of the vertices following:

▶ A translation by $\begin{pmatrix} {}^-4 \\ 3 \end{pmatrix}$ $\qquad$ ▶ A reflection in the line $y = {}^-2$

▶ A rotation by 90° clockwise, centre (0, 0).
Discuss how the results describe the symmetry of the parallelogram.

Further activities

Students could investigate the shapes made by reflecting a triangle in each of its sides.

Differentiation

Core questions:
The exercise is a review of Year 8 work.
▶ Question 1 focuses on reflection.
▶ Question 2 focuses on rotation.
▶ Question 3 involves all three transformations.

Extension tier: focuses on reviewing transformations.

Support tier: focuses on finding bearings.

Exercise S3.1

1 Make five copies of this diagram.

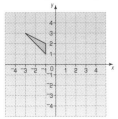

Using a new copy of the diagram each time, reflect the triangle in each of these mirror lines.
a $x = ^-1$ b $y = 2$
c $x = 1$ d the x-axis
e the y-axis.

2 Make six copies of this diagram.

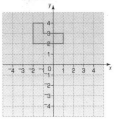

Using a new copy of the diagram each time, draw the image after each of these rotations.
a 90° clockwise about (1, 2)
b $\frac{1}{2}$ turn about (1, 3)
c $\frac{1}{2}$ turn about (0, 0)
d 90° clockwise about (0, 0)
e 90° anticlockwise about ($^-$2, 2)
f $\frac{1}{2}$ turn about ($^-$1, $^-$2).

3 Make three copies of this diagram.

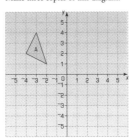

On the first copy:
a Reflect shape A in the x-axis.
   Label the reflection B.
b Reflect A in the y-axis.
   Label the reflection C.

On the second copy:
c Rotate A by $\frac{1}{4}$ turn anticlockwise, centre (0, 0).
   Label the rotation P.
d Rotate A by $\frac{1}{4}$ turn clockwise, centre (0, 0).
   Label the rotation Q.
e Rotate A by $\frac{1}{2}$ turn, centre (1, 0).
   Label the rotation R.

On the third copy:
f Translate A using the vector $\begin{pmatrix} 5 \\ -2 \end{pmatrix}$.
   Label the translation X.

g Translate X using the vector $\begin{pmatrix} -2 \\ 6 \end{pmatrix}$.
   Label the translation Y.

h What translation will move Y back to A?

149

Exercise commentary

The questions assess objectives on Framework Pages 203 and 209.

Problem solving
The exercise assesses objectives on Framework Page 27.

Group work
The exercise is suitable for paired work.

Misconceptions
Students often mix up the equations of lines, using $y = 2$ instead of $x = 2$. Encourage students to write down two or three points on the line before deciding on the equation.
Students often find rotations difficult. Encourage them to turn the page to help visualise where the image will be. Emphasise that the vertices will be the same distance from the centre throughout. Students may find it useful to visualise a circle, passing through each vertex using the same centre.

Links
Coordinates: Framework Page 219.

Homework

S3.1HW gives more practice in carrying out the three transformations on a coordinate grid.

Revision

Students should work through S1 in the 5–7 Revision Book.

Answers

1

2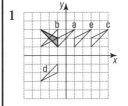

3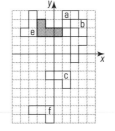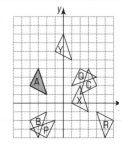

3h ($^-$3, $^-$4)

149

S3.2 Describing transformations

Mental starter

Give me another

Draw a scalene triangle on a grid (**R8**) on OHP.

Ask students to work in small groups (of three to five) to find the coordinates of the shape following a transformation of their choice. Each group shows their image on the OHP and challenges the others to find the transformation.

Useful resources

R8 – coordinate grid
S3.2OHP – example from the Students' Book

Introductory activity

Refer to the mental starter.

Discuss how to spot which transformation is which.

Emphasise that the movements are sliding, turning and flipping over.

Discuss the information that you need to give to ensure the position of the image is uniquely defined.

Discuss what all the shapes have in common.

Emphasise that they are all exactly the same shape and size, just different orientations.

Encourage students to remember the technical term: congruent.

Discuss the example in the Students' Book shown on **S3.2OHP**.

Encourage students to suggest congruent shapes.

Emphasise that all the shapes are congruent.

Discuss how to map pairs of shapes onto each other.

Encourage students to give full and precise definitions.

Emphasise that you can map the image back onto the object and record ways of doing this so students can generalise.

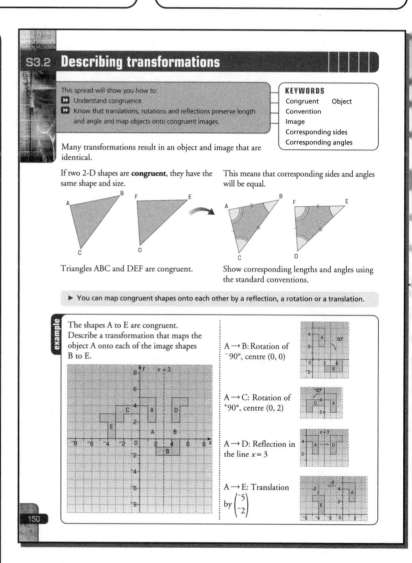

Plenary

Draw these parallelograms on a coordinate grid (**R8**).

1 Coordinates: (2, 0) (5, 0) (4, 2) (1, 2)
2 Coordinates: (⁻2, ⁻2) (⁻1, ⁻4) (⁻4, ⁻4) (⁻5, ⁻2)

Discuss the transformation that would map shape 1 onto shape 2.

Encourage students to find more than one way [translation or rotation of 180° about (0, ⁻1)].

Discuss how to ensure that only one of the transformations is defined by the image – label the vertices ABCD and A′B′C′D′.

Further activities

Students could make up a problem like question 3, using congruent shapes, for a partner to solve.

Differentiation

Core questions:
▸ Question 1 revises congruence.
▸ Questions 2 and 3 focus on describing transformations.
▸ Question 4 involves drawing shapes following given transformations.

Extension tier: focuses on reviewing enlargement work from Year 8.

Support tier: focuses on simple transformations.

Exercise S3.2

1 Which of these shapes are congruent?

2 The diagram shows six congruent triangles labelled A to F.
Describe these transformations:
   a A to B
   b B to C
   c E to F
   d C to E
   e C to B
   f B to A.

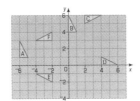

3 The diagram shows six congruent shapes labelled A to G.

A is the object.

Match each of these transformations with the correct image.
   a reflection in $x = {}^-1$
   b rotation 90° clockwise about (0, 0)
   c reflection in $y = 0$
   d rotation 180° anticlockwise about (0, 0)
   e reflection in $y = 3$
   f translation with vector $\begin{pmatrix} 1 \\ -3 \end{pmatrix}$.

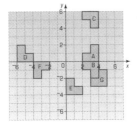

4 Copy the diagram and draw these transformations of shape A:
   a reflection in $y = 2$ (label B)
   b reflection in $x = 2$ (label C)
   c 180° rotation about (0, 0) (label D)
   d translation with vector $\begin{pmatrix} 8 \\ -4 \end{pmatrix}$ (label E)
   e rotation 90° clockwise, centre (0, 2) (label F).

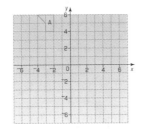

151

Exercise commentary

The questions assess objectives on Framework Page 203.

Problem solving
Questions 2–4 assess objectives on Framework Page 27.

Group work
The exercise is suitable for paired work.

Misconceptions
Students often fail to give a complete description of a transformation, particularly a rotation.
Emphasise that there are three pieces of information needed to specify a rotation: angle, direction and centre – it's as easy as ADC.
The acronym CARD may be useful.
Students can discuss their strategies as a class.
Students may not recognise that $y = 0$ is in fact the x-axis.
Encourage them to plot a few points to help them visualise the line.

Links
Straight-line graphs: Framework Pages 165–167.

Homework

S3.2HW give more practice in drawing and identifying transformations.

Revision

Students should work through S2 in the 5–7 Revision Book.

Answers

1 A and B
2 a Translation $\binom{6}{3}$
   b Rotation of ${}^-90°$, centre (2, 4)
   c Reflection in $y = 1$
   d Rotation of 180°, centre (0, 2) ✗
   e Rotation of ${}^+90°$, centre (2, 4)
   f Translation $\binom{-6}{-3}$
3 a D **b** E **c** B **d** F **e** C **f** G

4

2 reflections

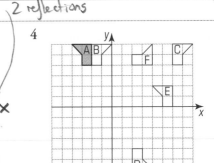

151

S3.3 Combining transformations

Useful resources

R8 – coordinate grids

Introductory activity

Refer to the mental starter.
Discuss what students notice about the orientation of each image.
Encourage them to make generalisations – you may need to combine results to show to the class.
Emphasise that if you:
▸ Reflect a shape with line symmetry it looks the same as a translation.
▸ Rotate a shape with rotational symmetry it looks the same as a translation.

Emphasise that there is often more than one way to get back to the original object following a series of transformations.

Give students the coordinates of a shape to plot on a grid (R8):
(1, 1) (4, 1) (3, 1).
Encourage them to reflect the shape in $x = 1$ then in $y = ^-1$.
Discuss how to get back to the object: 180° rotation centre (1, $^-$1).

With the same object, students now reflect it in the x-axis then rotate clockwise through 90°, centre (0, 0).
Discuss how to get back to the object: reflect in $y = ^-x$.

Discuss what would happen if you change the order of the transformations.
Encourage students to repeat the previous transformations but in a different order.
Discuss results.

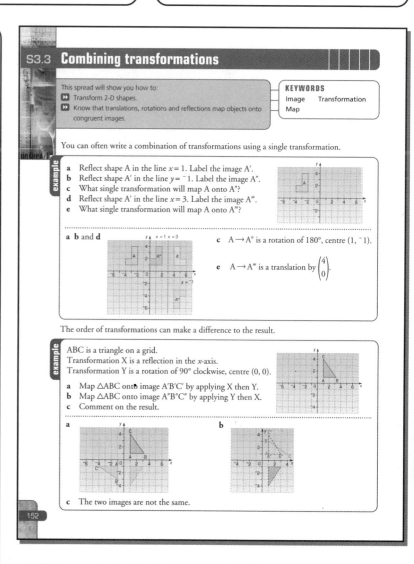

S3.3 Combining transformations

This spread will show you how to:
▶▶ Transform 2-D shapes.
▶▶ Know that translations, rotations and reflections map objects onto congruent images.

KEYWORDS
Image   Transformation
Map

You can often write a combination of transformations using a single transformation.

example

a Reflect shape A in the line $x = 1$. Label the image A′.
b Reflect shape A′ in the line $y = ^-1$. Label the image A″.
c What single transformation will map A onto A″?
d Reflect shape A′ in the line $x = 3$. Label the image A‴.
e What single transformation will map A onto A‴?

a b and d

c A → A″ is a rotation of 180°, centre (1, $^-$1).

e A → A‴ is a translation by $\binom{4}{0}$.

The order of transformations can make a difference to the result.

example

ABC is a triangle on a grid.
Transformation X is a reflection in the x-axis.
Transformation Y is a rotation of 90° clockwise, centre (0, 0).

a Map △ABC onto image A′B′C′ by applying X then Y.
b Map △ABC onto image A″B″C″ by applying Y then X.
c Comment on the result.

a

b

c The two images are not the same.

152

Plenary

Students draw the rectangle with coordinates
(0, 0) (0, 3) (3, 2) (2, 0) on a grid and label it A. They could:
▸ Reflect A in $y = 2$ and label it B.
▸ Rotate B 90° clockwise, centre (0, 0) and label it C.
▸ Rotate A 90° clockwise, centre (0, 0) and label it D.
▸ Reflect D in $y = 2$ and label it E.
Discuss results.

Further activities

In **S3.3ICT** students practise investigating combinations of transformations using a geometry package.

Alternatively

Students could transform the shapes in questions 1, 4 and 5 by using a combination of transformations and ask a partner to identify the transformations used. Is there a single transformation that is equivalent?

Differentiation

Core questions:

▶ Questions 1 and 2 are straightforward combined reflections.
▶ Questions 3–5 focus on combining transformations, including reflections overlapping the mirror line.
▶ Question 6 and 7 invite students to generalise.

Extension tier: focuses on identifying congruent triangles and explaining the reasons.

Support tier: focuses on transformations and combinations of them.

Exercise S3.3

1 Copy the diagram.

  a Reflect shape A in the y-axis and label the new shape A'.
  b Reflect A' in the x-axis and label it A".
  c What single transformation will transform A to A"?

2 Repeat question 1 but change the order of the transformations:

  ▶ Reflect shape A in the x-axis and label the new shape A'.
  ▶ Reflect A' in the y-axis and label it A".

  What do you notice?

3 Copy the diagram.

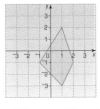

  a Reflect the quadrilateral in the x-axis.
  b Use colour to show which lines and angles are equal in size.

4 Copy the diagram.

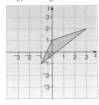

  a Reflect the triangle in the x-axis.
  b Reflect both shapes in the y-axis.
  c Use colour to show which lines and angles are equal in size.

5 Copy the diagram.

  a Rotate the flag F through 90° clockwise centre (0, 0) and label the new flag F'.
  b Reflect F' in the x-axis and label it F".
  c Show that F can be transformed to F" by reflection in $y = x$.
  d Describe other ways of transforming F to F".

6 Investigate combinations of reflections, for example the effect of a reflection in $x = 2$ followed by a reflection in $y = 2$.

7 Investigate combinations of rotations. What single transformation is equivalent to two rotations?

Exercise commentary

The questions assess objectives on Framework Pages 203 and 205.

Problem solving

Questions 1–5 assess objectives on Framework Page 27.
Questions 6 and 7 assess Page 15.

Group work

The exercise is suitable for group work.

Misconceptions

It is easy to lose track of the various images once the diagrams start to get complicated. Encourage students to label an image carefully before moving on to the next part.
Students need to read the questions carefully to ensure they are transforming the required shape.

Links

Straight-line graphs: Framework Pages 165–169.

Homework

S3.3HW focuses on the effect of combining transformations, and whether the order of reflections is important.

Revision

Students should work through S3 in the 5–7 Revision Book.

Answers

1 a, b Appropriate reflections
  c Reflection in $y = x$ or rotation of 180°, centre (0, 0)
2 The order does not matter.   **3, 4** Appropriate reflections
5 Appropriate reflections
  d For example, by 90° anticlockwise then reflection
6 Reflection in two perpendicular lines is equivalent to a half turn rotation.
7 A rotation through the combined angle.

Symmetrical shapes

Ask students to sketch three shapes with:

▶ 0 lines of symmetry
▶ 1 line of symmetry
▶ 2 lines of symmetry
▶ 3 or more lines of symmetry.

Useful resources

R14 – triangles
R15 – quadrilaterals
R16 – 3-D shapes
Set of solids
Multilink cubes for the plenary

Introductory activity

Refer to the mental starter.
Discuss any other 2-D shapes that have line symmetry.
Check that students recognise all the line symmetries of triangles and quadrilaterals – **R14** and **R15** may be useful.

Use a set of solids or show **R16**.
Ask students to name a solid shape which is symmetrical.
Encourage students to describe the symmetry as precisely as possible.
Emphasise that rather than a line, the symmetry of the 3-D shape is shown by a cross-section – a cut directly through the shape.
Emphasise that this cut results in two congruent 2-D shapes, called planes.

Encourage students to describe cross-sections of the shape that are not planes of symmetry.
Emphasise that the planes may be congruent but that the two halves of the 3-D shape must be exactly the same shape and size too.

Discuss the symmetry of shapes that have the same cross-section throughout their length: prisms.
Encourage students to generalise: all prisms have at least one plane of symmetry.

Discuss pyramids.
Emphasise that the symmetry will depend on the shape of the base and the position of the apex.

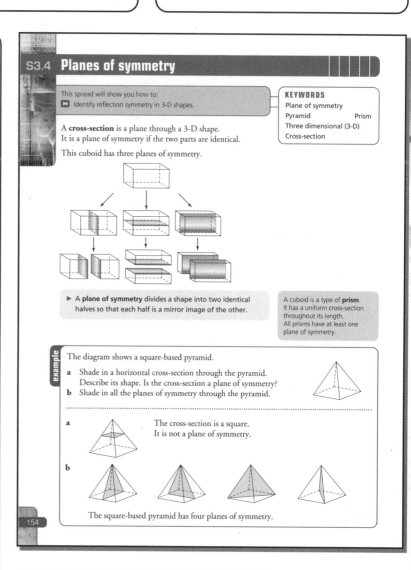

S3.4 Planes of symmetry

This spread will show you how to:
▶ Identify reflection symmetry in 3-D shapes.

KEYWORDS
Plane of symmetry
Pyramid   Prism
Three dimensional (3-D)
Cross-section

A **cross-section** is a plane through a 3-D shape.
It is a plane of symmetry if the two parts are identical.

This cuboid has three planes of symmetry.

▶ A **plane of symmetry** divides a shape into two identical halves so that each half is a mirror image of the other.

A cuboid is a type of **prism**. It has a uniform cross-section throughout its length. All prisms have at least one plane of symmetry.

example

The diagram shows a square-based pyramid.
a Shade in a horizontal cross-section through the pyramid. Describe its shape. Is the cross-section a plane of symmetry?
b Shade in all the planes of symmetry through the pyramid.

a The cross-section is a square. It is not a plane of symmetry.

b

The square-based pyramid has four planes of symmetry.

154

Plenary

Students work in groups.
Each group has four multilink cubes.
Challenge them to find as many different 3-D shapes as they can and to identify any planes of symmetry.

Further activities

Students could use four multilink cubes to make as many different shapes as possible. For each shape they should identify any planes of symmetry. Which shapes are mirror images of each other?

Differentiation

Core questions:
▸ Question 1 revises lines of symmetry.
▸ Questions 2–5 focus on describing symmetries and planes for 3-D shapes.
▸ Question 6 extends to include a cone.

Extension tier: focuses on identifying similar triangles.

Support tier: focuses on symmetry and geometrical properties of shapes.

Exercise S3.4

1 Copy these shapes and draw in any lines of symmetry.

a
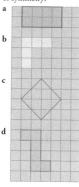
b

c

d

2 Make sketches to show the planes of symmetry of these shapes:

a cube

b triangular prism

c regular tetrahedron

d regular octahedron.

3 There are many ways to slice a cube.

Can you slice a cube so that the cross-section is:
a a square
b a rectangle
c a triangle
d a circle
e a pentagon
f a hexagon?
Give reasons for your answers.

4 Repeat question 3 using a cuboid rather than a cube.

5 Investigate other 2-D shapes you can make when you slice other 3-D shapes.

6 You can slice a cone in many different ways:

Explain how to slice a cone so that the cross-section is:
a a circle
b an isosceles triangle
c an oval.

Exercise commentary

The questions assess objectives on Framework Page 207.

Problem solving
Questions 3 and 4 assess objectives on Framework Page 31.

Group work
The exercise is suitable for group work.

Misconceptions
Students often find it difficult to visualise planes of 3-D shapes.
Having a set of solids available should help.
Students need to remember the vocabulary and properties of 2-D shapes.
Prominent posters displaying the various shapes are a useful reference.

Links
Properties of shapes: Framework Pages 185–189.

Homework

S3.4HW focuses on sketching planes of symmetry of 3-D shapes, and slicing shapes to give different cross-sections.

Revision

Students should work through S4 in the 5–7 Revision Book.

Answers

1 Number of lines of symmetry: **a** 2 **b** 1 **c** 4 **d** none
2 Number of planes of symmetry: **a** 5 **b** 4 **c** 3 **d** 5
3 **a** Yes **b** Yes **c** Yes **d** No **e** Yes **f** Yes
4 **a** Yes **b** Yes **c** Yes **d** No **e** Yes **f** Yes
5 Student's own answers
6 **a** Parallel to the base **b** Through the vertex, perpendicular to the base **c** Entirely through the curved surface, not parallel to the base

155

155

S3.5 Enlargement and similarity

Mental starter

What's my shape?
Give students a plane of symmetry (a rectangle) and ask them to sketch a 3-D shape with that plane of symmetry.
Discuss results.
Repeat for other planes: circle, isosceles triangle, equilateral triangle.
Challenge students to find other shapes with the same plane of symmetry.

Useful resources

S3.5OHP – diagram from the Students' Book example
A3 paper for the plenary
Squared paper
Photocopied shapes for Further activities

Introductory activity

Discuss the diagram in the example in the Students' Book shown on **S3.5OHP**.
Encourage students to describe the relationship between the two shapes.
Expect responses such as 'it's bigger'.
Discuss what is meant by 'bigger'.
Emphasise that you want a precise relationship – how much bigger?
Encourage students to explain their reasoning.

Encourage the use of technical terms: proportion, enlargement.
Discuss what students understand by the term 'enlargement'.
Referring to photograph sizes is a useful example that students often understand.
Discuss the features of an enlargement.
Emphasise that corresponding lengths are in the same proportion.

Discuss the scale factor of the enlargement from the example.
Emphasise that this gives the number of times the enlargement is bigger.

Discuss whether there is any other information you need to specify the position of the enlargement exactly.
Sketch the enlargement on another part of the grid to illustrate it is not uniquely specified by size.
Emphasise that you find the centre by joining corresponding vertices as for rotations.

Discuss how to describe shapes that are enlargements of each other – they are not congruent but similar.

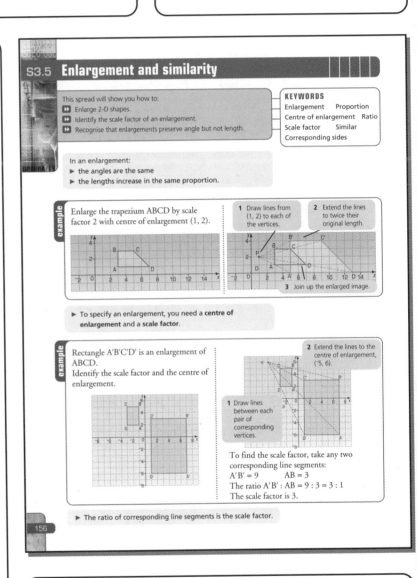

Plenary

Encourage students to work in groups.
They have an A3 piece of paper and measure the edges.
They fold it in half and measure the edges.
They then fold it in half again and measure the edges.

Discuss the scale factor of enlargement in each case.
Challenge students to estimate the area of each size.
Discuss the scale factor of the areas.

Further activities

Students could look at enlarged simple shapes from a photocopier and estimate the scale factor of the enlargement as accurately as possible.

Differentiation

Core questions:
▶ Question 1 focuses on the effect of an enlargement on dimensions.
▶ Questions 2–4 focus on describing and drawing enlargements.
▶ Questions 5 and 6 focus on the effect of an enlargement on the perimeter and area of a shape.

Extension tier: focuses on drawing enlargements, and finding the centre and scale factor of an enlargement.
Support tier: focuses on simple enlargements, with and without a centre.

Exercise S3.5

1 Write down the dimensions of this book following an enlargement of 10%.
[Its size is 246 mm × 189 mm.]

2 Copy these diagrams onto squared paper and draw enlargements with the given scale factor and centre, C.

a   b

Scale factor 3   Scale factor 2

c   d

Scale factor 3   Scale factor 3

3 Copy this grid four times.

Using a new grid each time, draw each of these enlargements of shape R:
a scale factor of 2, centre (0, 0)
b scale factor of 2, centre (1, 1)
c scale factor of 3, centre (⁻1, 0)
d scale factor of 2, centre (⁻2, ⁻2).

4 Find the scale factor and the coordinates of the centre of enlargement.
The small shape in each case is the object.

a

b

5 **Investigation**
a Sketch three triangles which are similar to this one.

Enlargements are similar shapes.

b Find the perimeter of each triangle in part **a**.
What do you notice?
c Draw some other simple shapes and enlarge them to different scale factors. Investigate the relationship between enlargement and perimeter.

6 A shape has an area of 12 cm² and a perimeter of 14 cm.
Find the area and perimeter of the shape following an enlargement with scale factor 3.

157

Exercise commentary

The questions assess objectives on Framework Page 213.

Problem solving
Questions 5 and 6 assess objectives on Framework Page 29.

Group work
The exercise is suitable for paired work.

Misconceptions
Some students misinterpret the scale factor, making the area twice as big for a scale factor of 2.
Emphasise that a scale factor of 2 means all lengths will be twice as long. Encourage students can use the method of counting squares to check.

Links
Maps and scales: Framework Page 217.
Ratio and proportion: Pages 79–81.

Homework

S3.5HW gives more practice in drawing enlargements on squared grids, and identifying centres and scale factors of enlargements.

Revision

Students should work through S5 in the 5–7 Revision Book.

Answers

1 270.6 mm by 207.9 mm
2, 3 Grids with appropriate enlargement
4 a Scale factor 2, centre (1, 6)   b Scale factor 2, centre (3, 4)
5 a Sketches of similar triangles.
   b The scale factor for the perimeter is the same as the enlargement scale factor.
   c Student's own investigation
6 Area = 108 cm², perimeter = 42 cm

S3.6 Scale and proportion

Mental starter

Imagine a journey

Ask students to draw sketches for these journeys:

▶ Start at a bus stop. Go straight for 2 km. Turn right. Go straight for 400 m then turn left. Go straight for 880 m then turn left. The bus stop is 60 m along this road.

▶ Start at a port. Go straight for 50 km. Turn on a bearing of 120°. Go straight for 80 km. Turn on a bearing of 060° for 35 km to the port.

Useful resources

S3.6OHP – map for the plenary. It is better to use a map of your local area if possible.
Rulers
String for the plenary

Introductory activity

Refer to the mental starter.
Check that students remember the conventions regarding bearings – you may want to revise them quickly in between the two examples.
Discuss how you could draw an accurate diagram of each journey.
Emphasise that you need to use a scale.

Discuss an appropriate scale to use in each situation.
Emphasise that a scale should be easy to use and allow the diagram to fit into the required size.

Discuss each of the suggested scales. Encourage students to convert each of the measures into the scale, explaining each step.

Discuss other scales such as 2 cm to 5 km and 1.5 cm to 1 m.
Encourage students to explain their methods for converting between the scales. Emphasise the use of the unitary method as shown in the first example.

Discuss how to write each of the scales as a ratio with no units.
Emphasise that you need to convert the distances to use the same measure.

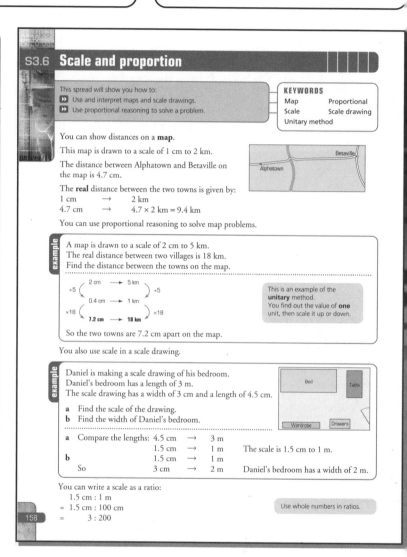

Plenary

Use a map of your local area, or use **S3.6OHP**.
Discuss what 1 cm represents on the map.
Discuss how to find the distance from home to school.
Emphasise that you need to define which distance first – as the crow flies (use a ruler) or by road (use string).
Use the scale to work out the distance in m.
Repeat for other journeys.

Further activities

Students could work in pairs to make an accurate scale drawing of the classroom.

Differentiation

Core questions:

▶ Question 1 focuses on calculating real-life distances from a map.
▶ Questions 2–5 focus on interpreting scales on maps and diagrams.
▶ Questions 6–8 are more challenging problems involving scale.

Extension tier: focuses on making and interpreting accurate scale drawings.

Support tier: focuses on using scale ratios to interpret scale drawings.

Exercise S3.6

1   Here is a map of Luppitt village.
    The scale is 4 cm to 1 km.

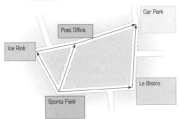

a   How far is it from the Sports Field to the Ice Rink?
b   How far is it from the Post Office to the Car Park?
c   Sarah walks from the Post Office to the Bistro by the shortest route. How far has she walked?
d   A new map is made using a scale of 2 cm to 1 km. On the map, what will be the distance from the Sports Field to the Ice Rink?

2   The scale on a map is 1 cm to 2 km.
a   If the distance between York and Scarborough is 60 km, find the distance between the towns on the map.
b   On the map, the distance between Scalby and Ravenscar is 5.5 cm. Find the actual distance.
c   Write the scale in the form 1 : n.

The scale of a map is 2 cm to 5 km.

d   If the distance between Poole and Plymouth is 100 km, find the distance between the towns on the map.
e   On the map, the distance between Plymouth and Taunton is 8.5 cm. Find the actual distance.
f   Write the scale in the form 1 : n.

For questions 3 to 8, look at this plan of a garden.
It is drawn to a scale of 0.5 cm to represent 2 m.

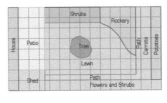

3   How long and wide is the garden?

4   Find the area of the garden, and the area of the lawn in m^2.

5   How wide is the path in cm?

6   Paving slabs come in three sizes:
    2 feet × 3 feet, 2 feet × 2 feet, and 2 feet × 1 foot.
    (1 foot is about 30 cm)
a   Which slabs would be best to use to cover the patio?
b   How many slabs are needed?

7   When the tree is fully grown the diameter of the branches will be about 3 m.
    This means that the tree should be at least 5 m from the house.
    Is the tree planted too near the house?

8   Carrots should be planted in rows 20 cm apart.
    How many rows of carrots can be planted longways in the carrot bed?

159

Exercise commentary

The questions assess objectives on Framework Pages 79–81 and 217.

Problem solving

Questions 5, 6 and 8 assess objectives on Framework Page 29.

Group work

The exercise is suitable for paired work.

Misconceptions

Students will often confuse units, in particular mixing the units from a map with the real-life distance.
Encourage students to think about the size and suitability of an answer before deciding on the units.
Emphasise the real-life unit will be the larger one and the diagram unit will be smaller (this is the case on Key Stage 3 papers).

Links

Enlargement: Framework Page 213.

Homework

S3.6HW focuses on measuring and interpreting lengths on a scale drawing and making an accurate scale drawing.

Revision

Students should work through S6 in the 5–7 Revision Book.

Answers

1 a 550 m   b 775 m   c 1.5 km   d 1.1 cm
2 a 30 cm   b 11 km   c 1 : 200 000   d 40 cm
  e 21.25 km   f 1 : 250 000
3 28 m × 16 m   4 448 m^2, 160 m^2
5 100 cm   6 a 2 feet × 3 feet   b 120 slabs
7 No   8 10 rows

Summary

The key objectives for this unit are:
- ▶ Know that translations, rotations and reflections preserve length and angle and map objects onto congruent images. (203–207)
- ▶ Use proportional reasoning to solve a problem. (79–81)
- ▶ Present a concise, reasoned argument using symbols and related explanatory text. (31)

Plenary activity

Discuss the symmetries of real objects, such as a (symmetrical) building, different shaped food packaging, items in the classroom, etc.

Discuss suitable scales for drawing a map/plan of the classroom/school/neighbourhood.

Check out commentary

1 Emphasise that reflection, rotation and translation transform a shape to a congruent shape, which helps in drawing the image.
Tracing paper may help with the rotation. There are two possible answers for part **c**.

2 Emphasise that reflections do not change the proportions of the shape as images are always congruent. Different colours for the different images may be helpful. Images D and E are identical.

3 Encourage students to draw diagrams and explain clearly what each shows. Encourage them to build up their reasoning by first showing one possible line, then two, etc.

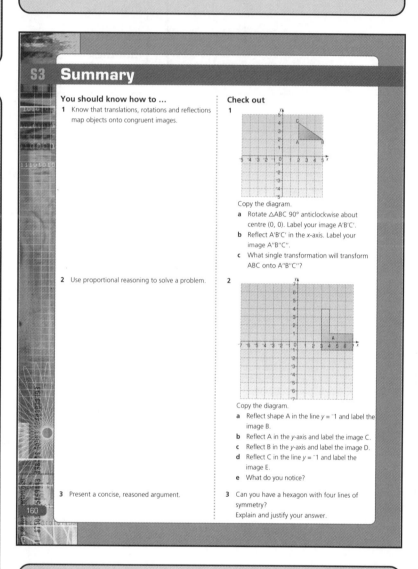

S3 Summary

You should know how to ...

1 Know that translations, rotations and reflections map objects onto congruent images.

2 Use proportional reasoning to solve a problem.

3 Present a concise, reasoned argument.

Check out

1

Copy the diagram.
a Rotate △ABC 90° anticlockwise about centre (0, 0). Label your image A'B'C'.
b Reflect A'B'C' in the x-axis. Label your image A"B"C".
c What single transformation will transform ABC onto A"B"C"?

2

Copy the diagram.
a Reflect shape A in the line $y = {}^-1$ and label the image B.
b Reflect A in the y-axis and label the image C.
c Reflect B in the y-axis and label the image D.
d Reflect C in the line $y = {}^-1$ and label the image E.
e What do you notice?

3 Can you have a hexagon with four lines of symmetry?
Explain and justify your answer.

160

Development

The work on prisms, and maps and scales is developed in **S4**.
Students will revise transformations in **P1**.

Links

The work on maps and scales can be applied practically in everyday life and in other subjects, particularly geography.
The transformations and symmetry work has links to technology.

Revision

This unit is covered in S7 of the 5–7 Revision Book.
Students should revise S8–S12 in the 5–7 Revision Book. They should also revise the work of the last three units, unless they have already done so: N2, N3, A5, A6, D7, D8, D9 and S7.

Mental starters

Objectives covered in this unit:

▶ Count on or back in steps.
▶ Order, add, subtract, multiply and divide integers and fractions.
▶ Know and use squares, cubes, roots and index notation.
▶ Convert between fractions, decimals and percentages.
▶ Find the outcomes of a given percentage increase of decrease.
▶ Recall multiplication and division facts.
▶ Use known facts to derive unknown facts.
▶ Visualise, describe and sketch 2-D shapes.
▶ Solve simple problems involving probabilities.
▶ Apply mental skills to solve simple problems.

Resources needed

* means class set needed
Essential:
P1.0OHP – problem-solving cycle
Counting stick
Key Stage 3 questions*
Useful:
P1.1OHP – bicycle example
P1.2OHP – probability example
P1.3OHP – algebra example
P1.4OHP – proportion example
P1.5OHP – geometry example and proof
P1.6OHP – checking results example
Recipes
Dice   R1 – digit cards

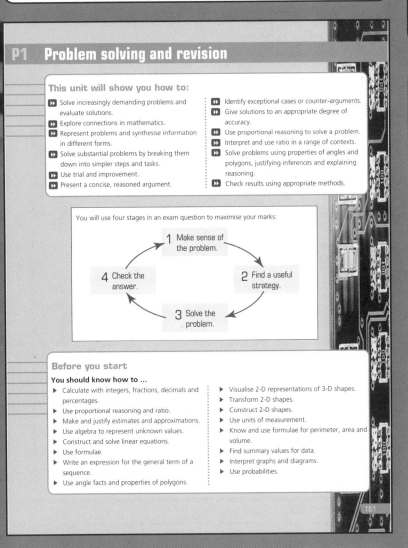

P1   Problem solving and revision

This unit will show you how to:

▶▶ Solve increasingly demanding problems and evaluate solutions.
▶▶ Explore connections in mathematics.
▶▶ Represent problems and synthesise information in different forms.
▶▶ Solve substantial problems by breaking them down into simpler steps and tasks.
▶▶ Use trial and improvement.
▶▶ Present a concise, reasoned argument.

▶▶ Identify exceptional cases or counter-arguments.
▶▶ Give solutions to an appropriate degree of accuracy.
▶▶ Use proportional reasoning to solve a problem.
▶▶ Interpret and use ratio in a range of contexts.
▶▶ Solve problems using properties of angles and polygons, justifying inferences and explaining reasoning.
▶▶ Check results using appropriate methods.

You will use four stages in an exam question to maximise your marks:

1 Make sense of the problem.
2 Find a useful strategy.
3 Solve the problem.
4 Check the answer.

Before you start

You should know how to ...

▶ Calculate with integers, fractions, decimals and percentages.
▶ Use proportional reasoning and ratio.
▶ Make and justify estimates and approximations.
▶ Use algebra to represent unknown values.
▶ Construct and solve linear equations.
▶ Use formulae.
▶ Write an expression for the general term of a sequence.
▶ Use angle facts and properties of polygons.

▶ Visualise 2-D representations of 3-D shapes.
▶ Transform 2-D shapes.
▶ Construct 2-D shapes.
▶ Use units of measurement.
▶ Know and use formulae for perimeter, area and volume.
▶ Find summary values for data.
▶ Interpret graphs and diagrams.
▶ Use probabilities.

Unit commentary

Aim of the unit

The unit focuses on the development and use of key strategies for solving problems. The last three lessons concentrate on using these skills in solving problems involving proportional or geometrical reasoning, and on methods for checking answers.

Introduction

Discuss the use of mathematics in 'real life', and use examples from building engineering, banking, advertising, etc. Encourage students to discuss examples they have seen, including from other subjects. Emphasise that one of the most important aspects of mathematics is to solve problems in different contexts.

Framework references:

Teaching objectives pages:
3–29, 31, 79–81, 185–187
Problem solving pages:
5, 7, 17, 21, 23–25, 29, 31

Check in activity

Write a calcualtion on the board, for example:
8.6 ÷ 2 = 4.3
Encourage students to think of 'word' problems this calculation could represent. For example, 8.6 m of fabric is cut into two equal lengths.
Discuss suggestions and try more complex initial calculations.

Differentiation

Support tier

Focuses on problem-solving techniques, problems involving geometrical and proportional reasoning, reading information from tables and checking results.

Extension tier

Focuses on using the same skills in more complex problems. The last lesson considers appropriate degrees of accuracy.

P1.1 Making sense of the problem

Mental starter

Quick quiz

Ask these questions in order, and give students ten seconds to work out each answer:

$140 - 67$; Value of $3x - 7$ when $x = 5$; 10% of £345; Area of a triangle 6 cm base by 4 cm height [draw on the board]; The ratio of men to women in a room is 4 : 3. If there are 52 men, how many women are there?; $(0.6)^2$; If $3x - y = 11$, what is the value of $9x - 3y$; Mean of 14, 13, 16 and 17.

Useful resources

P1.0OHP – problem-solving cycle
P1.1OHP – Students' book example
Key Stage 3 questions

Introductory activity

Discuss **P1.0OHP**, which shows the problem-solving cycle. Emphasise that this method of approaching a problem will help students answer questions during an exam.

Discuss the first part of the cycle, and emphasise that it is important to understand what a question is asking.

Discuss the example in the Students' Book, on P1.1OHP. Discuss that you are going to work through the problem-solving cycle, using this problem as an example.

Challenge students to work in pairs to work out exactly what the question is asking them to find. Discuss answers, Emphasise the **quantity** to find, and the **units**. [Part a – distance in cm; part b – number, no units.]

Encourage students to next write down the information that they need from the question and any formulae they have to use. Discuss answers. Encourage students to use numerical shorthand for information and formulae:

▶ Circumference = πd.

Challenge students to solve the problem. Discuss methods and strategies with the whole class.

Challenge students to solve a set of Key Stage 3 questions following the strategies in the cycle.

Emphasise:

▶ Read the problem.
▶ Identify what you need to find.
▶ Write down information in shorthand, including formulae.

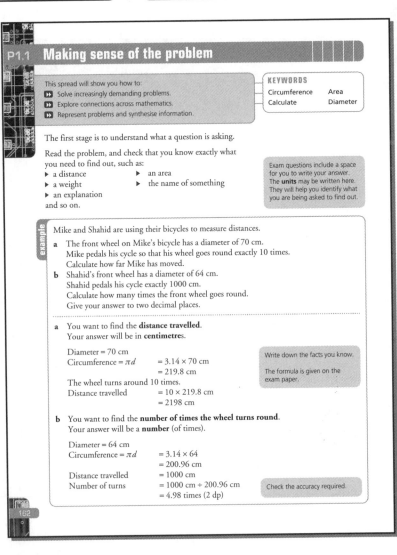

Plenary

Remind students of the problem-solving cycle on **P1.0OHP**. Challenge students to work together as a class to suggest what they should do for each stage of the cycle in solving this problem:

▶ Calculate the area of a church door, made from a rectangle and a semi-circle.

Discuss strategies.

2.2 m
1.1 m

Further activities

Students could play 'What's my shape?' One student draws a 2-D or 3-D shape and then describes it to the other, using accurate mathematical language. The student listening has to draw the shape.

Differentiation

Core questions:
▸ Question 1: approximately Level 5 Key Stage 3 style question.
▸ Questions 2–4: approximately Level 5/6 Key Stage 3 style questions.
▸ Questions 5 and 6: approximately Level 6/7 Key Stage 3 style questions.

Extension tier: focuses on questions from Level 6 to 8.

Support tier: focuses on questions from Level 4 to 6.

Exercise P1.1

For each of these questions, write down what the question is asking you to find out before you solve the problem.

1. This is a pattern made with matchsticks:

a Joanne wants to make the pattern with 10 squares in it.
How many matchsticks will she need?
b Richard uses 51 matchsticks to make a pattern.
How many squares are there in the pattern?

2. The graph shows the cost of buying and selling cappuccinos in Del's Cafe:

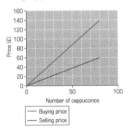

a How much does Del pay for 40 cappuccinos?
b For how much does he sell 55 cappuccinos?
c Del spends £45 on cappuccinos and sells all of them.
How much profit does he make?

3. Alan buys 6 trees for £110.70.
How much would 11 trees cost?

4. Calculate:
a 9% of £28.50
b 17.5% of £212.

5. The shaded face of this prism is in the shape of a trapezium.
Calculate the volume of the prism.

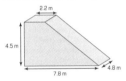

6. A large pond has a diameter of 4.8 metres.

a Jonathon wants to put curved paving stones around the circumference of the pond.
Each curved paving stone would cover 35 cm of the circumference.
Jonathon has 45 curved paving stones.
Can Jonathon completely surround the pond with his paving stones?
b Kevin wants to build a circular fountain with a radius of 1.4 m in the centre of the pond.

What area of pond will be left?

163

Exercise commentary

The questions assess objectives on Framework Pages 3–29.

Problem solving

Question 6 assesses objectives on Framework Page 29.
Question 3 assesses objectives on Framework Page 5.

Group work

All questions are suitable for working in pairs, with the focus on understanding the question.

Misconceptions

Students may use the diameter instead of the radius when calculating the area of a circle.
Encourage students to write down the information needed for each part of the problem, and to ensure that they substitute the correct value into the formula.

Links

Problem solving links to all other aspects of the Framework.

Homework

P1.1HW provides further practice at Key Stage 3 style questions, focusing on a problem-solving approach.

Revision

Students should work through R1 in the 5–7 Revision Book.

Answers

1 a 33   b 16
2 a £30   b £95   c £60
3 £202.95
4 a £2.57   b £37.10
5 108 m^3
6 a Yes   b 11.9 m^2

P1.2 Answering the question

Mental starter

Challenge students to count up a counting stick in steps of 23.
Encourage them to count using strategies they already know.
Count up the stick again after each strategy:

▶ What do we know already – $1 \times 23 = 23$, $10 \times 23 = 230$.
▶ Which numbers can you work out quickly – 5×23 – halve 230, 2×23 – double 23.
▶ What else can you work out – use doubling answers and subtracting 23.

Useful resources

P1.0OHP – problem-solving cycle
P1.2OHP – Students' Book example
Counting stick
Key Stage 3 questions

Introductory activity

Discuss **P1.0OHP**, which shows the problem-solving cycle.
Discuss the first part of the cycle again, and emphasise that it is important to fully answer all parts of the questions, including explaining working if needed.

Discuss the example in the Students' Book, on P1.2OHP.
Challenge students to work in pairs to:
▶ Work out exactly what the question is asking them to find.
▶ Highlight the key words.
▶ Write down the information given in shorthand.

Discuss answers. Emphasise what the key words are [in bold] and the need for explanation.
Challenge students to solve the problem.
Discuss methods and strategies with the whole class. Emphasise that an explanation should go with any working out. Discuss the features of a good explanation.

Challenge students to solve a set of Key Stage 3 questions following the strategies in the cycle.
Emphasise:
▶ Read the problem.
▶ Identify what you need to find including an explanation if necessary.
▶ Highlight key words.
▶ Write down information in shorthand, including formulae.
▶ Identify the area of mathematics required to solve the problem.

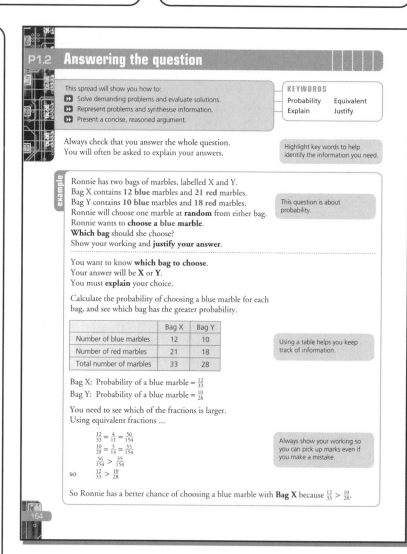

P1.2 Answering the question

This spread will show you how to:
▶ Solve demanding problems and evaluate solutions.
▶ Represent problems and synthesise information.
▶ Present a concise, reasoned argument.

KEYWORDS
Probability   Equivalent
Explain   Justify

Always check that you answer the whole question.
You will often be asked to explain your answers.

Highlight key words to help identify the information you need.

example

Ronnie has two bags of marbles, labelled X and Y.
Bag X contains **12 blue** marbles and **21 red** marbles.
Bag Y contains **10 blue** marbles and **18 red** marbles.
Ronnie will choose one marble at **random** from either bag.
Ronnie wants to **choose a blue marble**.
Which bag should she choose?
Show your working and **justify your answer**.

This question is about probability.

You want to know **which bag to choose**.
Your answer will be **X** or **Y**.
You must **explain** your choice.

Calculate the probability of choosing a blue marble for each bag, and see which bag has the greater probability.

	Bag X	Bag Y
Number of blue marbles	12	10
Number of red marbles	21	18
Total number of marbles	33	28

Using a table helps you keep track of information.

Bag X: Probability of a blue marble = $\frac{12}{33}$
Bag Y: Probability of a blue marble = $\frac{10}{28}$

You need to see which of the fractions is larger.
Using equivalent fractions ...

$\frac{12}{33} = \frac{4}{11} = \frac{56}{154}$
$\frac{10}{28} = \frac{5}{14} = \frac{55}{154}$
$\frac{56}{154} > \frac{55}{154}$
so $\frac{12}{33} > \frac{10}{28}$

Always show your working so you can pick up marks even if you make a mistake.

So Ronnie has a better chance of choosing a blue marble with **Bag X** because $\frac{12}{33} > \frac{10}{28}$.

164

Plenary.

Challenge students to write a poster or short guide for answering Key Stage 3 questions. Discuss answers and collect ideas together to produce an overview. Emphasise general strategies, with reference to a real Key Stage 3 question:
▶ Read through the paper at the beginning.
▶ Always show working out.
▶ Look at the number of marks as a time guide.
▶ Look at the answer space for clues about units or quantities.

Further activities

Students could research areas of countries and their populations and calculate population densities to find which of a group of countries is least 'crowded'.

Differentiation

Core questions:
▶ Question 1: approximately Level 5 Key Stage 3 style question.
▶ Questions 2 and 3: approximately Level 5/6 Key Stage 3 style questions.
▶ Question 4: approximately Level 6/7 Key Stage 3 style question.

Extension tier: focuses on questions from Level 6 to 8.

Support tier: focuses on questions from Level 4 to 6.

Exercise P1.2

1 These charts show information about the pets kept by pupils at Smallton School and Big City Academy.

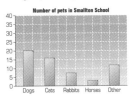

Number of pets in Smallton School

Number of pets at Big City Academy

- Dogs
- Cats
- Rabbits
- Horses
- Other

  a Steve says: 'The charts show that there are more pet cats at Smallton School than at Big City Academy'.
  Decide if you agree or disagree with Steve.
  Use the charts to explain your answer carefully.

  b Susan says: 'The charts show that a greater proportion of the pupils at Smallton School have rabbits as pets compared with Big City Academy'.
  Decide if you agree or disagree with Susan.
  Use the charts to explain your answer carefully.

2 a Which colour is this spinner most likely to land on?
Explain and justify your answer.

  b Describe how to shade the spinner so that the chance of getting a red section is a third of the chance of getting a blue section.

3 Year 10 are trying to decide the colour of the new Year 11 school jumper. There are four colours to choose from – black, red, blue or pink.
All the pupils and teachers get one vote for their favourite colour. All the votes are then put in a box.
A voting card is then chosen at random from the box. Jade says that there are only four colours to choose from so the probability of the voting card being for the colour pink is $\frac{1}{4}$.
Explain why Jade is wrong.

4 This table shows some information about planets in the Coughalot galaxy.

Planet	Surface area (km²)	Population
Ticho	5.44 million	57.5 million
K'aargghhh	0.42 million	15.3 million
Hmmm 2	5.05 million	49.8 million
Ear Ak	2.44 million	32.6 million

  a Which planet gives you the most room in which to live?
  Explain and justify your answer.
  b On the planet Ticho, all the land is shared out equally amongst the people who live there. How much land, in m², does each person own?

1 km² = 1 000 000 m²

165

Exercise commentary

The questions assess objectives on Framework Pages 3–31.

Problem solving
Questions 3 and 4 assess objectives on Framework Pages 23–25.

Group work
All questions are suitable for working in pairs, with the focus on understanding the question.

Misconceptions
Students may have difficulty finding population densities, and may calculate the surface area divided by the population, looking for the smallest answer as being the one with the most room.
Encourage students to say in words what their division represents [amount of land shared by number of people, so the amount of land per person]. The place with the most room will have the largest amount of land per person.

Links
Problem solving links to all other aspects of the Framework.

Homework

P1.2HW provides further practice at Key Stage 3 style questions, focusing on answering the question correctly.

Revision

Students should work through R2 in the 5–7 Revision Book.

Answers

1 a Disagree, the number of cats at Big City Academy is not known.
  b Agree, the proportion for Smallton School is about 12% compared with about 8%.
2 a Red b 3 blue sections, 1 red section, 2 yellow sections
3 There will be different numbers of cards for each colour, so the colours are not equally likely.
4 a Hmmm 2, it has 0.101 km² per person. b 94 609 m²

P1.3 Choosing a strategy

Mental starter

Give students ten seconds to work out each answer:
Value of $12x$ when $x = 15$; £130 – £69; 3000 – 78; Value of $x - 3$ if $x + 5$ is 15; A ticket increases in price from £2.50 to £3.00. What is the percentage increase? Tom is 1.7 m tall. Sarah is $\frac{11}{100}$ of a metre shorter than Tom. How tall is Sarah? In a class there are 14 boys and 16 girls. If a student is chosen at random, what is the probability of choosing a boy, in its simplest form?

Useful resources

P1.0OHP – problem-solving cycle
P1.3OHP – Students' Book example
Key Stage 3 questions

Introductory activity

Discuss **P1.0OHP**, which shows the problem-solving cycle.
Discuss the second part of the cycle and emphasise that it is important to choose the right strategy to solve the problem.

Discuss the first example in the Students' Book, on P1.3OHP. Challenge students to work in pairs to:
▸ Work out exactly what the question is asking them to find.
▸ Highlight the key words.
▸ Write down the information given.
▸ Identify the area of mathematics needed to solve the problem.
Discuss methods and strategies with the whole class. Emphasise the different strategies:
▸ Breaking the problem down into steps.
▸ Trial and improvement (not really appropriate in this case).
▸ Using algebra (most useful strategy).
▸ Using a diagram.

Discuss the second example in the Students' Book. Emphasise that trial and improvement, if appropriate, should be used systematically.
Challenge students to solve a set of Key Stage 3 questions or work through the exercise following the cycle. Emphasise:
▸ Read the problem.
▸ Identify what you need to find.
▸ Highlight key words.
▸ Write down information in shorthand, including formulae.
▸ Choose a strategy.
▸ Identify the area of mathematics required.

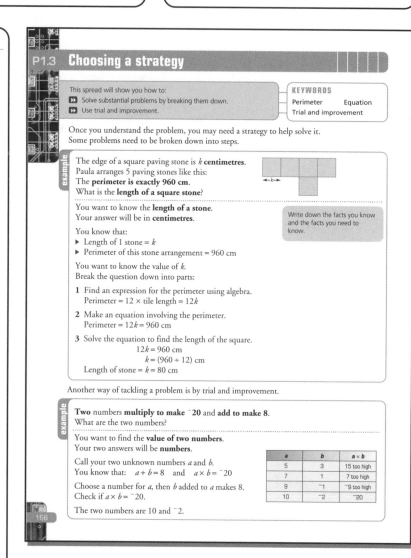

P1.3 Choosing a strategy

This spread will show you how to:
▸▸ Solve substantial problems by breaking them down.
▸▸ Use trial and improvement.

KEYWORDS
Perimeter   Equation
Trial and improvement

Once you understand the problem, you may need a strategy to help solve it.
Some problems need to be broken down into steps.

example

The edge of a square paving stone is k **centimetres**.
Paula arranges 5 paving stones like this:
The **perimeter is exactly 960 cm**.
What is the **length of a square stone**?

You want to know the **length of a stone**.
Your answer will be in **centimetres**.

You know that:
▸ Length of 1 stone = k
▸ Perimeter of this stone arrangement = 960 cm

Write down the facts you know and the facts you need to know.

You want to know the value of k.
Break the question down into parts:

1 Find an expression for the perimeter using algebra.
   Perimeter = 12 × tile length = $12k$

2 Make an equation involving the perimeter.
   Perimeter = $12k$ = 960 cm

3 Solve the equation to find the length of the square.
   $12k = 960$ cm
   $k = (960 ÷ 12)$ cm
   Length of stone = k = 80 cm

Another way of tackling a problem is by trial and improvement.

example

Two numbers **multiply to make ⁻20 and add to make 8**.
What are the two numbers?

You want to find the **value of two numbers**.
Your two answers will be **numbers**.

Call your two unknown numbers a and b.
You know that: $a + b = 8$ and $a × b = ⁻20$

Choose a number for a, then b added to a makes 8.
Check if $a × b = ⁻20$.

a	b	$a × b$
5	3	15 too high
7	1	7 too high
9	⁻1	⁻9 too high
10	⁻2	⁻20

The two numbers are 10 and ⁻2.

166

Plenary.

Discuss answers to questions in the exercise, emphasising the strategies students use to solve the problems. Challenge students to solve this problem using two different strategies:
▸ Jack and Jill have a combined age of 30 years. In three years Jack will be half the age of Jill. How old is Jack?
Encourage students to discuss their ideas. Emphasise:
▸ Trial and improvement is useful when you are stuck.
▸ Algebra is a more powerful strategy. $x + y = 30$; $2(x + 3) = y + 3$.

Further activities

Students could repeat question 7 to show possible dimensions of a cuboid with volume 20 cm³, 30 cm³, etc.

Differentiation

Core questions:
▶ Question 1: approximately Level 5 Key Stage 3 style question.
▶ Questions 2–6: approximately Level 5/6 Key Stage 3 style questions.
▶ Question 7: approximately Level 6/7 Key Stage 3 style question.

Extension tier: focuses on questions from Level 6 to 8.

Support tier: focuses on questions from Level 4 to 6.

Exercise P1.3

1 From this list of numbers:

‾6 ‾5 ‾3 ‾1 0 2 5 6 8

a Find two numbers with a total of 1.
b Find two numbers with a difference of 7.
c Choose three numbers that have the lowest possible total.

2 Lindsey and Robert want to pack 44 bottles of pop into a box.
Each bottle weighs 570 g.
The box weighs 5 kg.
They read a notice that recommends the maximum weight for filling the box.

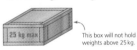

This box will not hold weights above 25 kg.

Is the box safe to lift?
Explain and justify your answer.

3 David has made up a number puzzle:

Multiplying my number by 3 and subtracting 4 gives the same answer as multiplying my number by 2 and adding 1.

Solve David's number puzzle.

4 Geoff and his father have a combined age of 62 years. In 5 years' time, Geoff will be exactly one third of his father's age.
How old is Geoff now?

5 Here are five expressions:

$x - 3$ $4x$ x^2 $\frac{x}{5}$ $\frac{10}{x}$

a Which expression gives the greatest value when x is between 0 and 1?
b Which expression gives the smallest value when x is between 3 and 4?
c Calculate the values of x that make each of the expressions equal to 1.

6 Cassie and Lucy each have four cards, numbered 2, 3, 4 and 5.

They each choose one of their own cards and multiply the numbers on the two cards together to make the answer.
a Calculate the probability that the answer is an odd number.
b The probability of the answer being less than x is $\frac{5}{8}$.
Give a possible value for x.

7 This trapezium has an area of 20 cm².

Copy and complete this table to show three possible values for h, b and a.

a	b	h
3 cm		
		2.5 cm

Exercise commentary

The questions assess objectives on Framework Pages 3–29.

Problem solving

Question 2 assesses objectives on Framework Page 21.
Question 6 assesses objectives on Framework Page 23.

Group work

All questions are suitable for working in pairs, with the focus on understanding the question and choosing an appropriate strategy.

Misconceptions

Students may fail to understand all the information in a problem. For example, in question 4 they may fail to realise that both Geoff and his father are five years older.
Encourage students to set out the problem algebraically where appropriate.
Ask students to think of the combined age in five years' time. Geoff and his father are both five years older, so students need to add on ten years.

Links

Problem solving links to all other aspects of the Framework.

Homework

P1.3HW provides further practice at Key Stage 3 style questions, focusing on using different strategies.

Revision

Students should work through R3 in the 5–7 Revision Book.

Answers

1 a ‾5 and 6, or ‾1 and 2   b ‾5 and 2, or ‾1 and 6   c ‾6, ‾5 and ‾3
2 No, it weighs 30 kg.
3 5   4 13 years old
5 a $\frac{10}{x}$ b $x - 3$ c 4, $\frac{1}{4}$, ±1, 5, 10
6 a $\frac{1}{4}$ b 13, 14 or 15
7 Examples: 3 cm, 7 cm, 4 cm; 6 cm, 10 cm, 2.5 cm

Mental starter

Use number cards with these values: $\frac{3}{8}$, $\frac{2}{5}$, 0.45, 0.5, 40%, 48%.
Challenge students to:
▶ Put the cards in order from highest to lowest.
▶ Sum some of the cards.
▶ Work out $\frac{3}{8}$ of £250, 40% of 250, etc.
▶ Work out ratios: 0.45 to 0.5 in its simplest form, etc.
Encourage students to discuss methods.

Useful resources

P1.0OHP – problem-solving cycle
P1.4OHP – Students' Book example
Recipes for Further activities

Introductory activity

Discuss **P1.0OHP**, which shows the problem-solving cycle.
Discuss the third part of the cycle and emphasise that this lesson will focus on solving problems using proportion.

Discuss the example in the Students' Book, on **P1.4OHP**.
Challenge students to work in pairs to:
▶ Work out exactly what the question is asking them to find.
▶ Identify the area of mathematics needed.
▶ Choose a strategy.
Discuss methods and strategies with the whole class. Emphasise that the problem uses proportion. Discuss the key ideas:
▶ Equivalence of fractions, decimals and percentages.
▶ A proportion is part of the whole. (In this case, the total number of sales.)
▶ Use a mental approximation first.

Discuss this example:
£3 is the same as $4.62. How many:
▶ Dollars would you get for £1?
▶ Pounds would you get for $1?
Discuss strategies.
Emphasise the key ideas:
▶ Sets of proportional numbers have a fixed ratio. In this case it is the conversion factor, 1 : 1.54.
▶ Link between proportionality and proportion, ratio, fractions, decimals and percentages.
▶ Different strategies for solving proportional problems, including unitary and scale factor methods.

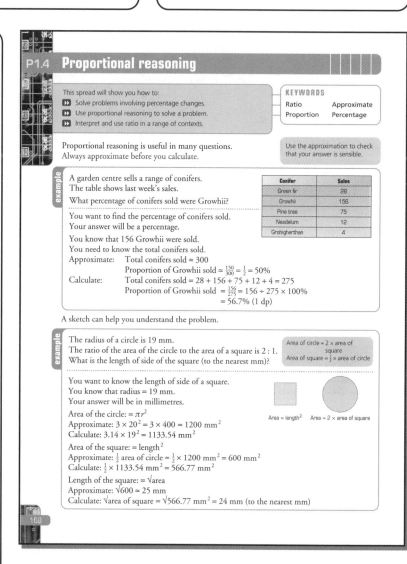

Plenary.

Discuss answers to questions in the exercise, emphasising the strategies students use to solve the problems.
Discuss the second example in the Students' Book, emphasising that the ratio of area gives a proportion.
Encourage students to answer further questions on proportion and proportionality in the example, such as:
▶ How many times bigger is the are of the circle?
▶ What fraction of the area of the circle is the area of the square?

Further activities

Students could rewrite real-life recipes for different numbers of servings.

Differentiation

Core questions:
▶ Question 1: approximately Level 5 Key Stage 3 style question.
▶ Questions 2–5: approximately Level 5/6 Key Stage 3 style questions.
▶ Question 6: approximately Level 6/7 Key Stage 3 style question.

Extension tier: focuses on questions from Level 6 to 8.

Support tier: focuses on questions from Level 4 to 6.

Exercise P1.4

1 Shoaib, Imran and Inzimam share £12 600 in the ratio of their ages.
   Shoaib is $1\frac{1}{2}$ times as old as Imran.
   Inzimam is 7 years older than Imran.
   Shoaib is 15 years old.
   Calculate how much money each person receives.

2 A farmer decides to divide her field into sections for planting different crops.
   She uses $\frac{1}{6}$ of the field for potatoes.
   She uses $\frac{1}{4}$ of the field for carrots.
   She uses $\frac{5}{9}$ of the field for swedes.
   a In total, what fraction of the field does she not plant with crops?
   b Each year the cost to rent a similar sized field is £150 for each $\frac{1}{36}$ of the field.
      i How much would it cost to rent $\frac{2}{9}$ of the field?
      ii What fraction of the field could the farmer rent for £1350?

3 The table shows the tins of cat food sold in one week in Katsave supermarket.

Cat food	Number of tins sold	Takings
Kitty Chunks	145	£68.15
Kat–u–Fat	570	£222.30
Purrfect Pieces	48	£31.20
Meow!	17	£14.28
Katsave own brand	76	£26.60
Total	856	£362.53

   a What percentage of the total number of tins sold was Kat-u-Fat?
   b What percentage of the total takings was Kat-u-Fat?
   c Kristof says that the percentage of the total number of tins sold that are Kat-u-Fat should be the same as the percentage of the total takings that are Kat-u-Fat.
      Explain why this is not true.

4 Kieran collects caps.
   He has red caps, white caps, green caps and blue caps.
   K stands for the number of red caps that Kieran owns.
   a Kieran has the same number of white caps as red caps.
      How many white caps does Kieran own?
   b Kieran has three times as many green caps as white caps.
      How many green caps does Kieran own?
   c Kieran has 7 more blue caps than red caps.
      If Kieran has 43 caps, how many does he have of each colour?

5 Johann is cooking a vegetable casserole.
   Here is the recipe for 4 people.

   > 400g potatoes
   > 350g carrots
   > 2 onions
   > 180g mushrooms
   > 100ml of vegetable stock

   a Johann is cooking for 11 people. What weight of carrots will he need to use?
   b He has 500 g of mushrooms in his fridge.
      Does he have enough mushrooms to make the casserole for 11 people?
      Explain and justify your answer.

6 Judith is driving her car on a motorway.
   The normal speed of the car on the motorway is 105 kmph.
   On average, the car uses 5 ml of fuel for every 70 metres travelled.
   How many litres of fuel does the car use if it travels for one hour at the normal speed?

Exercise commentary

The questions assess objectives on Framework Pages 3–25 and 79–81.

Problem solving

Questions 1, 5 and 6 assess objectives on Framework Page 5.

Group work

All questions are suitable for working in pairs, with the focus on using proportional reasoning.

Misconceptions

Students often find the scale factor correctly in a problem but then don't know whether to multiply or divide by it. Encourage them to try both, and see which answer is more sensible.

Links

Problem solving links to all other aspects of the Framework.

Homework

P1.4HW provides further practice at Key Stage 3 style questions, with an emphasis on proportional reasoning.

Revision

Students should work through R4 in the 5–7 Revision Book.

Answers

1 Shoaib £4500, Imran £3000, Inzimam £5100
2 **a** $\frac{1}{36}$ **b i** £1200 **ii** $\frac{1}{4}$
3 **a** 66.6% **b** 61.3%
   c Kat-u-Fat is a different price to the other brands.
4 **a** K **b** $3K$ **c** 6 red, 6 white, 18 green, 13 blue
5 **a** 963 g **b** Yes, he needs 495 g.
6 7.5 litres

P1.5 Geometrical reasoning

Mental starter

Challenge students to close their eyes and visualise these problems:

▶ Imagine a rectangular sheet of paper. Tear the rectangle in half along one of the diagonals and rearrange the triangles to make a new shape. Draw your shape.
▶ Imagine two equilateral triangles. Bring them together so that they line up exactly along one edge. Draw the new shape.
▶ Now start with three equilateral triangles, etc.

Discuss answers and encourage students to draw their answers.

Useful resources

P1.0OHP – problem-solving cycle
P1.5OHP – Students' Book example, plus proof diagram
Key Stage 3 questions

Introductory activity

Discuss **P1.0OHP**, which shows the problem-solving cycle.

Discuss the third part of the cycle and emphasise that this lesson will focus on solving problems using geometrical reasoning.

Discuss the example in the Students' Book, on P1.5OHP.

Challenge students to solve the problem, and write down any strategies that they use that involve geometrical reasoning. Discuss answers and emphasise the key points:

▶ Write down all the given facts and unknowns to find.
▶ Label unknowns using letters.
▶ Write down any useful information, for example, angles in a triangle add to 180°.
▶ Show all steps of the calculation.
▶ Give a reason for each step.
▶ Choose a method. Often angle questions can be done mentally.

Emphasise that some geometrical questions will involve proof.

Challenge students to work in pairs to prove that the angles in a triangle add up to 180°, using the diagram on **P1.5OHP**. Discuss solutions and strategies on the board.

Emphasise the key strategies, and that they are identical to those for the first example, but without any actual calculation.

Challenge students to solve a set of Key Stage 3 questions or work through the exercise following the geometrical strategies covered. Emphasise that students should use all the strategies from the previous lessons to help them solve problems.

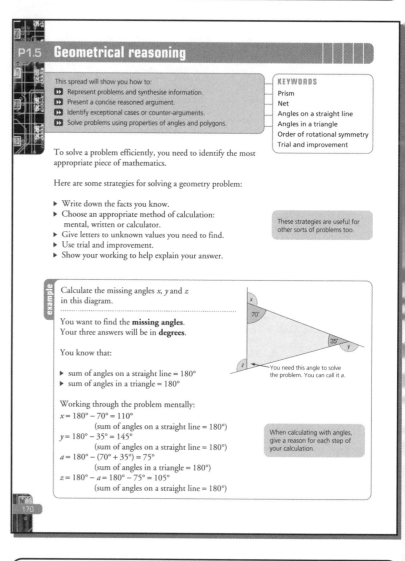

P1.5 Geometrical reasoning

This spread will show you how to:

▶▶ Represent problems and synthesise information.
▶▶ Present a concise reasoned argument.
▶▶ Identify exceptional cases or counter-arguments.
▶▶ Solve problems using properties of angles and polygons.

KEYWORDS
Prism
Net
Angles on a straight line
Angles in a triangle
Order of rotational symmetry
Trial and improvement

To solve a problem efficiently, you need to identify the most appropriate piece of mathematics.

Here are some strategies for solving a geometry problem:

▶ Write down the facts you know.
▶ Choose an appropriate method of calculation: mental, written or calculator.
▶ Give letters to unknown values you need to find.
▶ Use trial and improvement.
▶ Show your working to help explain your answer.

These strategies are useful for other sorts of problems too.

example

Calculate the missing angles x, y and z in this diagram.

You want to find the **missing angles**. Your three answers will be in **degrees**.

You know that:

▶ sum of angles on a straight line = 180°
▶ sum of angles in a triangle = 180°

You need this angle to solve the problem. You can call it a.

Working through the problem mentally:

$x = 180° - 70° = 110°$
　(sum of angles on a straight line = 180°)
$y = 180° - 35° = 145°$
　(sum of angles on a straight line = 180°)
$a = 180° - (70° + 35°) = 75°$
　(sum of angles in a triangle = 180°)
$z = 180° - a = 180° - 75° = 105°$
　(sum of angles on a straight line = 180°)

When calculating with angles, give a reason for each step of your calculation.

170

Plenary.

Challenge students to solve this problem:

▶ A cuboid has a volume of exactly 2000 cm³. What dimensions could the cuboid have? Calculate its surface area. What dimensions will produce the smallest surface area?
[953 cm³ – 12.6 cm square]

Discuss answers and collect responses in a table, showing possible dimensions and surface area. Discuss how to continue to solve the problem, by using trial and improvement, a spreadsheet, etc.

Further activities

Students could write an explanation of
▶ a convention
▶ a definition
▶ a derived property, giving an example in each case.

Differentiation

Core questions:
▶ Question 1: approximately Level 5 Key Stage 3 style question.
▶ Questions 2–4: approximately Level 5/6 Key Stage 3 style questions.
▶ Question 5: approximately Level 6/7 Key Stage 3 style question.

Extension tier: focuses on questions from Level 6 to 8.

Support tier: focuses on questions from Level 4 to 6.

Exercise P1.5

1 Look at these shapes:

i 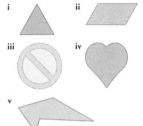 ii

iii iv

v

a Match a correct description to each shape from this list:
   ▶ 1 line of symmetry; rotational symmetry of order 1
   ▶ 3 lines of symmetry; rotational symmetry of order 3
   ▶ 2 lines of symmetry; rotational symmetry of order 0
   ▶ 0 lines of symmetry; rotational symmetry of order 2
   ▶ 2 lines of symmetry; rotational symmetry of order 2
   ▶ 0 lines of symmetry; rotational symmetry of order 1.
b One of the descriptions cannot be matched to any of the shapes above. Explain why it is impossible to draw a shape that fits this description.

2 a Explain exactly how you would map triangle A onto triangle B.

b Explain how you would map triangle B onto triangle C.

3 Here is a triangular prism.

a Which of these nets can be folded to make a triangular prism?

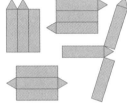

b Explain why one of the nets cannot be folded to make a triangular prism.

4 Wendy is calculating missing angles. Calculate the size of the angles x, y and z.

5 Each of these shapes has an area of 20 cm².
a Calculate the length of this parallelogram.

b Calculate the length and width of this rectangle.

$5y - 5$

$2y + 1$

171

Exercise commentary

The questions assess objectives on Framework Pages 15–17 and 185–187.
Problem solving
Questions 1–3 assess objectives on Framework Page 31.
Group work
All questions are suitable for pair work.
Misconceptions
Students may assume information from a diagram that they have not been given. Encourage students to say what the notation is actually describing about the diagram. Emphasise what the parallel and equal-length symbols on lines can say about the angles.
Encourage students to extend lines where appropriate so that all corresponding angles can be seen.
Students may not carry through to the final solution of a problem, especially when substituting in values. Encourage them to work out exactly what the question asks them to find and check that their answer matches.
Links
Problem solving links to all other aspects of the Framework.

Homework

P1.5HW provides practice at more complex problems to be solved in steps using geometrical reasoning.
Revision

Students should work through R5 in the 5–7 Revision Book.

Answers

1 a i 3 lines, order 3   ii 0 lines, order 2   iii 2 lines, order 2
     iv 1 line, order 1   v 0 lines, order 1
   b Rotational symmetry of order 0 is impossible. A shape with no rotational symmetry has order 1 not 0.
2 a Rotation 90° clockwise about (0, 0)   b Reflection in the line $y = x$
3 a All except the first one   b The triangular faces would overlap.
4 $x = 70°$, $y = 70°$, $z = 40°$ 5 a 5 cm   b 5 cm × 4 cm

171

Mental starter

Hit the target
Roll three dice, or pick from number cards to generate a three-digit target number.
Challenge students to use these numbers, plus operations and brackets, to make up the target number: 3, 7, 8, 12, 25, 30. Students can use each number only once, and have to get as close to the target as possible. They can score points for how close their number is to the target.

Useful resources

P1.0OHP – problem-solving cycle
P1.6OHP – Students' Book example
Dice or **R1** – digit cards
Key Stage 3 questions

Introductory activity

Discuss **P1.0OHP**, which shows the problem-solving cycle.
Discuss the last part of the cycle and emphasise that this lesson will focus on checking answers.

Discuss the example in the Students' Book, on P1.6OHP.
Challenge students to solve the problem. Emphasise the importance of a checking strategy. Discuss answers and make a list of the strategies students' use for checking their answers. Discuss examples:
▸ Checking that students have answered the question, used the correct units and given the answer tot the appropriate degree of accuracy.
▸ Making an approximation or estimate.
▸ Checking against the right order of magnitude, including multiplying by a number between 0 and 1.
▸ Working the problem backwards.
▸ Substituting numbers into expressions in algebra to see if they are equivalent.
Challenge students to make up an example problem to be checked by each method.

Challenge students to solve a set of Key Stage 3 questions or work through the exercise. Emphasise that students should use all the strategies from the previous lessons to help them solve problems, including checking their answers.

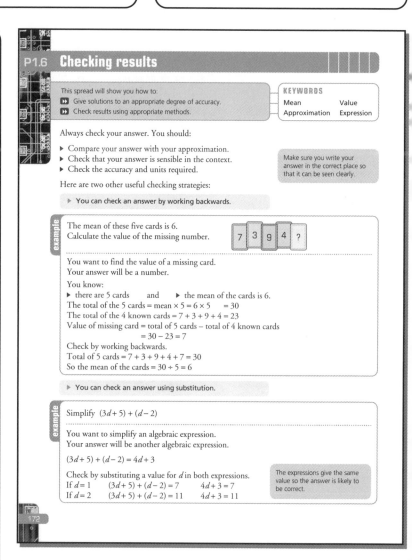

P1.6 **Checking results**

This spread will show you how to:
▸▸ Give solutions to an appropriate degree of accuracy.
▸▸ Check results using appropriate methods.

KEYWORDS
Mean   Value
Approximation Expression

Always check your answer. You should:
▸ Compare your answer with your approximation.
▸ Check that your answer is sensible in the context.
▸ Check the accuracy and units required.

Make sure you write your answer in the correct place so that it can be seen clearly.

Here are two other useful checking strategies:

▸ You can check an answer by working backwards.

example

The mean of these five cards is 6.
Calculate the value of the missing number.

7 3 9 4 ?

You want to find the value of a missing card.
Your answer will be a number.
You know:
▸ there are 5 cards   and   ▸ the mean of the cards is 6.
The total of the 5 cards = mean × 5 = 6 × 5   = 30
The total of the 4 known cards = 7 + 3 + 9 + 4 = 23
Value of missing card = total of 5 cards – total of 4 known cards
                      = 30 – 23 = 7
Check by working backwards.
Total of 5 cards = 7 + 3 + 9 + 4 + 7 = 30
So the mean of the cards = 30 ÷ 5 = 6

▸ You can check an answer using substitution.

example

Simplify $(3d + 5) + (d - 2)$

You want to simplify an algebraic expression.
Your answer will be another algebraic expression.
$(3d + 5) + (d - 2) = 4d + 3$

Check by substituting a value for d in both expressions.
If $d = 1$ $(3d + 5) + (d - 2) = 7$ $4d + 3 = 7$
If $d = 2$ $(3d + 5) + (d - 2) = 11$ $4d + 3 = 11$

The expressions give the same value so the answer is likely to be correct.

172

Plenary.

Discuss answers to questions in the exercise, emphasising the strategies used to solve the problems.

Discuss some of the questions, students' answers and their strategies.

Emphasise all the strategies covered in the past six lessons.

Further activities

Students could discuss in pairs the methods they used to check their answers to the questions in the exercise.

Differentiation

Core questions:
- ▸ Question 1: approximately Level 5 Key Stage 3 style question.
- ▸ Questions 2–6: approximately Level 5/6 Key Stage 3 style questions.
- ▸ Questions 7 and 8: approximately Level 6/7 Key Stage 3 style questions.

Extension tier: focuses on questions from Level 6 to 8.

Support tier: focuses on questions from Level 4 to 6.

Exercise P1.6

1 This is a sketch of an ice-cream wafer in the shape of a sector of a circle.

Make an accurate, full-size scale drawing of this sector.

2 Angie needs to stack 140 tins of beans on the shelves of a supermarket.
A tray of 12 tins of beans weighs 5.28 kg.
What is the weight of the tins Angie has to stack?

3 In a badminton game, each player can score between 0 and 11 points.
Albert plays four games of badminton in a tournament. His mean score for the four games was 9 points.
What points might Albert have scored in each of his four games?

4 Here are two cuboids.

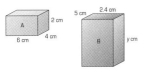

The volume of cuboid A is $\frac{1}{2}$ the volume of cuboid B.
Find the length of the edge marked y.

5 Simplify these algebraic expressions:
a $6 + 4x + 8x$
b $5y + 5 - 3y + 6$

6 Samina and Jack are packing boxes.
They have to pack 1040 tins into the boxes.
Each box can hold 39 tins.
They have already packed 21 boxes.
How many more boxes do they need to pack?

7 ABCD is a rectangle. Calculate the size of the angle p in this rectangle.

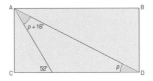

8 This is the graph of $y = 3x - 2$.

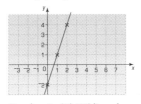

a Does the point (34, 100) lie on the line $y = 3x - 2$?
Explain and justify your answer.
b Write the coordinates of the point which lies on both of the straight lines $y = 2x + 1$ and $y = 6x - 17$.

Exercise commentary

The questions assess objectives on Framework Pages 3–29.

Problem solving

Question 7 assesses objectives on Framework Page 17.
Questions 3 and 6 assess objectives on Framework Page 7.

Group work

All questions are suitable for working in pairs to discuss solutions.

Misconceptions

Students may make mistakes in just one step of their solution.
Encourage students to highlight key words and write down information given. Then encourage them to approximate the answer by estimating using proportion or another method, or by judging if their answer is bigger or smaller than the information given.

Links

Problem solving links to all other aspects of the Framework.

Homework

P1.6HW provides practice at more complex Key Stage 3 style problems.

Revision

Students should work through R6 in the 5–7 Revision Book.

Answers

1 Accurate scale drawing
2 61.6 kg
3 Any four numbers between 0 and 11 that total 36
4 8 cm
5 a $12x + 6$ b $2y + 11$
6 6 (or 5 with 26 tins left over)   7 18°
8 a Yes, $3 \times 34 - 2 = 100$ b (4.5, 10)

Summary

The key objectives for this unit are:
▶ Solve substantial problems by breaking them down into simpler steps and tasks. (29)
▶ Present a concise, reasoned argument. (31)
▶ Give solutions to an appropriate degree of accuracy. (31)
▶ Use proportional reasoning to solve a problem. (79–81)
▶ Solve problems using properties of angles and polygons. (185–187)

Check out commentary

1 Encourage students to use the problem-solving cycle. They should decide on what information they know and what the question is asking for.

2 Encourage students to sketch a rectangle and mark on what they know, then construct expressions for the missing lengths and thus the area. Emphasise that in these questions marks will be given for the working out.

3 To make the maximum amount of paint you need to use all of the red paint but not all of the yellow paint. For students who struggle to understand this, encourage them to use a trial and improvement method, using different starting quantities of red paint.

4 Some students see travel graphs as pictures and may interpret this graph as climbing up a hill. Encourage them to describe the position of the person every 30 minutes. For example after $\frac{1}{2}$ hour the person is 1 km from home, so the person is walking at 2 km/h.

5 Students may struggle to make a start on this problem. Encourage them to look at each angle in turn and decide whether they can work out its size immediately or whether they need to calculate some other angles first.

Plenary activity

Discuss questions from past Key Stage 3 papers. Follow the problem-solving cycle and discuss the strategies to use, without actually solving the problems.

Discuss simple strategies for exams, for example, reading all the instructions on the cover page, reading each question twice, allowing more time for questions with more marks.

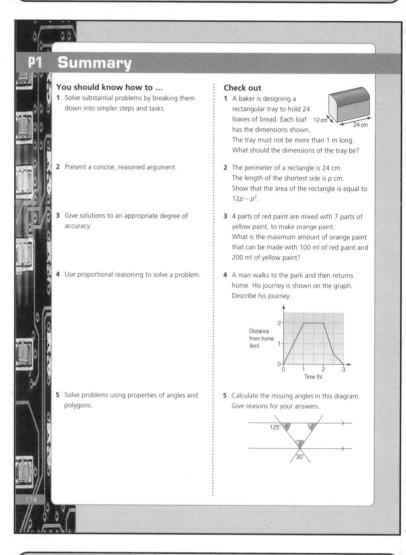

P1 Summary

You should know how to ...

1 Solve substantial problems by breaking them down into simpler steps and tasks.

2 Present a concise, reasoned argument.

3 Give solutions to an appropriate degree of accuracy.

4 Use proportional reasoning to solve a problem.

5 Solve problems using properties of angles and polygons.

Check out

1 A baker is designing a rectangular tray to hold 24 loaves of bread. Each loaf has the dimensions shown.
The tray must not be more than 1 m long. What should the dimensions of the tray be?

2 The perimeter of a rectangle is 24 cm. The length of the shortest side is p cm. Show that the area of the rectangle is equal to $12p - p^2$.

3 4 parts of red paint are mixed with 7 parts of yellow paint, to make orange paint. What is the maximum amount of orange paint that can be made with 100 ml of red paint and 200 ml of yellow paint?

4 A man walks to the park and then returns home. His journey is shown on the graph. Describe his journey.

5 Calculate the missing angles in this diagram. Give reasons for your answers.

Development

Problem-solving skills are developed throughout Mathematics, particularly in Key Stage 3 test practice.

Links

Problem-solving skills are used throughout Mathematics and particularly in coursework.

Revision

Students should take the mock papers in the 5–7 Revison Book.

Mental starters

Objectives covered in this unit:
▸ Add, subtract, multiply and divide negative numbers.
▸ Know or derive quickly the prime factorisation of numbers to 30 and factor pairs of a number.
▸ Find highest common factors and lowest common multiples.
▸ Order, add and subtract fractions.
▸ Solve equations.
▸ Discuss and interpret graphs.
▸ Simplify fractions by cancelling.
▸ Know or derive complements of 0.1, 1, 10.

Resources needed

Essential:
A5.5OHP – function machine and inverse
R8 – grid in all four quadrants

Useful:
A5.2OHP – expanding brackets
A5.6OHP – equations of graphs
R3 – fraction cards
A5.3ICT* – solving equations using graphs

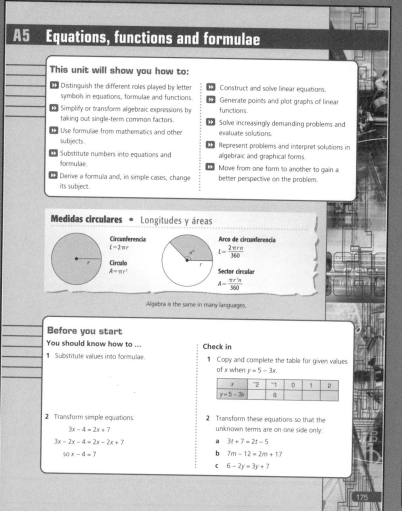

A5 Equations, functions and formulae

This unit will show you how to:

▸▸ Distinguish the different roles played by letter symbols in equations, formulae and functions.
▸▸ Simplify or transform algebraic expressions by taking out single-term common factors.
▸▸ Use formulae from mathematics and other subjects.
▸▸ Substitute numbers into equations and formulae.
▸▸ Derive a formula and, in simple cases, change its subject.

▸▸ Construct and solve linear equations.
▸▸ Generate points and plot graphs of linear functions.
▸▸ Solve increasingly demanding problems and evaluate solutions.
▸▸ Represent problems and interpret solutions in algebraic and graphical forms.
▸▸ Move from one form to another to gain a better perspective on the problem.

Medidas circulares • Longitudes y áreas

Circunferencia
$L = 2\pi r$

Círculo
$A = \pi r^2$

Arco de circunferencia
$L = \dfrac{2\pi r n}{360}$

Sector circular
$A = \dfrac{\pi r^2 n}{360}$

Algebra is the same in many languages.

Before you start

You should know how to ...
1 Substitute values into formulae.

2 Transform simple equations.
$$3x - 4 = 2x + 7$$
$$3x - 2x - 4 = 2x - 2x + 7$$
$$\text{so } x - 4 = 7$$

Check in
1 Copy and complete the table for given values of x when $y = 5 - 3x$.

x	$^{-}2$	$^{-}1$	0	1	2
$y = 5 - 3x$		8			

2 Transform these equations so that the unknown terms are on one side only:
a $3t + 7 = 2t - 5$
b $7m - 12 = 2m + 17$
c $6 - 2y = 3y + 7$

175

Unit commentary

Aim of the unit

This unit focuses on developing students' ability to solve equations. Students consider equations involving brackets and go on to study algebraic fractions, a topic which many students will find very challenging. Students then use some of the techniques to transform formulae and finally consider how graphs can be used to help solve equations.

Introduction

Discuss students' understanding of what algebra is.
Emphasise that it is a way of generalising number and is the same in many parts of the world.
Explain that you will focus on solving equations and working with formulae using the same techniques as students in other countries.

Framework references

This unit focuses on:
Teaching objectives pages:
111–113, 117–119, 123–125, 129, 139–141, 165–167.
Problem solving pages:
7, 9, 27, 29, 35.

Check in activity

Function

Give students the function $y = 3x - 2$.
Ask for values of y given values of x.
Ask for values of x given values of y.
Discuss how to transform the function so that the subject is x.

Differentiation

Support tier

Focuses on solving linear equations involving brackets and fractions and using graphs to solve real-life simultaneous equations.

Extension tier

Focuses on algebraic manipulation and problem solving, including algebraic fractions and the difference of squares.

A5.1 Equations, functions, formulae and identities

Who am I?

Practise work involving negative numbers.

Ask questions like these:

▶ I think of a number, triple it and the answer is ⁻18.
What is my number?

▶ I am 3 more/less than ⁻4. What is my number?

▶ I am double ⁻3. What is my number?

Useful resources

A5.2OHP – grid method for expanding brackets

Introductory activity

Refer to the mental starter.

Check that students know the basic rules for multiplying and dividing with negative numbers.

Write these expressions on the board:

$5x - 7$

$6x + 7$

$5(2x - 1)$

$2(3x - 5) - x + 3$

Ask students to find two expressions that have the same value when $x = 5$.

Challenge students to find two expressions that are always equal, whatever the value of x.

Emphasise that this is an identity:

$5x - 7 \equiv 2(3x - 5) - x + 3$

Encourage students to expand the brackets in the second expression and combine like terms to see this is true. (**A5.2OHP** shows the grid method for reference.)

Encourage students to find the value of x for which the other two expressions are equal:

$5(2x - 1) = 6x + 7$

Emphasise that this is an equation – it can be solved to find the unknown value.

Discuss what students understand by the terms 'function' and 'formula'.

Emphasise that the functions they use most often are those of the form $y = mx + c$ which produce straight-line graphs.

Discuss formulae that students know and emphasise that you often have more than two unknown values.

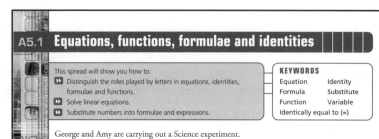

A5.1 Equations, functions, formulae and identities

This spread will show you how to:

▶▶ Distinguish the roles played by letters in equations, identities, formulae and functions.

▶▶ Solve linear equations.

▶▶ Substitute numbers into formulae and expressions.

KEYWORDS

Equation	Identity
Formula	Substitute
Function	Variable
Identically equal to (≡)	

George and Amy are carrying out a Science experiment.

They measure the distance rolled by a metal ball along a glass surface.

Here are their notes:

$8t + 4 = 28$

$4(2t + 1) = 8t + 4$

$s = 8t + 4$

$t = time$

$s = ut + 4$ $s = distance$

$u = speed$

▶ The equation $8t + 4 = 28$ can be solved to find a particular value.

$8t + 4 - 4 = 28 - 4$

$8t = 24$

$8t \div 8 = 24 \div 8$

$t = 3$

This is the balance method – you make sure the sides stay in balance.

▶ The function $s = 8t + 4$ links two variables.

You can substitute the value of one variable to find the value of the other variable:

$s = 8t + 4$

when $t = 2$, $s = 8 \times 2 + 4$

$s = 18$

For every value you substitute there is only one possible solution.

▶ The formula $s = ut + 4$ links two or more variables.

▶ The identity $4(2t + 1) \equiv 8t + 4$ is true for every value.

$4(2t + 1)$ is equal to $8t + 4$ no matter what the value of t.

Plenary

Discuss question 6.

Encourage students to explain the errors in the working.

Discuss how to solve the equations correctly.

Able students could challenge each other to spot the error in working, devising problems as in question 6 for a partner to solve.

Differentiation

Core questions:

▶ Questions 1 and 2 involve simplifying and substituting values into expressions.
▶ Questions 3–5 focus on solving equations and recognising identities.
▶ Question 6 involves finding the error in working.

Extension tier: focuses on proof.

Support tier: focuses on forming and solving simple linear equations.

Exercise A5.1

1 Rewrite these expressions in their simplest form:
   a $3m + 5m - 6m$ b $4m - 5 - 3m + 3$
   c $(6 - 2m) + (15 - 3m)$
   d $2 \times m \times 3$ e $2 \times m \div 3$
   f $2(3m + 1) - 8$ g $m \times m \div 2$
   h $m \div 3$ i $m \times 3 - 7$
   j $6 \times m \times m \div 3$

2 a If $m = 3$ work out the value for each of the expressions in question 1.
   b There are eight expressions of equal value when $m = 3$. Write them as equations in pairs, for example,
   $2m = m + 3$.

3 a Solve these two sets of equations:
   Set A   **Set B**
   i $3a - 4 = 11$ p $2p - 4 = p + 8$
   ii $16 - 3b = 10$ q $2(q + 2) = 11$
   iii $15 = 2c + 8$ r $3r + 1 = 5r - 9$
   iv $d - 7 = 5$ s $\frac{t}{3} + 7 = 9$
   v $\frac{e}{2} = 3$ t $15 - 3t = 4t + 1$

   b Match each answer from set A to one from set B.
   Write down each pair, for example,
   $a = s$.

4 Here are six expressions:

   a Two are identical for all values of x. Write them out using an identity ($\equiv$) sign.
   b When $x = 4$, which other pair of expressions are equal?
   c The final two expressions are equal. Write them as an equation and find the value of x.

5 Here are three algebra expressions:

   a When $x = 7$, work out the values of each expression.
   b If each expression is equal to 13, work out each value for x.
   c Two of the expressions are equal. Write all the different equations that could be true and work out the different possible values for x.

6 In a recent Key Stage 3 paper, Paul had his work marked as shown:

> 9 Solve these equations. Show your working.
> i $4k - 1 = 15$
> $3k = 15$ $k = \underline{5}$ ✗
> ii $2m + 3 = 10$
> $m + 3 = 5$ $m = \underline{2}$ ✗
> iii $3t + 5 = t + 9$
> $4t = 14$ $t = \underline{3.5}$ ✗
> iv $2(3n + 2) = 10$
> $6n + 2 = 10$ $n = \underline{2}$ ✗
> $6n = 12$

   a Work out the correct answer for each question.
   b Explain what Paul got wrong in each part of the question.

177

Exercise commentary

The questions assess objectives on Framework Pages 113, 123–125 and 139.

Problem solving
The exercise assesses objectives on Framework Page 27 and 35.
Questions 4–6 assess Pages 7–9.

Group work
Question 3 is ideal for small group discussion.

Misconceptions
Many students will need support in starting questions 4 and 5 and it is important that students are confident with the strategies introduced in the introductory activity before they start. Students will often make mistakes when expanding brackets, failing to multiply each term.
Encourage them to use the grid method – you may wish to revise this as part of the introductory activity.

Links
Brackets: Framework Pages 117–119.

Homework

A5.1HW focuses on identifying errors in working.

Answers

1 a $2m$ b $m - 2$ c $21 - 5m$ d $6m$ e $\frac{2m}{3}$ f $6m - 6$ g $\frac{m^2}{2}$ h $\frac{m}{3}$
   i $3m - 7$ j $2m^2$

2 a 6, 1, 6, 18, 2, 12, 4.5, 1, 2, 18 b $2m = 21 - 5m$, $m - 2 = \frac{m}{3}$, $6m = 2m^2$, $\frac{2m}{3} = 3m - 7$

3 a i $a = 5$ ii $b = 2$ iii $c = 3.5$ iv $d = 12$ v $e = 6$ p $p = 12$
   q $q = 3.5$ r $r = 5$ s $s = 6$ t $t = 2$ b $a = r$, $b = t$, $c = q$, $d = p$, $e = s$

4 a $3(2x + 5) \equiv 2(x + 6) + 4x + 3$ b $5x - 6$ and $3x + 2$ c $5x - 6 = 3x + 2$, $x = 4$

5 a 21, 33, 1 b 3, 3, 3 c $2x + 7 = 5x - 2$, $x = 3$; $2x + 7 = 22 - 3x$, $x = 3$;
   $5x - 2 = 22 - 3x$, $x = 3$ 6 a i $k = 4$ ii $m = 3.5$ iii $t = 2$ iv $n = 1$

A5.2 Using brackets

Mental starter

Addition pyramids

Encourage students to work in pairs or small groups to complete these addition pyramids, which involve negative numbers:

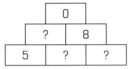

Challenge students to find as many solutions as they can.

Useful resources

A5.2OHP – grid method for expanding brackets

Introductory activity

Refer to the mental starter.

Discuss strategies.

Discuss how to use algebra to set up equations, and how it can help you decide whether there is more than one solution (if only in x then only one solution – if you need a second variable you have an infinite number of solutions).

Discuss how to expand brackets as in the expression: $6(3x - 2) - 3(5x - 6)$.

Encourage students to work out each bracket separately.

A5.2OHP has some grids so you can illustrate the grid method.

Emphasise that you multiply the second bracket by $^-3$ then add, or by 3 then subtract.

Discuss which method students find easier and why.

Give students an expression such as $12x - 18$.

Discuss how to factorise the expression.

Encourage students to give as many different factorisations as they can.

Repeat for the expression $15x + 45x^2$.

Emphasise that to factorise the expression completely, you take out the highest common factor.

Recap how to find the HCF – you list all the prime factors and take out the common ones.

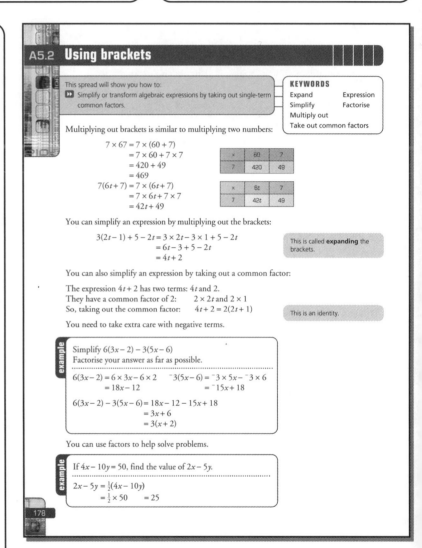

A5.2 Using brackets

This spread will show you how to:
▶ Simplify or transform algebraic expressions by taking out single-term common factors.

KEYWORDS
Expand   Expression
Simplify   Factorise
Multiply out
Take out common factors

Multiplying out brackets is similar to multiplying two numbers:

$7 \times 67 = 7 \times (60 + 7)$
$\qquad = 7 \times 60 + 7 \times 7$
$\qquad = 420 + 49$
$\qquad = 469$

×	60	7
7	420	49

$7(6t + 7) = 7 \times (6t + 7)$
$\qquad = 7 \times 6t + 7 \times 7$
$\qquad = 42t + 49$

×	6t	7
7	42t	49

You can simplify an expression by multiplying out the brackets:

$3(2t - 1) + 5 - 2t = 3 \times 2t - 3 \times 1 + 5 - 2t$
$\qquad = 6t - 3 + 5 - 2t$
$\qquad = 4t + 2$

> This is called **expanding** the brackets.

You can also simplify an expression by taking out a common factor:

The expression $4t + 2$ has two terms: $4t$ and 2.
They have a common factor of 2: $2 \times 2t$ and 2×1
So, taking out the common factor: $4t + 2 = 2(2t + 1)$

> This is an identity.

You need to take extra care with negative terms.

example

Simplify $6(3x - 2) - 3(5x - 6)$
Factorise your answer as far as possible.

$6(3x - 2) = 6 \times 3x - 6 \times 2$ $^-3(5x - 6) = ^-3 \times 5x - ^-3 \times 6$
$\qquad = 18x - 12$ $\qquad = ^-15x + 18$

$6(3x - 2) - 3(5x - 6) = 18x - 12 - 15x + 18$
$\qquad = 3x + 6$
$\qquad = 3(x + 2)$

You can use factors to help solve problems.

example

If $4x - 10y = 50$, find the value of $2x - 5y$.

$2x - 5y = \frac{1}{2}(4x - 10y)$
$\qquad = \frac{1}{2} \times 50$ $= 25$

178

Plenary

Give students the equation $20p + 8q = 18$.
Challenge them to work out:

▶ $10p + 4q$
▶ $60p + 24q$

Ask them to find the expressions that total 36 and 4.5.

Differentiation

Core questions:
▶ Questions 1 focuses on simplifying expressions.
▶ Questions 2–4 focus on expanding brackets and factorising expressions.
▶ Questions 5 and 6 focus on using algebra to solve area and perimeter problems.

Extension tier: focuses on expanding double brackets and difference of squares.

Support tier: focuses on expanding brackets in the context of area.

Exercise A5.2

1 In these algebra towers the expression in each cell is made by adding the two expressions below it.
Copy the towers, fill in the missing expressions and write them as simply as possible.

a
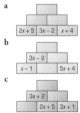
| $2x + 5$ | $3x - 2$ | $x + 4$ |

b
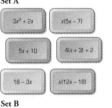
| | $3x - 2$ | |
| $x - 1$ | | $5x + 4$ |

c

| | $3x + 2$ | |
| $2x + 5$ | | $3x + 1$ |

2 Equivalent pairs
Take each expression from Set A and find an equivalent expression in Set B.

Set A

$3x^2 + 2x$	$x(5x - 7)$
$5x + 10$	$4(x + 3) + 2$
$18 - 3x$	$x(12x - 18)$

Set B

$4x + 14$	$6(2x^2 - 3x)$
$5x^2 - 7x$	$x(3x + 2)$
$5(x + 1) + 5$	$3(6 - x)$

3 Multiply out the brackets and simplify these expressions:
a $3(x + 2) + 5$
b $2(3x - 2) + 5$
c $14x - 3(2x + 5)$
d $2(3x + 4) + 3(5x - 2)$
e $5(6 - x) - 2(3x + 4)$
f $x(3x + 2) + 4(3x^2 + 2x)$

4 Factorise these expressions.
The first one is started for you.
a $3x + 6y = 3($ $)$
b $2x^2 + 5x =$
c $18x - 12y$
d $5x^2 - 7x =$
e $6x^2 - 8x =$
f $4x^3 - 3x^2 + 9x =$

5 a For each of these rectangles, find the area and perimeter:

i
$3x + 4$

x

ii
$6x - 7$

5

b The perimeters of the rectangles are equal.
Find the value of x and use this to find the area of each rectangle.

6 The area of another rectangle is $2x^2 + 6x$.
a Suggest suitable lengths for its sides.
b Find the perimeter of your rectangle.

179

Exercise commentary

The questions assess objectives on Framework Pages 117 and 123.

Problem solving
The exercise assesses objectives on Framework Page 27.
Questions 1 and 2 assess Pages 7–9.

Group work
Question 4 is ideal for discussion – encourage students to discuss which is the best answer.

Misconceptions
Students will continue to make mistakes when expanding brackets.
Encourage students to use the grid method until they can expand brackets confidently without support.
A quick check may involve substituting a suitable value into the expression and into the expansion to see if they give the same value.

Links
Factors: Framework Pages 55.

Homework

A5.2HW provides practice in expanding brackets and simple factorisation.

Answers

1 a $9x + 5$; $5x + 3$, $4x + 2$ **b** $10x + 1$; $7x + 3$; $2x - 1$ **c** $8x + 8$; $5x + 6$; $x + 3$
2 $3x^2 + 2x = x(3x + 2)$, $x(5x - 7) = 5x^2 - 7x$, $5x + 10 = 5(x + 1) + 5$,
    $4(x + 3) + 2 = 4x + 14$, $18 - 3x = 3(6 - x)$, $x(12x - 18) = 6(2x^2 - 3x)$
3 a $3x + 11$ **b** $6x + 1$ **c** $8x - 15$ **d** $21x + 2$ **e** $22 - 11x$ **f** $15x^2 + 10x$
4 a $3(x + 2y)$ **b** $x(2x + 5)$ **c** $6(3x - 2y)$ **d** $x(5x - 7)$ **e** $2x(3x - 4)$
    f $x(4x^2 - 3x + 9)$
5 a i Area $= x(3x + 4)$, perimeter $= 8x + 8$ **ii** Area $= 5(6x - 7)$, perimeter $= 12x - 4$
    b $x = 3$, areas are 39 and 55   **6** Example: **a** $2x$, $x + 3$ **b** $6x + 6$

Matching fractions

Give students these fractions and ask them to match them into equivalent pairs.

$$\frac{2}{3} \qquad \frac{3}{4} \qquad \frac{3}{5} \qquad \frac{4}{5} \qquad \frac{5}{8} \qquad \frac{6}{8}$$

$$\frac{10}{15} \qquad \frac{12}{20} \qquad \frac{16}{20} \qquad \frac{15}{24}$$

Useful resources

A5.2OHP – grid method for expanding brackets

Introductory activity

Write these expressions on the board:

$5(x + 3)$

$2(2x + 7)$

$3(4x - 2)$.

Encourage students to find values when two of the expressions are equal.

Emphasise that this means students will solve these three equations:

1 $5(x + 3) = 2(2x + 7)$
2 $5(x + 3) = 3(4x - 2)$
3 $2(2x + 7) = 3(4x - 2)$

Discuss how to solve the first equation.

Emphasise that the unknown is on each side and you need to collect them on one side.

Discuss the complication of the bracket. Emphasise that you can expand the bracket and then proceed as for any other equation. **A5.2OHP** shows the grid method for reference.

Discuss each stage of the working. Emphasise that you collect the unknown terms on the side where most are to start with.

Encourage students to check the answer you find by substituting into each side of the original equation.

Discuss how to set out working.

Repeat for the second and third equations.

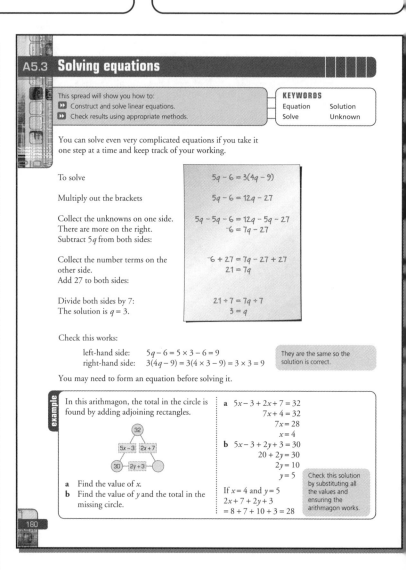

Plenary

Discuss question 5.

Discuss which was the easiest equation to write down and which was the hardest, and why.

Discuss how to solve each equation.

Encourage students to justify each stage of their working.

Further activities

A5.3ICT provides practice at using a spreadsheet to solve equations by plotting and drawing graphs.

Alternatively

Challenge able students to write their own problem similar to question 6 for a partner to solve.

Differentiation

Core questions:

▶ Question 1 focuses on solving equations with the unknown on one side.

▶ Questions 2–4 focus on the unknown on both sides and include brackets.

▶ Questions 5–7 focus on using algebra to solve problems.

Extension tier: focuses on expanding brackets and solving equations in the context of geometry and shape.

Support tier: focuses on solving linear equations involving brackets.

Exercise A5.3

1 Solve these equations using a suitable method.
  a $5x + 8 = 23$
  b $3x - 7 = 11$
  c $18 = 4x + 10$
  d $3(2x - 7) = 15$
  e $2(7x - 9) = 10$
  f $5(2x + 3) - 10 = 25$

2 Each of these expressions is equal to $2x + 3$. Form an equation with each expression and solve to find a value for x.
  a $x + 10$ b $3x - 8$
  c $5x - 12$ d $2(3x - 7)$
  e $5(x + 6)$

3 In an arithmagon, the total in the circle is found by adding adjoining rectangles.
  a

  b

  i For each arithmagon, find the value of x.
  ii Use this value of x to find the totals in the other two circles.

4 Solve these equations using an appropriate method:
  a $5m - 7 = 6$
  b $4(2x + 5) = 34$
  c $9x - 5 = 2(3x + 7)$
  d $3(2 - x) + 4(2x - 3) = 0$
  e $\frac{3x}{4} = 5$ f $2 = \frac{11}{x}$

5 Form an algebraic equation for each of these problems and solve it.

  a I multiply a number m by 3 and add 7 to give the same answer as subtracting the number m from 25.
  b I add 6 to a number n and multiply by 7 to give the same answer as subtracting double the number from 60.
  c If I take three times a number y away from 100, I get the same answer as nine times the number add 4.

6 Work out the values of the letters in these equations.

  $3a + 5 = 16 - a$
  $8 - 3b = 0$
  $5c - 3 = 11$

  Complete the inequality statement using the values for a, b and c to fill each ☐.

  ☐ < ☐ < ☐

7 Two of these expressions are equal.

  $3x - 7$ $^{-}2(5 - x)$
  $3(2x + 3)$
  a Write each of the equations that could be true.
  b Find the different possible values for x.
  c If $^{-}4 < x < 0$, what is the value of x?

Exercise commentary

The questions assess objectives on Framework Pages 111, 123 and 125.

Problem solving

The exercise assesses objectives on Framework Page 27. Students may be encouraged to use trial and improvement to help solve problems, assessing Page 29. Questions 3, 5 and 6 assess Pages 7–9.

Group work

Less confident students would benefit from discussing all questions.

Misconceptions

There are many potential mistakes as there are so many steps in the working. Emphasise that students need to have a systematic approach and to set out their working in clear and logical steps. Encourage them to use a check at the end of their working to help avoid needless mistakes.

Links

Brackets: Framework Pages 117–119.

Homework

A5.3HW gives more practice in solving equations and substitution.

Answers

1 a $x = 3$ b $x = 6$ c $x = 2$ d $x = 6$ e $x = 2$ f $x = 2$

2 a $x + 10 = 2x + 3$, $x = 7$ b $3x - 8 = 2x + 3$, $x = 11$ c $5x - 12 = 2x + 3$, $x = 5$
  d $2(3x - 7) = 2x + 3$, $x = 4\frac{1}{4}$ e $5(x + 6) = 2x + 3$, $x = {}^{-}9$

3 a i 7 ii 39, 42 b i 2 ii 34, 18   4 a $m = 2\frac{3}{5}$ b $x = 1\frac{1}{4}$ c $x = 6\frac{1}{3}$
  d $x = {}^{-}\frac{3}{5}$ e $x = 6\frac{2}{3}$ f $x = 5\frac{1}{2}$ 5 a $3m + 7 = 25 - m$, $m = 4.5$
  b $7(n + 6) = 60 - 2n$, $n = 2$ c $100 - 3y = 9y + 4$, $y = 8$ 6 $a = 2\frac{3}{4}$, $c = 2\frac{4}{5}$, $b = 2\frac{2}{3}$; $b < a < c$

7 a $3x - 7 = {}^{-}2(5 - x)$; $3x - 7 = 3(2x + 3)$; $3(2x + 3) = {}^{-}2(5 - x)$
  b $x = {}^{-}3$; $x = {}^{-}\frac{16}{3}$; $x = {}^{-}\frac{19}{4}$ c $x = {}^{-}3$

A5.4 Algebraic fractions

Mental starter

Adding fractions
Give students these fractions:

$\frac{2}{3}$ $\frac{1}{4}$ $\frac{3}{5}$ $\frac{3}{8}$

Ask for the common denominator needed to add two of the
fractions:

For $\frac{2}{3} + \frac{1}{4}$ you use 12.

Ask for the common denominator needed to add all the fractions.

R3 – fraction cards may be useful.

Useful resources

R3 – fraction cards for the mental starter
and Further activities.

Introductory activity

Refer to the mental starter.

Discuss how to add two fractions such
as $\frac{1}{4} + \frac{3}{5}$.

Emphasise that you use a common
denominator – in this case 20.

Encourage students to show how to set out
the working in clear and logical steps.

Emphasise the strategy of working out the
equivalent fractions and then adding.

Discuss how to work out $\frac{x}{4} + \frac{3x}{5}$.

Emphasise the link with $\frac{1}{4} + \frac{3}{5}$ – they are
the same fractions but with an extra factor
of x.

Discuss how to adapt the method used for
numbers to algebraic fractions.

Emphasise that you find the common
denominator and use it to work out
equivalent fractions:

$\frac{x}{4} = \frac{5x}{20}$ and $\frac{3x}{5} = \frac{12x}{20}$

Then it is straightforward to add them.

Discuss how to work out $\frac{3x}{5} + \frac{x}{3} = 7$.

Emphasise that you need to add the two
unknown terms and combine them into a
single term.

Discuss the steps involved and how to set
out working.

Briefly discuss how to work out:

$\frac{2}{x} = \frac{3}{(x + 1)}$.

Emphasise that you can multiply through
by each denominator in turn as there is
only one term on each side of the equals
sign.

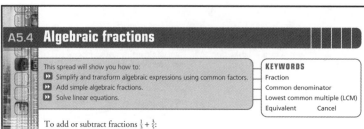

A5.4 **Algebraic fractions**

This spread will show you how to:
- Simplify and transform algebraic expressions using common factors.
- Add simple algebraic fractions.
- Solve linear equations.

KEYWORDS
Fraction
Common denominator
Lowest common multiple (LCM)
Equivalent   Cancel

To add or subtract fractions $\frac{1}{3} + \frac{3}{5}$:

▸ Find a common denominator: the lowest common multiple of 3 and 5 is 15.

▸ Find equivalent fractions:

$$\frac{1}{3} \xrightarrow[\times 5]{\times 5} \frac{5}{15} \qquad \frac{3}{5} \xrightarrow[\times 3]{\times 3} \frac{9}{15}$$

▸ Add the fractions: $\frac{1}{3} + \frac{3}{5} = \frac{5}{15} + \frac{9}{15} = \frac{14}{15}$

You add and subtract algebraic fractions in the same way.

To add $\frac{x}{6} + \frac{2x}{3}$

▸ The lowest common multiple of 3 and 6 is 6.
▸ Find equivalent fractions: $\frac{2x}{3} = \frac{4x}{6}$
▸ Now add: $\frac{x}{6} + \frac{2x}{3} = \frac{x}{6} + \frac{4x}{6} = \frac{5x}{6}$

You can multiply by the lowest common multiple to get rid
of fractions in equations.

> You must multiply every term in
> the equation.

example

Find the value of x in these equations:

a $\frac{x-4}{3} = \frac{x+2}{4}$ b $\frac{3}{t} + \frac{5}{2t} = 11$

a   The LCM of 3 and 4 is 12.
     Multiply each term by 12 and cancel.

$$\frac{{}^{4}\cancel{12}(x-4)}{\cancel{3}_{1}} = \frac{{}^{3}\cancel{12}(x+2)}{\cancel{4}_{1}}$$

so $4(x-4) = 3(x+2)$
      $4x - 16 = 3x + 6$
      $4x - 3x - 16 = 3x - 3x + 6$
      $x - 16 = 6$
      $x - 16 + 16 = 6 + 16$
      $x = 22$

b   The LCM of t and $2t$ is $2t$.
     Multiply each term by $2t$ and cancel.

$$2\cancel{t} \times \frac{3}{\cancel{t}} + {}^{1}\cancel{2t} \times \frac{5}{\cancel{2t}_{1}} = 11 \times 2t$$

Simplify:
      $6 + 5 = 22t$
      $11 = 22t$
      $11 \div 22 = 22t \div 22$
      $\frac{1}{2} = t$

Remember to check your solutions in each side of the equation:

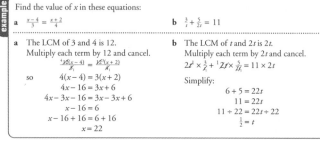

$\frac{22-4}{3} = \frac{18}{3} = 6$ and $\frac{x+2}{4} = \frac{22+2}{4} = \frac{24}{4} = 6$ $\frac{3}{t} + \frac{5}{2t} = \frac{3}{0.5} + \frac{5}{1} = 6 + 5 = 11$

Plenary

Discuss question 5.

Emphasise the strategy of multiplying through by the common
denominator (20 for 5a, 12 for 5b).

$\frac{x+2}{5} = \frac{x-1}{4}$ becomes $4(x+2) = 5(x-1)$.

Further activities

Less confident students should focus on adding and subtracting numeric fractions, using **R3** to generate pairs.

Differentiation

Core questions:
▸ Question 1 focuses on numeric fractions.
▸ Questions 2–5 focus on algebraic fractions.
▸ Questions 6–8 are for able students.

Extension tier: focuses on solving equations involving algebraic fractions in a range of contexts.

Support tier: focuses on solving equations involving fractions with more than one operation.

Exercise A5.4

1 Solve these fraction problems.

a $\dfrac{1}{3}+\dfrac{1}{4}$ b $\dfrac{3}{4}-\dfrac{1}{3}$

c $\dfrac{2}{5}+\dfrac{1}{4}$ d $\dfrac{3}{10}-\dfrac{1}{5}$

2 Solve these harder fraction problems.

a $\dfrac{a}{3}+\dfrac{a}{4}$ b $\dfrac{3b}{4}-\dfrac{b}{3}$

c $\dfrac{2c}{5}+\dfrac{c}{4}$ d $\dfrac{3d}{10}+\dfrac{2d}{5}$

3 Match a lowest common multiple with each of these questions and work out the value of x.

Lowest common multiple
15   6   12
8   10

a $\dfrac{x}{3}-\dfrac{x}{4}=2$ b $\dfrac{x}{5}+\dfrac{x}{2}=14$

c $\dfrac{2x}{3}-\dfrac{x}{6}=3$ d $\dfrac{x}{3}+\dfrac{2x}{5}=22$

e $\dfrac{5x}{8}-\dfrac{x}{2}=5$

4 Find the lowest common multiple to simplify and then solve these equations.

a $\dfrac{x}{2}+\dfrac{x}{3}=25$ b $\dfrac{x+1}{2}+\dfrac{x+2}{3}=7$

c $\dfrac{x-1}{3}+\dfrac{x+1}{4}=4$ d $\dfrac{x+5}{6}+\dfrac{x-2}{5}=3$

e $\dfrac{x+5}{2}+\dfrac{x+2}{5}=5$ f $\dfrac{x-2}{3}+\dfrac{x+4}{6}=7$

5 Solve these equations:

a $\dfrac{x+2}{5}=\dfrac{x-1}{4}$

b $\dfrac{2x+5}{3}=\dfrac{3x+4}{4}$

6 Solve these harder equations:

a $\dfrac{2}{(x+1)}=\dfrac{3}{(x+2)}$

b $\dfrac{4}{(x-1)}=\dfrac{8}{(x+3)}$

> The common denominator of $\frac{1}{(x+1)}$ and $\frac{1}{(x+2)}$ is $(x+1)(x+2)$

7 If x is an integer and $2 \leqslant x \leqslant 5$:
a What different values can x take?
b Substitute integer values for x into this expression:
$$\dfrac{16}{x}+\dfrac{12}{2x}$$
What are the different values of this expression?
c As the value of x increases, what happens to the value of the expression?

8 If $x=12$, what is the value of each of these expressions?
Give your answer as a fraction in its simplest form.

a $\dfrac{3}{x}+\dfrac{x-6}{9}$

b $\dfrac{5x+4}{x^2}-\dfrac{16-x}{3x}$

c $\dfrac{4(x-3)}{(x+3)(x-8)}$

Exercise commentary

The questions assess objectives on Framework Pages 117, 119, 123 and 125.

Problem solving
The exercise assesses objectives on Framework Page 27.

Group work
The first two questions are suitable for class discussion.
Less confident students would benefit from discussing all questions.

Misconceptions
A common error in adding fractions is to add the denominators as well as the numerators.
One useful strategy is to encourage students to say the fractions out loud: one twentieth plus three twentieths equals four twentieths.

Links
Fractions: Framework Pages 61–65.

Homework

A5.4HW focuses on solving equations involving algebraic fractions.

Answers

1 a $1\frac{1}{12}$ b $\frac{5}{12}$ c $\frac{13}{20}$ d $\frac{1}{10}$ **2** a $\frac{13a}{12}$ b $\frac{5b}{12}$ c $\frac{13c}{20}$ d $\frac{7d}{10}$

3 a $12, x=24$ b $10, x=20$ c $6, x=6$ d $15, x=30$ e $8, x=40$

4 a $x=30$ b $x=7$ c $x=7$ d $x=7$ e $x=3$ f $x=14$

5 a $x=13$ b $x=8$

6 a $x=1$ b $x=5$

7 a $2, 3, 4, 5$ b $x=11; 7\frac{1}{3}; 5\frac{1}{2}; 4\frac{2}{5}$ c Decreases

8 a $\frac{11}{12}$ b $\frac{1}{3}$ c $\frac{3}{5}$

Mental starter

Make my fraction

Give students these fractions: $\frac{1}{2}$ $\frac{1}{4}$ $\frac{3}{8}$

Challenge them to use two fractions and any one of the four operations to make an answer:

‣ Between 0 and 1
‣ More than 1
‣ Less than 1
‣ Between $\frac{1}{2}$ and 1.

Useful resources

A5.5OHP – function machines and inverses

Introductory activity

Discuss how to solve the equation:

$15 = 7(x - 3) + 1$

Encourage students to explain each step in the working and to set out working logically and clearly.

Emphasise that:

‣ you rearrange the equation to make x the subject, and
‣ you do the same thing to both sides to keep the equation in balance.

Discuss how to rearrange the formula $s = ut + v$ so that v is the subject.

Emphasise that you want the v term on its own so you subtract ut from both sides.

Discuss how to rearrange the formula so that u is the subject.

Emphasise that you want the u term on its own.

Encourage students to describe how the formula is built up, starting with u.

You can use the function machines and inverses on **A5.5OHP** to help.

Encourage students to describe the inverse function.

Emphasise that this will help rearrange the formula.

Discuss the example in the Students' Book – rearrange $F = \frac{9C}{5} + 32$ to make C the subject.

Encourage students to think about how the function machine builds up to help them rearrange the formula in logical steps.

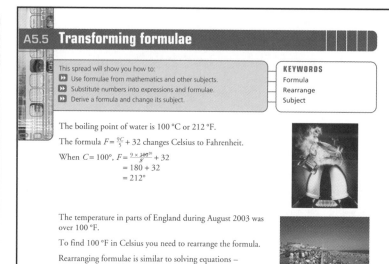

A5.5 Transforming formulae

This spread will show you how to:
▶ Use formulae from mathematics and other subjects.
▶ Substitute numbers into expressions and formulae.
▶ Derive a formula and change its subject.

KEYWORDS
Formula
Rearrange
Subject

The boiling point of water is 100 °C or 212 °F.

The formula $F = \frac{9C}{5} + 32$ changes Celsius to Fahrenheit.

When $C = 100°$, $F = \frac{9 \times 100^{20}}{5^1} + 32$
$= 180 + 32$
$= 212°$

The temperature in parts of England during August 2003 was over 100 °F.

To find 100 °F in Celsius you need to rearrange the formula.

Rearranging formulae is similar to solving equations – you do the same thing to both sides.

example

Rearrange the formula $F = \frac{9C}{5} + 32$ to make C the subject.
Use the formula to change 100 °F to Celsius.

You want the C term on one side. $F = \frac{9C}{5} + 32$

Subtract 32: $\quad F - 32 = \frac{9C}{5} + 32 - 32$

$\quad F - 32 = \frac{9C}{5}$

Multiply by 5: $\quad 5(F - 32) = \frac{5 \times 9C}{5}$

$\quad 5(F - 32) = 9C$

Divide by 9: $\quad \frac{5(F - 32)}{9} = \frac{9C}{9}$

$\quad \frac{5}{9}(F - 32) = C$

When $F = 100°$, $\quad C = \frac{5}{9}(100 - 32) = 5 \times \frac{68}{9} = 37.8°$ (1 dp)

184

Plenary

Discuss question 2.

Encourage students to explain how they decided which formulae were for area and which for volume.

Discuss strategies – emphasise that assigning any known formulae first helps narrow down the choices.

Discuss how to make h the subject of the formula in part **v**.

Further activities

Students could find examples of formulae used in other subjects, such as Science, and change the subjects.

Differentiation

Core questions:
▶ Question 1 focuses on substituting into formulae.
▶ Questions 2–4 focus on recognising, rearranging and substituting into formulae.
▶ Questions 5 and 6 are extension questions for able students.

Extension tier: focuses on substituting into and rearranging formulae.

Support tier: focuses on substituting into formulae.

Exercise A5.5

1 These formulae give the number of lines T(n), in a sequence of patterns.

  i   T(n) = $4n + 4$
  ii T(n) = $4n + 5$
  iii T(n) = $3n^2 + 9n$

  a Find T(n) for the third pattern in each sequence ($n = 3$).
  b Find T(n) for each of the formulae when $n = 5$.

2 Here are formulae for the area and volume of different shapes.
  Match the correct formula to each shape and find the area or volume of the shapes.

  i $A = \pi r^2$
  ii $A = \frac{1}{2}(a + b)h$
  iii $A = \frac{1}{2}\pi r^2$
  iv $V = \frac{1}{2}\pi r^2 l$
  v $V = \frac{1}{2}bhl$
  vi $V = WLH$

  a   b
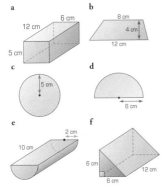

  c   d

  e   f

3 Make x the subject of each of these formulae:

  a $a = 2b - x$
  b $a = bx$
  c $a = 5x - 2b$
  d $a = 3bx + 2$
  e $a = \frac{x}{3} - 3b$
  f $a = \frac{x + 2b}{3}$

4 Find the value of x in each equation in question 3 when $a = {}^-2$, $b = 2$.

5 The area of this circle is 154 cm^2.

  Use the formula $A = \pi r^2$ to:
  a make r^2 the subject
  b find the value of r^2 (take $\pi = 3.142$)
  c find the value of r.

6 The area of an ellipse is given by $A = \pi ab$.

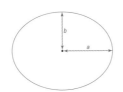

  a Calculate a to 1 decimal place if $A = 30$ cm^2 and $b = 3$ cm.
  b If $A = 15$ cm^2 and $b = 3$ cm, work out the length of a.

185

Exercise commentary

The questions assess objectives on Framework Pages 139 and 141.

Problem solving
The exercise assesses objectives on Framework Page 27 and 35.

Group work
Students can work together usefully on question 3 – students take turns to decide the next step to take while their partner writes the step down.

Misconceptions
Students often make mistakes when rushing through problems.
Encourage them to follow a structured step-by-step approach.
Students having difficulties with working out the steps should use the function machine approach.

Links
Perimeter, area and volume: Framework Pages 235–241.

Homework

A5.5HW provides practice in changing the subject of a formula.

Answers

1 a i 16 ii 17 iii 54 b i 24 ii 25 iii 120
2 a v 360 cm^3 b ii 40 cm^2 c i 78.54 cm^2
  d iii 56.55 cm^2 e iv 62.83 cm^3 f v 216 cm^3
3 a $x = 2b - a$ b $x = \frac{a}{b}$ c $x = a + 2b$ d $x = \frac{(a - 2)}{3b}$
  e $x = 3(a + 3b)$ f $x = 3a - 2b$
4 a 6 b $^-$1 c 2 d $\frac{-2}{3}$ e 12 f $^-$10
5 a $r^2 = \frac{A}{\pi}$ b 49.0 c 7 cm   6 a 3.2 cm b 1.6 cm

Mental starter

What's my gradient?

Show students these equations of graphs (on **A5.6OHP**):

$y = 2x$ $y = 3x - 1$ $y = 2x - 1$ $y = x - 1$

$y = 2x + 3$ $y + x + 1 = 0$ $y - 2x = 2$ $y = 1 - 2x$

In pairs or groups, students sort the equations into graphs with the same gradient and those with the same intercept.

Ask them to identify which graph is the steepest.

Discuss answers.

Useful resources

A5.6OHP – equations of graphs

R8 – coordinate grid

Introductory activity

Refer to the mental starter.

Emphasise that a straight line has the general equation $y = mx + c$ where m is the gradient and c the intercept.

Discuss what a gradient of m means:

For every one unit along the x-axis you go up m units (or down if it is negative).

On a blank grid (R8) ask students how to draw $y = 2x + 1$.

Emphasise the use of the gradient and intercept.

Ask them how to draw $y = 2x + 3$ and $y = 2x - 2$ on the same axes.

Emphasise that the lines have the same gradient so they are parallel.

On a new grid, ask students how to sketch $y = 3x - 2$.

On the same grid ask them to describe how to sketch $y = 2x - 2$ and $y = x - 2$.

Emphasise that the lines have different gradients but cross the y-axis in the same place.

Discuss how to sketch $y = {}^-3x - 2$ on the same grid.

Emphasise that it will cross at the same intercept but will slope downward.

Discuss how to work with implicit equations as in the mental starter.

Emphasise that you need to rearrange them to make y the subject to be able to see the gradient and intercept.

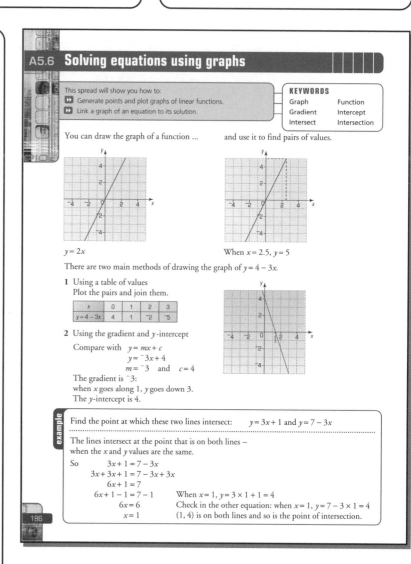

A5.6 Solving equations using graphs

This spread will show you how to:
- Generate points and plot graphs of linear functions.
- Link a graph of an equation to its solution.

KEYWORDS
Graph   Function
Gradient   Intercept
Intersect   Intersection

You can draw the graph of a function ...   and use it to find pairs of values.

$y = 2x$ When $x = 2.5$, $y = 5$

There are two main methods of drawing the graph of $y = 4 - 3x$.

1 Using a table of values
Plot the pairs and join them.

x	0	1	2	3
$y = 4 - 3x$	4	1	⁻2	⁻5

2 Using the gradient and y-intercept

Compare with $y = mx + c$
            $y = {}^-3x + 4$
            $m = {}^-3$ and $c = 4$

The gradient is ⁻3:
when x goes along 1, y goes down 3.
The y-intercept is 4.

---

example

Find the point at which these two lines intersect: $y = 3x + 1$ and $y = 7 - 3x$

The lines intersect at the point that is on both lines –
when the x and y values are the same.

So $3x + 1 = 7 - 3x$
     $3x + 3x + 1 = 7 - 3x + 3x$
         $6x + 1 = 7$
    $6x + 1 - 1 = 7 - 1$ When $x = 1$, $y = 3 \times 1 + 1 = 4$
           $6x = 6$ Check in the other equation: when $x = 1$, $y = 7 - 3 \times 1 = 4$
            $x = 1$ (1, 4) is on both lines and so is the point of intersection.

186

Plenary

Discuss question 4. Encourage students to explain how they decided whether the points lay on the line. Emphasise that you substitute the value of x and see if it gives the required value of y.

Discuss how to solve part **c**.

Emphasise that the graphs intersect when the expressions are equal so you could solve the equation instead of plotting the graph or just substitute the x value into each expression to show they are equal.

Further activities

Students could sketch graphs and find their point of intersection to solve equations such as $3x + 2 = 5x - 2$ [graphs of $y = 3x + 2$, $y = 5x - 2$].

Differentiation

Core questions:
▶ Question 1 focuses on matching equations to lines.
▶ Question 2 involves plotting curves given implicitly.
▶ Questions 3 and 4 focus on solving equations using graphs.

Extension tier: focuses on rearranging more complex formulae.

Support tier: focuses on writing equations, and solving a simple linear equation using a graph.

Exercise A5.6

1 a Match three of these equations to the lines drawn on the grid.

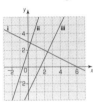

$y = 2x - 3$
$y = \frac{1}{2}x - 3$
$y = 3x + 2$
$y = 3 - \frac{1}{2}x$

b On a similar grid, sketch the line of the fourth equation.

2 Rearrange these linear equations to make y the subject of each equation.

Copy the grid and plot all the equations.

a $y + x - 4 = 0$
b $y - 2x + 3 = 0$
c $\frac{y}{3} - 2 = 0$
d $2y - 3x - 12 = 0$

3 This graph shows the line $y = 5x - 1$.

a Does the point $(3, 14)$ lie on the line? Explain how you know.
b Which of these points lie on the line?
$(7, 36)$ $(11, 54)$ $(^-5, ^-24)$ $(^-10, ^-51)$
c Show that the line $y = 2x + 14$ intersects the line $y = 5x - 1$ at the point $(5, 24)$.

4 a Copy the grid and plot at least six points whose x and y coordinates multiply together to make 12 (the point $(6, 2)$ has been plotted for you).

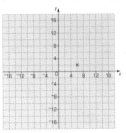

b Carefully draw in the curve $xy = 12$ joining the points you have plotted.
c If $x = ^-1$, what value of y makes $xy = 12$?
d Plot six points where x and y are both negative and $xy = 12$.
e Join up these points to form the second part of the graph for $xy = 12$.

Exercise commentary

The questions assess objectives on Framework Pages 129 and 165–167.

Problem solving
The exercise assesses objectives on Framework Page 27.
Question 3 assesses Pages 7–9.

Group work
Students can discuss question 4 in pairs.

Misconceptions
Students find rearranging formulae as in question 3 difficult.
Encourage them to work through the problems one step at a time, first transforming the x term to the right-hand side by adding or subtracting, then the number term.
A good checking strategy is to work out a pair of coordinates from the implicit equation and then check it is still on the line for the explicit equation.

Links
Solving equations: Framework Pages 123–125.

187

Homework

A5.6HW provides more practice in matching equations to graphs.

Answers

1 a, b sketch of: $y = \frac{1}{2}x - 3$ **i** $y = 3 - \frac{1}{2}x$ **ii** $y = 3x + 2$ **iii** $y = 2x - 3$
2 a $y = 4 - x$ **b** $y = 2x - 3$ **c** $y = 6$ **d** $y = 1\frac{1}{2}x + 6$
3 a Yes, $5 \times 3 - 1 = 14$ **b** $(11, 54)$, $(^-10, ^-51)$
  c $2 \times 5 + 14 = 24$ and $5 \times 5 - 1 = 24$, so both lines go through $(5, 24)$.
4 a, b Graph of $xy = 12$ **c** $^-12$
  d, e Graph of $xy = 12$ in negative quadrants.

187

The key objective for this unit is:
▶ Construct and solve linear equations using an appropriate method. (123–125)
Other objectives are:
▶ Use formulae and substitute numbers into equations and formulae. (139–141)
▶ Generate points and plot graphs of linear functions. (165–167)

Check out commentary

1 Students may need help in starting this question.
Encourage them to work through the question systematically, starting with the facts that they know.
There are a lot of stages to work through so there are many potential mistakes.
Emphasise that students should check their answers work in the original arithmagon.

2 Students find it difficult to rearrange formulae.
Encourage them to use a function machine to help consider how the formula is constructed.
Emphasise that they can often do the rest of the question without transforming the formula. In any event it is important to check answers in the original formula rather than the transformed one in case of errors.

3 Students may find the downward sloping line confusing and read the gradient and intercept the wrong way round.
Encourage students to check using a couple of points on each line. The intercept is often a useful and easy point to use as a check.

Plenary activity

Challenge students to devise two linear equations which are equal when $x = 3$. They can then give their equations to a partner to check that they are indeed equal.
Encourage students to use brackets in at least one of the expressions.

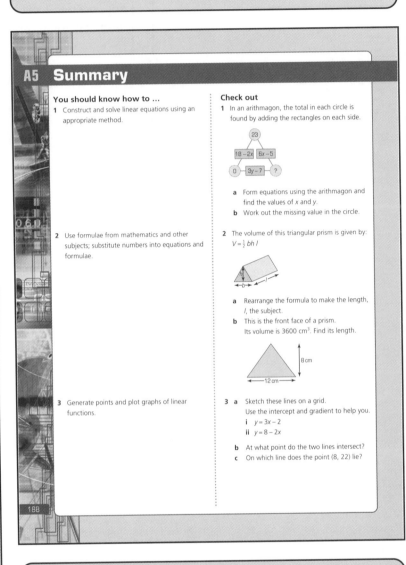

A5 Summary

You should know how to ...

1 Construct and solve linear equations using an appropriate method.

2 Use formulae from mathematics and other subjects; substitute numbers into equations and formulae.

3 Generate points and plot graphs of linear functions.

Check out

1 In an arithmagon, the total in each circle is found by adding the rectangles on each side.

a Form equations using the arithmagon and find the values of x and y.
b Work out the missing value in the circle.

2 The volume of this triangular prism is given by:
$V = \frac{1}{2} bh\, l$

a Rearrange the formula to make the length, l, the subject.
b This is the front face of a prism.
Its volume is 3600 cm³. Find its length.

3 a Sketch these lines on a grid.
Use the intercept and gradient to help you.
  i $y = 3x - 2$
  ii $y = 8 - 2x$

b At what point do the two lines intersect?
c On which line does the point (8, 22) lie?

Development

This is the last algebra unit in the course. Students will revise many of the techniques here in GCSE courses as they develop their skills in solving equations.

Links

Students will set up and solve equations and model situations using graphs in other subject areas so it is important that they can transfer these skills when appropriate.

Mental starters

Objectives covered in this unit:
▶ Order, add, subtract, multiply and divide integers.
▶ Apply mental skills to solve simple problems.
▶ Calculate a mean using an assumed mean.
▶ Discuss and interpret graphs.

Resources needed

* means class set needed
Essential:
R36 – handling data cycle
Graph paper*

Useful:
D3.1OHP – examples of data
D3.2OHP – examples of tables
D3.3OHP – scatter graphs
D3.4OHP – skewed and symmetric distributions
D3.5OHP – distributions
D3.3ICT* – scatter graphs

D3 Statistical reports

This unit will show you how to:

▶▶ Discuss how data relate to a problem and identify possible sources.
▶▶ Construct tables for large sets of raw data.
▶▶ Design and use two-way tables.
▶▶ Gather data from specified secondary sources.
▶▶ Find summary values that represent the raw data, and select the most appropriate statistics.
▶▶ Select, construct and modify suitable graphical representation to progress an enquiry.
▶▶ Interpret graphs and diagrams and draw inferences.
▶▶ Have a basic understanding of correlation.

▶▶ Compare two or more distributions and make inferences.
▶▶ Communicate interpretations and results of a statistical enquiry using selected tables, graphs and diagrams in support.
▶▶ Solve increasingly demanding problems in handling data and evaluate solutions.
▶▶ Present a concise, reasoned argument using symbols, diagrams, graphs and related explanatory text.
▶▶ Represent problems and interpret solutions in graphical form.
▶▶ Identify exceptional cases and counter-examples.

What shall we produce next?

Let's ask our customers.

We'll have to give choices, we can't produce just **anything**.

You have to think carefully before you start to research.

Before you start

You should know how to ...

1 Organise raw data into a frequency table.

2 Calculate the mean, median, mode and range of a set of data.

3 Draw statistical diagrams to represent data.

Check in

1 Some students from class 9B ran a race. Their times were:
  17.2 s, 18.3 s, 20.4 s, 16.5 s
  19.4 s, 19.2 s, 17.8 s, 21.5 s
  18.5 s, 19.2 s, 18.1 s, 17.0 s
  Organise this data in a grouped frequency table.

2 Find the mean, median and modal class of the data in question 1.

3 Draw a suitable diagram to represent the data in question 1.

Unit commentary

Aim of the unit

This unit provides an opportunity for students to carry out a substantial piece of project work. The unit uses the theme of 'transport' and aims to discuss all stages in the handling data cycle. An alternative theme may be adopted, and the lesson plans and examples adapted as necessary. There is an emphasis on group work and discussion, and examples and techniques are provided that can be incorporated into students' own projects as they are developed.

Introduction

Remind students of the main ideas of the handling data cycle in **D1**. **D1.1OHP** may be useful. Emphasise that this unit covers a project, so it will give them an opportunity to put all the ideas into practice.

Framework references

This unit focuses on:
Teaching objectives pages:
251–257, 261, 267, 271–275.
Problem solving pages:
25, 27, 31.

Check in activity

Discuss a hypothesis that might be suitable for the data in Check in question 1.
▶ What do the averages confirm in the possible hypothesis?
▶ What features of the graph or chart support the hypothesis?
▶ What further information might be needed before a conclusion can be reached?
Emphasise that all these questions will be asked as students work on their own data projects.

Differentiation

Support tier

Focuses on students' handling data project, including revising and extending their skills.

Extension tier

Focuses on guiding students through writing a statisical report.

D3.1 Gathering data

Mental starter

Emphasise the theme of the statistical project to the class. Challenge students to work in pairs to discuss ideas for investigations on the theme. The theme for the examples in this unit is transport.

Record answers and ideas on the board in a spider diagram Challenge them to come up with some hypotheses they could test for these ideas.

Useful resources

R36 – handling data cycle
D3.1OHP – data tables from the Students' Book

Introductory activity

Discuss the first part of the handling data cycle on **R36**. Emphasise that to start projects students will need:
▶ To decide the area of enquiry
▶ To formulate a hypothesis
▶ To design their data collection by survey or experiment.

Discuss the example in the Students' book on **D3.1OHP**. Challenge students to describe a possible hypothesis for Karen's project. Emphasise that the hypothesis must be clear in its aims and testable. Discuss the usefulness of the data shown to the hypothesis chosen. Challenge students to suggest other data that could be used for Karen's project. Emphasise that they can use primary or secondary data. For primary data, remind students about:
▶ Use of a pilot survey
▶ Suitable sample size and degree of accuracy
▶ Appropriate questions
▶ Clear design of tables for data collection.
For secondary data, emphasise that the data must be carefully chosen, and students must be sure that they understand it all. Emphasise that some of Karen's data has too high a degree of accuracy to be useful and could be rounded.

Discuss the advantages and disadvantages of primary and secondary data.

Refer to the ideas suggested in the mental starter. Encourage students to decide on a hypothesis and plan their data collection. Use the questions in the exercise to help draw out key points, especially question 4.

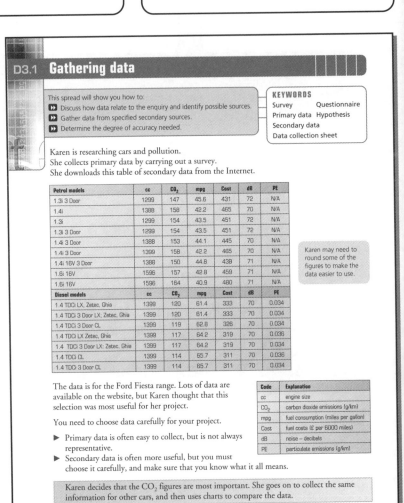

D3.1 Gathering data

This spread will show you how to:
▶ Discuss how data relate to the enquiry and identify possible sources.
▶ Gather data from specified secondary sources.
▶ Determine the degree of accuracy needed.

KEYWORDS
Survey   Questionnaire
Primary data   Hypothesis
Secondary data
Data collection sheet

Karen is researching cars and pollution.
She collects primary data by carrying out a survey.
She downloads this table of secondary data from the Internet.

Petrol models	cc	CO_2	mpg	Cost	dB	PE
1.3i 3 Door	1299	147	45.6	431	72	N/A
1.4i	1388	158	42.2	465	70	N/A
1.3i	1299	154	43.5	451	72	N/A
1.3i 3 Door	1299	154	43.5	451	72	N/A
1.4i 3 Door	1388	153	44.1	445	70	N/A
1.4i 3 Door	1399	158	42.2	465	70	N/A
1.4i 16V 3 Door	1388	150	44.8	438	71	N/A
1.6i 16V	1596	157	42.8	459	71	N/A
1.6i 16V	1596	164	40.9	480	71	N/A
Diesel models	cc	CO_2	mpg	Cost	dB	PE
1.4 TDCi LX, Zetec, Ghia	1399	120	61.4	333	70	0.034
1.4 TDCi 3 Door LX; Zetec, Ghia	1399	120	61.4	333	70	0.034
1.4 TDCi 3 Door CL	1399	119	62.8	326	70	0.034
1.4 TDCi LX Zetec, Ghia	1399	117	64.2	319	70	0.036
1.4 TDCi 3 Door LX; Zetec, Ghia	1399	117	64.2	319	70	0.034
1.4 TDCi CL	1399	114	65.7	311	70	0.036
1.4 TDCi 3 Door CL	1399	114	65.7	311	70	0.034

Karen may need to round some of the figures to make the data easier to use.

The data is for the Ford Fiesta range. Lots of data are available on the website, but Karen thought that this selection was most useful for her project.

You need to choose data carefully for your project.

▶ Primary data is often easy to collect, but is not always representative.
▶ Secondary data is often more useful, but you must choose it carefully, and make sure that you know what it all means.

Code	Explanation
cc	engine size
CO_2	carbon dioxide emissions (g/km)
mpg	fuel consumption (miles per gallon)
Cost	fuel costs (£ per 6000 miles)
dB	noise – decibels
PE	particulate emissions (g/km)

Karen decides that the CO_2 figures are most important. She goes on to collect the same information for other cars, and then uses charts to compare the data.

190

Plenary

Encourage students to explain the hypotheses that they have chosen, and their plans for data collection. Discuss these hypotheses with the class, and encourage them to consider if:
▶ The hypothesis is clear and testable.
▶ The data collection plans include both primary and secondary data.
▶ The data has an appropriate sample size and is collected to an appropriate degree of accuracy.

Further activities

Students should continue with their own project work after completing the exercise.

Differentiation

Core questions:

▶ Question 1 focuses on forming a hypothesis and planning data collection.

▶ Questions 2–4 focus on assessing data, and features of primary and secondary data.

▶ Question 5 focuses on analysing data to test a hypothesis.

Extension tier: focuses on planning an investigation.

Support tier: focuses on organising and grouping data.

Exercise D3.1

1 Here are some hypotheses that could be tested in a statistical project.
   ▶ The level of traffic noise in some classrooms in your school is too high.
   ▶ People in the UK own more dogs than people in other parts of Europe.
   ▶ School students spend more time watching sport than playing sport.
   ▶ Britain's beaches are cleaner now than they were ten years ago.
   ▶ Travelling by car is the most common way of getting to school.
   For each of these hypotheses:
   a Make a list of the things that you would need to know before you could decide whether the hypothesis is correct.
   b Explain how you would collect the required data, and whether it would be primary or secondary data, or both. Justify your answers. Include the size and accuracy of your data.

2 Maria wants to find out if there has been a change in the popularity of different holiday destinations.
   a She carries out a survey, asking friends where they have gone on holiday. Comment on the likely reliability of Maria's survey results.
   b Maria's teacher shows her this data. Explain how Maria could use this data in her project.

Holidays abroad: by destination

United Kingdom				Percentages
	1971	1981	1991	2001
Spain	34	22	21	28
France	16	27	26	18
Greece	5	7	8	8
United States	1	6	7	6
Italy	9	6	4	4
Irish Republic	–	4	3	4
Other	35	28	31	32
All destinations (=100%) (millions)	4.2	13.1	20.9	36.7

3 Peter decides to test this hypothesis: Fewer children walk to school now than ever before.
   ▶ He asks 20 people in his class to fill in a questionnaire.
   ▶ They will have to say how they travel to school, and how their parents used to travel to school.
   He then collects the data in a data collection sheet.
   Do you think that Peter's project will give reliable results? Explain your answer, and suggest any improvements you would make.

4 Decide whether each of these comments is about primary data or secondary data.
   a The data is organised in the way you want it.
   b This type of data can often be collected quickly and easily.
   c The sample size will usually be large enough to be reliable.
   d You have to rely on somebody else to collect the data reliably.
   e The sample size may be too small to be useful.
   f You generally have no control about how the data is organised.
   g You should have a good idea of how reliable the data is.
   h You may have to spend time finding the data you want, and you might not be able to find it all.

5 Karen's dad says: Diesel cars are noisier than petrol cars, but they go about twice as far on a gallon of fuel. Does the data in the table on page 190 support these views? Explain your answer.

> Sound levels are measured in decibels (dB). The higher the number of decibels, the louder the sound.

Exercise commentary

The questions assess objectives on Framework Pages 251, 253 and 255.

Problem solving

Question 5 assesses objectives on Framework Page 31.

Group work

Students can work in small groups to discuss their hypothesis and plan data collection.

Misconceptions

Students can find planning an enquiry difficult. Encourage them to choose a hypothesis that interests them, and to refine it through discussion with others. Students may not plan their data collection in enough detail. Emphasise that the data collection should have sufficient detail and an appropriate degree of accuracy to the hypothesis being tested. Data sets should be large enough to give valid results, and both primary and secondary sources should be looked at.

Links

This topic links to practical investigations in other subject areas.

Homework

D3.1HW provides prompts for students to formulate their hypotheses and decide on the data they need to collect.

Answers

1 For example, measure traffic noise in classroom directly – Primary data, plus questionnaire of students and teachers.
2 a Perhaps small sample and unrepresentative. b Try to observe any trends in the data
3 Hypothesis is vague – it could mean children anywhere in the world. Sample is small and unrepresentative and will only give a local result.
4 a Primary b Primary or secondary c Secondary d Secondary
   e Primary f Secondary g Primary h Secondary
5 The data supports neither view. Fuel consumption is about 50% better for diesel cars (not 100%) and diesel cars are actually quieter.

Mental starter

Ask students to draw out a tally chart, based on the first table from the Students' book on **D3.2OHP**. Ask them to draw a third column headed 'Tally' on the end and leave the frequency column blank. Call out data using integers between 1 and 8.
Challenge students to tally up the data in their table. Discuss answers.
Repeat for the second table, using decimal numbers and multiples of 5. Discuss answers.

Useful resources

R36 – handling data cycle
D3.2OHP – Students' Book examples

Introductory activity

Discuss the second part of the handling data cycle on **R36**. Emphasise that when collecting data students must make sure it is well organised for useful analysis later. Emphasise that tables are a good way of sorting data, and that they make data easier to interpret.
Discuss examples of data that students have collected so far in their projects.
Discuss ways in which the data has been collected and organised.

Discuss the first two tables in the Students' Book on D3.2OHP. Check by asking questions, that students understand the data in the tables. Emphasise that:

▶ The first table is grouped discrete data. There is no overlap between the groups, as people are discrete units.
▶ The second table is continuous data as you can have any value for speed. You need inequality signs to ensure the groups don't overlap, and no data is counted twice.

Discuss the two-way table in the Students' Book, also on **D3.2OHP**. Emphasise that two-way tables organise data that have two different criteria. In this example, each vehicle can be driven by a man or a woman. Emphasise that you can do calculations on either of the criteria separately (men or women), or on the data as a whole (drivers).

Encourage students to work on collecting and organising their data for their projects. Discuss the kind of data in each question in the exercise and how it is organised.

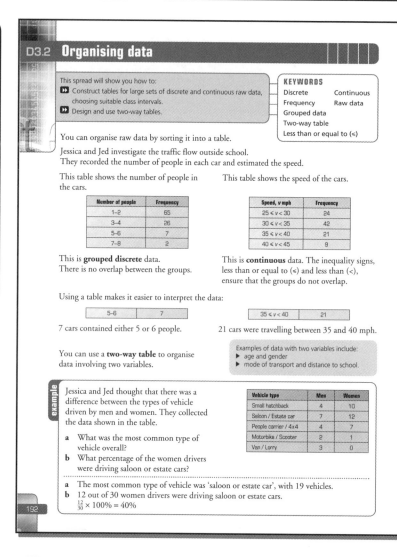

Plenary

Encourage students to explain the data they have collected for their project, and demonstrate how it is organised to the class.
Encourage them to consider different types of data: qualitative, discrete, continuous or grouped.
Encourage students to compare and evaluate the data and the way it has been organised. Is it easy to understand and interpret? If appropriate, challenge students to come up with a more suitable way of organising the data for each other's projects.

Further activities

Students should continue with their project work, organising their data in suitable tables.

Differentiation

Core questions:
▶ Question 1 focuses on grouped discrete data and drawing charts.
▶ Questions 2 and 3 focus on drawing and interpreting frequency diagrams and two-way tables.
▶ Questions 4 and 5 extend to choosing intervals and classes for sorting data.

Extension tier: focuses on sample size and sampling methods.

Support tier: focuses on finding the average from a frequency table.

Exercise D3.2

1 A technician tests samples of fabric produced by a machine.
She checks 20 samples each day, and records the number of faults in each.
The table shows the numbers of faults recorded over four days.

Grade	Number of faults	Number of samples
Excellent	0–1	37
Satisfactory	2–3	29
	4–5	11
Reject	6–7	3

The numbers of faults in the samples checked the next day were:

0, 4, 1, 2, 1, 0, 1, 0, 6, 2, 2, 3, 0, 0, 1, 1, 5, 1, 1, 0

a Make a new table, and find the total number of samples in each grade for all five days.
b Draw a bar chart to represent the data.
c Draw a pie chart to show the grades awarded to the samples tested over the five days.

2 In an athletics competition, there are four heats in the 100 metre sprint.
The times for the first three heats are shown in the table.

Time (t seconds)	Frequency
9.9 < t < 10.0	1
10.0 < t < 10.1	11
10.1 < t < 10.2	7
10.2 < t < 10.3	3
10.3 < t < 10.4	2

The times (in seconds) for the final heat were:

9.97, 10.03, 10.05, 10.11, 10.15, 10.19, 10.23, 10.31

a Copy the table, and fill in the frequency column for all four heats.
b Draw a frequency diagram to represent the data.

3 Sadie is checking the stock of coloured light bulbs at an electrical store.
There are three colours (red, green and yellow) and three powers (40, 60 and 100 watts).
Sadie writes 40R for a red 40-watt bulb.
Here is her data:

40R	60Y	60G	60G	40G	60G	60Y	60G
60Y	60G	100R	40G	60Y	60R	40R	100Y
60G	40G	60R	60R	60G	60Y	60G	100R
60Y	60R	100G	60G	40R	60Y	100R	60G
60Y	40G	60Y	60R	60Y	60G	60G	40G
60G	40R	60G	60Y	60R	100G	100G	60Y

a Organise the information into a two-way table.
b What percentage of the light bulbs is green?
c If Sadie picks a bulb at random, what is the probability that it will be a green 60-watt bulb?

4 The table shows the number of books taken out of a school library in one term by each of the students in a class.

0	12	4	8	3	9	17	0	4	11
2	7	4	10	11	18	10	8	6	10
4	7	15	14	0	4	5	9	9	8

a Organise the data into a frequency table, using equally sized groups.
b Draw a bar chart to show the data.

5 The table shows the mass (in kilograms to 3 decimal places) of 30 rock samples from a river-bed.

6.575	6.171	6.302	7.753	9.397	7.449	9.720	9.191	6.955	8.604
7.782	9.137	5.319	8.976	9.937	6.431	9.408	6.170	7.882	5.905
7.319	9.740	7.066	10.500	8.118	8.173	7.619	9.335	6.673	8.156

a Organise the data into a frequency table.
b Draw a frequency diagram for the data.

Exercise commentary

The questions assess objectives on Framework Pages 253 and 255.

Problem solving
The exercise assesses objectives on Framework Page 27.

Group work
Students can work in groups to discuss their data collection and organisation.

Misconceptions
Students can it difficult to organise data effectively. Encourage them to think carefully about the data that they are collecting, and what it describes. Encourage students to decide if the data is discrete or continuous, and if it is single or paired values. Then they can make the decision about what sort of table to use.

Links
This topic links to practical investigations in other subject areas.

Homework

D3.2HW requires students to organise their data and explain why they have organised it in this way.

Answers

1 a Number of samples: 50, 33, 13, 4   b Bar chart heights: 50, 33, 13, 4
  c Pie chart angles: 180°, 119°, 47°, 14°
2 a Frequency: 2, 13, 10, 4, 3   b Accurate frequency diagram drawn.
3 a 4, 6, 3; 6, 14, 2; 0, 12, 1   b 45.8%   c 0.29
4 a Example: 0–4: 10; 5–9: 10; 10–14: 7; 15–19: 3   b Accurate bar chart.
5 a Example: $5 \leqslant m < 6$: 2; $6 \leqslant m < 7$: 6; $7 \leqslant m < 8$: 7; $8 \leqslant m < 9$: 7;
      $9 \leqslant m < 10$: 7; $10 \leqslant m < 11$: 1   b Accurate frequency diagram.

D3.3 Scatter graphs and correlation

Mental starter

Sketch three scatter graphs on the board:

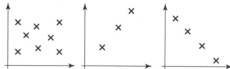

Challenge students to give examples of paired data from their project work. For example, distance and journey time. Challenge them to choose which diagram best describes the relationship between the pairs of data.

Useful resources

D3.3OHP – scatter graphs from Students' Book

Graph paper

Introductory activity

Refer to the mental starter.
Emphasise that when data has two variables you can use a scatter graph to show any relationship between them. Emphasise that there is a correlation when the points roughly form a line.

Discuss the first graphs from the Students' Book on D3.3OHP. Ensure that all the words are understood by the class. Challenge students to describe the relationship between the pairs of data in each graph in one sentence. Discuss if this relationship is what students would expect. Emphasise that both these graphs show positive correlation:

▶ As one variable increases, so does the other.

Refer to the mental starter and emphasise that there are three types of relationship: Positive, negative, and no correlation. **Discuss the second pair of graphs from the Students' Book**, also on **D3.3OHP**. Emphasise that these show negative correlation, and no correlation. Encourage students to describe the relationship in words, and give reasons.

Discuss the last graph from the Students' Book, on **D3.3OHP**. Challenge students to describe the correlation and give an explanation in words. Discuss possible causes of the increase in emissions. Emphasise that raising the price of a car does not **cause** it to have higher emissions, but that there is a positive trend.

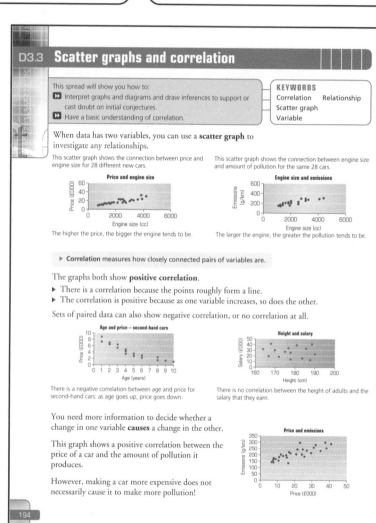

D3.3 Scatter graphs and correlation

This spread will show you how to:
▶▶ Interpret graphs and diagrams and draw inferences to support or cast doubt on initial conjectures.
▶▶ Have a basic understanding of correlation.

KEYWORDS
Correlation   Relationship
Scatter graph
Variable

When data has two variables, you can use a **scatter graph** to investigate any relationships.

This scatter graph shows the connection between price and engine size for 28 different new cars.

Price and engine size

The higher the price, the bigger the engine tends to be.

This scatter graph shows the connection between engine size and amount of pollution for the same 28 cars.

Engine size and emissions

The larger the engine, the greater the pollution tends to be.

▶ **Correlation** measures how closely connected pairs of variables are.

The graphs both show **positive correlation**.
▶ There is a correlation because the points roughly form a line.
▶ The correlation is positive because as one variable increases, so does the other.

Sets of paired data can also show negative correlation, or no correlation at all.

Age and price – second-hand cars

There is a negative correlation between age and price for second-hand cars: as age goes up, price goes down.

Height and salary

There is no correlation between the height of adults and the salary that they earn.

You need more information to decide whether a change in one variable **causes** a change in the other.

This graph shows a positive correlation between the price of a car and the amount of pollution it produces.

However, making a car more expensive does not necessarily cause it to make more pollution!

Price and emissions

194

Plenary

Encourage students to look at the data they have collected and describe any correlation they have found. Discuss the data with the class, and encourage them to consider what type of correlation is shown and suggest possible reasons for the relationships. Encourage students to discuss if one variable might cause a change in the other, or if there is no causal link. Emphasise that this is often a difficult question to judge.

Further activities

In **D3.3ICT** students construct and plot scatter graphs using a spreadsheet.

Alternatively

Students could continue with their project work, investigating the relationships from their data and drawing scatter graphs if appropriate.

Differentiation

Core questions:

▶ Questions 1–3 focus on drawing scatter graphs and interpreting correlation.

▶ Question 4 focuses on developing a reasoned argument using correlation.

▶ Questions 5 and 6 extend to using correlation to suggest causal relationships.

Extension tier: focuses on calculating statistics and drawing graphs for students' data.

Support tier: focuses on finding means, including using an assumed mean.

Exercise D3.3

1 Debbie is looking at portable hi-fis in a catalogue.
The table shows details of six different models.

Power (watts)	2	3	5	5	9	10	20
Price (£)	40	50	60	50	110	95	120

a Plot the data from the table as a scatter graph.
b Describe the correlation between power and price for these hi-fis.

2 Debbie's dad checks details of vacuum cleaners in the same catalogue.
The table shows his results.

Power (watts)	1300	1400	1400	1500
Price (£)	37	50	60	80

Power (watts)	1600	1600	1300	1800
Price (£)	90	100	50	90

Power (watts)	1100	1200	1400	1600	1500
Price (£)	120	60	90	170	140

a Plot this data as a scatter graph.
b Describe any correlation shown by your graph.

3 The table shows the heights of ten boys in Year 9, and the number of children in their families.

Height (cm)	167	172	178	156	168	159	161	162	165	163
Children in family	2	3	3	2	3	2	2	1	2	1

a Plot a scatter diagram for this data.
b Is there any correlation between a boy's height and the number of children in his family? Explain your answer.

4 A group of students did a maths test, a science test, and a sports assessment. They were given marks out of ten in each one.

Student	A	B	C	D	E	F	G	H	I	J
Maths	4	2	6	8	7	9	10	5	3	8
Science	3	3	7	6	7	8	7	4	5	5
Sports	5	5	2	3	5	8	9	2	8	1

a Draw a scatter graph to show the relationship between the maths scores and the science scores.
b Draw another scatter graph to show the relationship between the maths scores and the sports scores.
c Describe the correlation shown by each of your scatter graphs.
d Without drawing another graph, predict the correlation between the science scores and the sports scores.

5 Mrs Morgan is Karen's and Ben's maths teacher. She compares their marks (out of 20) for their last five maths homeworks.

Karen's mark	14	13	19	8	17
Ben's mark	14	13	19	8	17

a Draw a scatter diagram for these marks.
b What conclusions should Mrs Morgan draw from the graph? Explain your answer.

6 The table shows the number of sweets and pieces of fruit eaten by eight people in one day.

Fruit	2	1	0	2	5	3	1	2
Sweets	4	8	6	4	2	4	5	6

Draw a scatter graph for this data, and describe any correlation that it shows.

Exercise commentary

The questions assess objectives on Framework Pages 267 and 271.

Problem solving

Questions 3b and 5b assess objectives on Framework Page 31.
The exercise assesses objectives on Page 27.

Group work

Students can work in pairs to discuss interpretations of the relationships from their project data.

Misconceptions

Students may find it difficult to interpret low levels of correlation. They may expect a clear line or tight clustering before describing the variables as correlated. Encourage them to look at general positive or negative trends in the data overall, for example, in question 3.
Students may also wrongly describe a causal relationship between variables where there is none. Encourage students to consider, 'What happens when y increases? What direct effect might this have on x?'

Links

This topic links to practical investigations in other subject areas.

Homework

D3.3HW provides practice in interpreting scatter graphs.

Answers

1 a Accurate scatter graph b Positive correlation
2 a Accurate scatter graph b No correlation
3 a Accurate scatter graph b No, a family having more children doesn't make the children taller or shorter.
4 a, b Accurate scatter graphs c Maths and science show positive correlation; maths and sports show no correlation. d No correlation
5 a Accurate scatter graph b The two have worked together, or one has copied the other. 6 Accurate scatter graph, plus negative correlation

D3.4 Choosing the correct statistics

Introductory activity

Refer to the mental starter.

Emphasise that the mode, median and mode are all averages. They summarise the features of a set of data.

Discuss the third part of the handling data cycle on R36. Emphasise that when representing and analysing data it is important to decide carefully which average to use.

Discuss the first charts from the Students' Book on D3.4OHP. Emphasise that a skewed distribution has a tendency to very large or very small values. Challenge students to calculate the averages for the three groups of data. Discuss answers. Emphasise that the mean and median are the same for a symmetric distribution. Discuss the averages for the skewed data, and encourage students to relate them to the shape of the chart.

Discuss the numerical examples in the Students' Book, emphasising the difference in the averages for the different data sets. Challenge students to pick an average that they think represents each data set and justify their answer. Emphasise that the average should be a good representation of the data set as a whole. Discuss the last example. Emphasise that the mode is often not a very representative value for data.

Encourage students to work on finding appropriate averages for the data from their projects. Discuss the averages in each question in the exercise and how they are affected by the distribution.

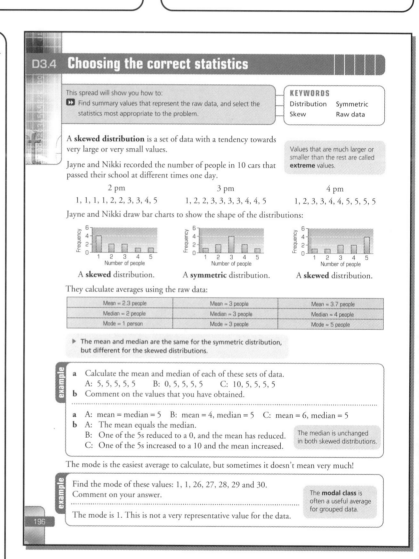

D3.4 Choosing the correct statistics

This spread will show you how to:
▶▶ Find summary values that represent the raw data, and select the statistics most appropriate to the problem.

KEYWORDS
Distribution   Symmetric
Skew   Raw data

A **skewed distribution** is a set of data with a tendency towards very large or very small values.

Jayne and Nikki recorded the number of people in 10 cars that passed their school at different times one day.

Values that are much larger or smaller than the rest are called **extreme** values.

2 pm	3 pm	4 pm
1, 1, 1, 1, 2, 2, 3, 3, 4, 5	1, 2, 2, 3, 3, 3, 3, 4, 4, 5	1, 2, 3, 3, 4, 4, 5, 5, 5, 5

Jayne and Nikki draw bar charts to show the shape of the distributions:

A **skewed** distribution.   A **symmetric** distribution.   A **skewed** distribution.

They calculate averages using the raw data:

Mean = 2.3 people	Mean = 3 people	Mean = 3.7 people
Median = 2 people	Median = 3 people	Median = 4 people
Mode = 1 person	Mode = 3 people	Mode = 5 people

▶ The mean and median are the same for the symmetric distribution, but different for the skewed distributions.

example

a Calculate the mean and median of each of these sets of data.
   A: 5, 5, 5, 5, 5   B: 0, 5, 5, 5, 5   C: 10, 5, 5, 5, 5
b Comment on the values that you have obtained.

a A: mean = median = 5   B: mean = 4, median = 5   C: mean = 6, median = 5
b A: The mean equals the median.
   B: One of the 5s reduced to a 0, and the mean has reduced.
   C: One of the 5s increased to a 10 and the mean increased.

The median is unchanged in both skewed distributions.

The mode is the easiest average to calculate, but sometimes it doesn't mean very much!

example

Find the mode of these values: 1, 1, 26, 27, 28, 29 and 30.
Comment on your answer.

The modal class is often a useful average for grouped data.

The mode is 1. This is not a very representative value for the data.

196

Plenary

Encourage students to give examples of some of the averages that they have calculated for their projects. Discuss with the class and encourage students to discuss the appropriateness of the statistics chosen.

Encourage students to discuss what other statistics might be appropriate for the data given.

Further activities

Students could continue with their project work, choosing and calculating appropriate averages to represent their data.

Differentiation

Core questions:
▸ Questions 1 and 2 focus on finding and choosing appropriate averages.
▸ Questions 3–6 investigate relationships between the three averages.
▸ Question 7 extends to finding modal groups with different groupings of the same data.

Extension tier: focuses on finding median and quartiles and drawing a box-and-whisper plot.

Support tier: focuses on drawing graphs.

Exercise D3.4

1 Here are three sets of data:

Set A
17, 20, 21, 19, 16, 20, 21

Set B
15, 14, 78, 16, 15, 13, 15

Set C
48, 52, 46, 3, 3, 45, 47

For each set of data, calculate:
a the mean
b the median
c the mode.
Explain whether each average represents the data fairly.

2 Calculate the mean, median and mode of each of these sets of data.
Explain which average gives the most representative value for each set of data.

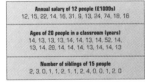

Annual salary of 12 people (£1000s)
12, 15, 22, 14, 16, 31, 9, 13, 24, 74, 18, 16

Ages of 20 people in a classroom (years)
14, 13, 13, 13, 14, 14, 13, 14, 52, 14, 13, 14, 28, 14, 14, 13, 14, 14, 13

Number of siblings of 15 people
2, 3, 0, 1, 1, 2, 1, 1, 2, 4, 0, 0, 1, 2, 0

3 **Puzzle**
Here are five number cards.

1 3 4 5 9

a Show how you could choose three of these cards so that the mean of the three numbers is bigger than the median.
b Now pick another three cards to make the median bigger than the mean.
c Finally, choose three cards where the mean and the median are equal.

4 **Puzzle**
Suki has two number cards. Each card has a whole number written on it.
The mean of the numbers is 8, and the range is 4.
What are the numbers on the cards?

5 **Puzzle**
Three people have a mean age of 25.
The range of the ages is 8 years, and the median age is 27.
How old is each person?

6 **Puzzle**
Suneeta has 5 number cards. Each card has a whole number between 1 and 10.
Suneeta says:
> The mode of the numbers is 4. The range is 6 and the mean is 5.

What cards does Suneeta have?
(There are two possible solutions.)

7 The table shows the UK population for different ages groups in 2002.

a Find the modal class for this data.
b Reorganise the data into intervals 0–9 years, 10–19 years, and so on. Find the new modal class.
c Now reorganise the data into intervals covering 20 years each. The first interval should be 0–19 years, and the last one will be '80+'. Find the modal class.

Age	Population (1000s)
0–4	3558
5–9	3833
10–14	3867
15–19	3737
20–24	3652
25–29	4078
30–34	4639
35–39	4775
40–44	4181
45–49	3756
50–54	4042
55–59	3231
60–64	2870
65–69	2575
70–74	2930
75–79	1998
80–84	2381
85–89	757
90+	390

Exercise commentary

The questions assess objectives on Framework Pages 257 and 261.

Problem solving

The exercise assesses objectives on Framework Page 25.

Group work

Students can work in pairs to discuss questions 3–7. Encourage students to find averages for their project work individually where appropriate.

Misconceptions

Students may calculate all three averages, even when they are not appropriate or not needed. Encourage them to justify a reasoned choice of an appropriate average, after considering all three.
Similarly, students may only calculate one average that may be unrepresentative. Encourage them to look at all three averages carefully and work out a choice of average, giving reasons.

Links

This topic links to practical investigations in other subject areas.

Homework

D3.4HW requires students to design data sets with given averages.

Answers

1 a 19, 23.7, 34.9 b 20, 15, 46 c 20 and 21, 15, 3; The mean is only fair for A. The median is fair for all of them. The mode is fair for B.
2 22, 16, 16, median; 16.25, 14, 14, mode; 1.33, 1, 1, mean. Salaries: median; age: mode (or median); no. of siblings: mean. 3 Examples: a 1, 3, 9 b 1, 4, 5 c 1, 3, 5
4 6, 10   5 20, 27, 28   6 2, 4, 4, 7, 8 or 3, 4, 4, 5, 9
7 a 35–39 b Population: 7401, 7604, 7730, 9414, 7947, 7273, 5445, 4328, 3138, 390; Modal class 30–39 c Population: 15 005, 17 144, 15 220, 9773, 3528; Modal class 20–39

D3.5 The shape of a distribution

Mental starter

Challenge students to find the mean, median and mode of two sets of test scores:

▶ 0, 7, 11, 12, 20
▶ 0, 0, 11, 19, 20.

Discuss answers. Challenge students to chose most representative average for each set of scores. Discuss if the statistics on their own give a representative picture.

Useful resources

D3.5OHP – Students' Book examples
Graph paper.

Introductory activity

Refer to the mental starter.

Discuss what else would be needed to give a full picture of the distribution of a set of data. Examples could include:

▶ Graphs or charts
▶ A short report in words
▶ Relevant data in tables with explanation.

Discuss the first charts from the Students' Book on D3.5OHP. Emphasise that you can use the shape of a graph to compare distributions. Challenge students to identify the key features of each distribution from its graph. Discuss answers and justifications for choices. Now challenge students to compare the graphs with each other. Emphasise that the graph for Year 9 is more symmetrical, whereas Years 7 and 8 have a similar, skewed distribution.

Discuss the second example from the Students' book. Emphasise that only one appropriate average and the range are given. Challenge students to justify if this gives a good overall impression of the two distributions. Discuss what features cannot be found from this data:

▶ Whether the distribution is skewed
▶ If there are any extreme values.

Encourage students to analyse the distribution of data from their projects. Encourage them to use both diagrams and words, and to consider what information is needed to give a full description of the distribution.

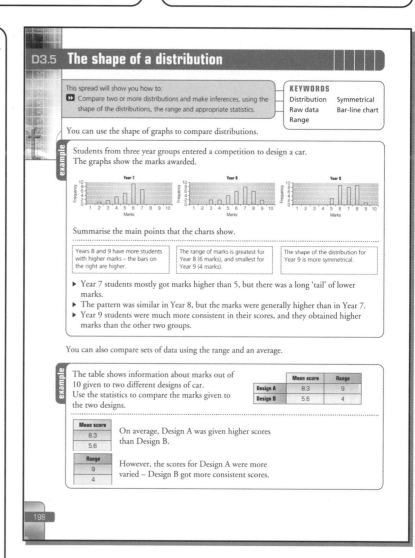

D3.5 The shape of a distribution

This spread will show you how to:
▶▶ Compare two or more distributions and make inferences, using the shape of the distributions, the range and appropriate statistics.

KEYWORDS
Distribution   Symmetrical
Raw data   Bar-line chart
Range

You can use the shape of graphs to compare distributions.

example

Students from three year groups entered a competition to design a car. The graphs show the marks awarded.

Summarise the main points that the charts show.

| Years 8 and 9 have more students with higher marks – the bars on the right are higher. | The range of marks is greatest for Year 8 (6 marks), and smallest for Year 9 (4 marks). | The shape of the distribution for Year 9 is more symmetrical. |

▶ Year 7 students mostly got marks higher than 5, but there was a long 'tail' of lower marks.
▶ The pattern was similar in Year 8, but the marks were generally higher than in Year 7.
▶ Year 9 students were much more consistent in their scores, and they obtained higher marks than the other two groups.

You can also compare sets of data using the range and an average.

example

The table shows information about marks out of 10 given to two different designs of car.
Use the statistics to compare the marks given to the two designs.

	Mean score	Range
Design A	8.3	9
Design B	5.6	4

Mean score
8.3
5.6

On average, Design A was given higher scores than Design B.

Range
9
4

However, the scores for Design A were more varied – Design B got more consistent scores.

Plenary

Encourage students to give examples of some of the distributions that they have calculated for their projects. Discuss what description and analysis might be needed to give a fair picture of the data sets.
Encourage students to discuss what other information might be needed. Emphasise the use of both charts and brief descriptions in words, as well as use of suitable averages and the range.

Further activities

Students could continue with their project work, considering the distribution of their data using tables, graphs and statistics.

Differentiation

Core questions:
▶ Question 1 practises comparing two simple distributions.
▶ Question 2 focuses on comparing distributions from a frequency table.
▶ Questions 3 and 4 extend to comparing distributions and interpreting results data.

Extension tier: focuses on interpreting and summarising graphs and statistics.
Support tier: focuses on stem-and-leaf diagrams.

Exercise D3.5

1 A panel of judges awards marks (out of ten) to two different chocolate cakes. The table shows the scores awarded.

Judge	A	B	C	D	E	F	G	H	I	J	K	L
Cake X	9	9	4	9	5	8	4	8	7	3	1	2
Cake Y	6	7	8	5	7	6	7	8	9	7	5	6

For each cake:
a calculate: **i** the mean score
            ii the modal score
b draw a bar line chart to show the frequencies.
c Describe and compare the distribution of scores for both cakes.
d Which cake do you think the judges preferred overall? Explain your answer.

2 The head teacher of Grange Park School collects attendance data for three classes in Year 9.
The table shows the number of days with a particular number of absences.
For example, there were five days when there was nobody absent in class 9A.

Absences	0	1	2	3	4	5	6
9A	5	28	24	7	7	3	1
9B	0	5	14	37	16	3	0
9C	2	2	6	7	9	29	20

For each class:
a draw a bar line chart, to show how many days there were with each number of absences
b calculate the mean number of absences
c find the median number of absences
d write down the modal number of absences.

e Describe and compare the distribution of the number of absences for all three classes. You should use your answers to parts a to d to justify your description.

3 The head office of MegaCorp plc has three computer networks.
The computer manager keeps a record of how many times each network crashes.
The table shows the number of crashes each day for 15 days.

Network A	1	1	2	1	5	0	3	2	1	6	8	7	2	4	3
Network B	3	2	0	0	1	4	2	0	1	1	0	2	2	1	0
Network C	4	3	3	3	4	5	4	3	3	4	3	4	4	3	3

For each network:
a draw a bar line chart to show how often each number of crashes occurred
b work out the mean number of crashes
c find the range of the number of crashes.

d Use your answers to parts a, b and c to compare the reliability of the networks.

4 Two athletics clubs, the Sprinters and the Harriers, enter runners in a marathon.
The times for the runners from each club are shown in the table.

Time, t (hours:minutes)	Sprinters	Harriers
$2{:}30 < t < 3{:}00$	6	8
$3{:}00 < t < 3{:}30$	9	15
$3{:}30 < t < 4{:}00$	10	9
$4{:}00 < t < 4{:}30$	2	6
$4{:}30 < t < 5{:}00$	6	4
$5{:}00 < t < 5{:}30$	0	2
$5{:}30 < t < 6{:}00$	6	0
$6{:}00 < t < 6{:}30$	4	0
$6{:}30 < t < 7{:}00$	2	0

For each athletic club:
a draw a frequency diagram
b find:
   i the modal class   **ii** the range.
c Compare the results for the two clubs.

Exercise commentary

The questions assess objectives on Framework Page 273.

Problem solving
The exercise assesses objectives on Framework Pages 27 and 31.

Group work
Students may discuss results for the exercise questions in groups.

Misconceptions
Students often compare individual values in distributions.
Emphasise that they should compare the shape of the graphs or the average(s).

Links
This topic links to practical investigations in other subject areas.

Homework

D3.5HW gives practice at comparing two distributions. Students will need graph paper.

Answers

1 a i 5.75, 6.75 ii 9, 7 b Bar charts with frequencies for X: 1, 1, 1, 2, 1, 0, 1, 2, 3; Y: 0, 0, 0, 0, 2, 3, 4, 2, 1 c The range of marks is less for Y but it has fewer top scores. d Y, it had a higher mean score and more consistent marks.
2 a Appropriate bar charts. b 1.9, 3.0, 4.5 c 2, 3, 5 d 1, 3, 5 e Most absences in 9C overall. 3 a Frequencies for A: 1, 4, 3, 2, 1, 1, 1, 1, 1; B: 5, 4, 4, 1, 1, 0, 0, 0, 0; C: 0, 0, 0, 8, 6, 1, 0, 0, 0 b 3.1, 1.3, 3.5 c 8, 4, 2 d Network B is most reliable; C is slightly less reliable than A overall, but more consistent.
4 a Appropriate frequency diagrams. b i Sprinters $3{:}30 \leqslant t < 4{:}00$, Harriers $3{:}00 \leqslant t < 3{:}30$ ii Sprinters 4:30, Harriers 3:00 c Harriers are generally faster.

Mental starter

Ask students to give examples of the hypotheses from their projects, and discuss with the class what conclusions they have come to so far. Discuss the evidence they have used to come to any conclusion. Include the data they have collected and any chart or statistics used in analysis. Challenge the class to think of any suggestions for further questions or hypotheses that could be used to extend their projects.

Useful resources

R36 – handling data cycle
Graph paper

Introductory activity

Refer to the mental starter.

Discuss the last part of the handling data cycle on R36. Emphasise that this involves drawing together all the data and analysis into a written report.

Discuss what sort of report students could write to finish their projects.

Emphasise that this is the final stage of interpreting what their results mean and describing them to other people.

Encourage students to think about their original hypothesis. Emphasise that their report should justify, with the use of statistics and diagrams, if their original hypothesis is correct.

Discuss the example report from the Students' Book. Challenge students to identify the elements of the report:

▶ State your hypotheses.
▶ Interpret your data in tables, diagrams and words.
▶ Include relevant statistics.
▶ Write down and justify your conclusions.

Discuss Tom's conclusions and any justifications for them from the information in the report. Emphasise that Tom's report is from secondary data. Encourage them to ask what information is missing [Reference to the source of the data]. Challenge students to think of other diagrams or words that might be needed if primary data was included. For example:

▶ Sample data collection sheet
▶ Information about the sample size and accuracy.

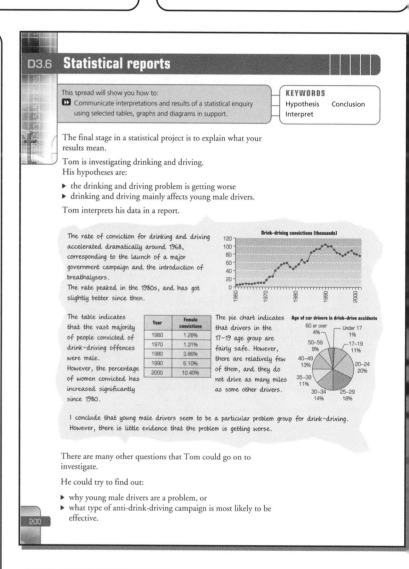

D3.6 Statistical reports

This spread will show you how to:
▶▶ Communicate interpretations and results of a statistical enquiry using selected tables, graphs and diagrams in support.

KEYWORDS
Hypothesis   Conclusion
Interpret

The final stage in a statistical project is to explain what your results mean.

Tom is investigating drinking and driving. His hypotheses are:

▶ the drinking and driving problem is getting worse
▶ drinking and driving mainly affects young male drivers.

Tom interprets his data in a report.

The rate of conviction for drinking and driving accelerated dramatically around 1968, corresponding to the launch of a major government campaign and the introduction of breathalysers.
The rate peaked in the 1980s, and has got slightly better since then.

Drink-driving convictions (thousands)

The table indicates that the vast majority of people convicted of drink-driving offences were male. However, the percentage of women convicted has increased significantly since 1980.

Year	Female convictions
1960	1.28%
1970	1.31%
1980	3.86%
1990	6.10%
2000	10.40%

The pie chart indicates that drivers in the 17–19 age group are fairly safe. However, there are relatively few of them, and they do not drive as many miles as some other drivers.

Age of car drivers in drink-drive accidents
60 or over 4%, Under 17 1%, 17–19 11%, 20–24 20%, 25–29 18%, 30–34 14%, 35–39 11%, 40–49 13%, 50–59 8%

I conclude that young male drivers seem to be a particular problem group for drink-driving. However, there is little evidence that the problem is getting worse.

There are many other questions that Tom could go on to investigate.
He could try to find out:

▶ why young male drivers are a problem, or
▶ what type of anti-drink-driving campaign is most likely to be effective.

200

Plenary

Discuss the whole handling data cycle, on **R36**. Emphasise that you have now been through the whole cycle once, and have completed a thorough statistical investigation.

Encourage students to raise any points that they are unclear about before they write their final reports.

Emphasise that the same approach applies to all statistical projects, including those that are set for statistics coursework at GCSE level.

Further activities

Students could continue with their project work, writing a report for their results.

Differentiation

Core questions:
▶ Questions 1–3 focus on justifying conclusions from graphs and charts.
▶ Questions 4 and 5 focus on discussing conclusions drawn from tables.
▶ Question 6 extends to interpreting a scatter graph.

Extension tier: focuses on analysing students' investigation and its relevance to real life.
Support tier: focuses on drawing conclusions from data.

Exercise D3.6

Here are six extracts from statistical reports, each containing a diagram or table and a conclusion.

▶ For each extract, write a paragraph explaining whether you think the conclusion is justified.
▶ If you think that there is a better conclusion, explain carefully what it is.

1 Emergency calls to the ambulance service in England.

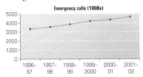

Conclusion: 'People have more accidents every year.'

2 Number of books read by students in class 9J during School Book Month.

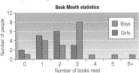

Conclusion: 'Boys are keener on reading books than girls are.'

3 Age of people using the Leisure Centre Swimming Pool (Tuesday 2 pm–4 pm during term-time).

Conclusion: 'Older people take more exercise than younger people.'

4 Finishing times for the school cross-country competition.
Results for Year 8 (Wednesday afternoon) and Year 9 (Thursday morning).

Time, t minutes	Year 8	Year 9
$25 < t < 30$	4	0
$30 < t < 35$	26	7
$35 < t < 40$	35	40
$40 < t < 45$	11	19
$45 < t < 50$	4	9
$50 < t < 55$	0	5

Conclusion: 'Year 8 students are better runners than Year 9 students.'

5 Mean and range of prices of 100 cars sold by two different auction companies.

Company	Mean price	Range
GT Sales	£2850	£4350
A1 Auctions	£2270	£3950

Conclusion: 'GT Sales will get you a better price for your car than A1 Auctions.'

6 Heights and weights of 21 dogs at a show.

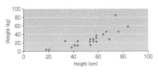

Conclusion: 'The more you feed your dog, the taller it will get.'

201

Exercise commentary

The questions assess objectives on Framework Pages 273–275.

Problem solving
The exercise assesses objectives on Framework Page 25.

Group work
Students may work in pairs to draft and revise conclusions to their projects.

Misconceptions
Students may have difficulties justifying their conclusions. Encourage them to explain their conclusions in pairs, and then write down exactly what they have said. Students may also jump to immediate conclusions without thinking of alternative interpretations of their data. Encourage them to work through the examples in the exercise and think carefully about all possible conclusions.

Links
This topic links to practical investigations in other subject areas.
Interpreting graphs: Framework Pages 173–177.

Homework

D3.6HW prompts students to write a report for their own project.

Answers – Alternative conclusions

1 People may be more ready to call an ambulance without real justification.
2 Boys may read shorter books. No information about time spent reading.
3 Young people in school at this time, so conclusion invalid.
4 Conclusion may not be true e.g. heavy rain on Wednesday night could have slowed Year 9 down.
5 You would need to know that both companies dealt with similar cars.
6 The heavier dogs are taller, but they are probably different breeds. Feeding a small dog more may make it heavier, but probably not taller.

Summary

The key objectives for this unit are:

▶ Communicate interpretations and results of a statistical enquiry using selected tables, graphs and diagrams in support. (273–275)

▶ Present a concise, reasoned argument. (31)

Plenary activity

Discuss the stages of the handling data cycle, including examples from the students' own projects.

Discuss any difficulties or unexpected conclusions. Do any of the conclusions have real-life consequences/implications?

Do they suggest further hypotheses for investigations?

Check out commentary

1 Students may be unsure what graph or diagram to draw. Emphasise that the diagram has to show the outlier value (32). Grouping the data too closely, for example 70–90 in together, will not show enough detail.

Encourage students to explain why they did not select some of the alternative graphs.

2 **a** Students should now be familiar with the four stages of the handling data cycle.

b Students may have trouble interpreting the data as a list. Encourage them to think of what both variables are first.

A time series would be the most appropriate graph.

Encourage students to interpret their graph in their criticism of Jon's statement, including defining much larger in relation to the previous years' growth.

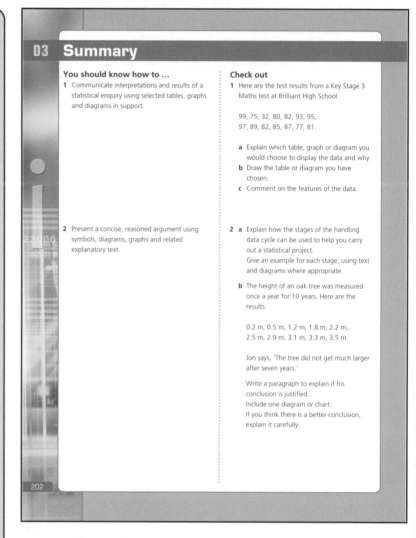

D3 Summary

You should know how to ...

1 Communicate interpretations and results of a statistical enquiry using selected tables, graphs and diagrams in support.

2 Present a concise, reasoned argument using symbols, diagrams, graphs and related explanatory text.

Check out

1 Here are the test results from a Key Stage 3 Maths test at Brilliant High School:

99, 75, 32, 80, 82, 93, 95,
97, 89, 82, 85, 87, 77, 81.

a Explain which table, graph or diagram you would choose to display the data and why.

b Draw the table or diagram you have chosen.

c Comment on the features of the data.

2 **a** Explain how the stages of the handling data cycle can be used to help you carry out a statistical project.
Give an example for each stage, using text and diagrams where appropriate.

b The height of an oak tree was measured once a year for 10 years. Here are the results:

0.2 m, 0.5 m, 1.2 m, 1.8 m, 2.2 m,
2.5 m, 2.9 m, 3.1 m, 3.3 m, 3.5 m.

Jon says, 'The tree did not get much larger after seven years.'

Write a paragraph to explain if his conclusion is justified.
Include one diagram or chart.
If you think there is a better conclusion, explain it carefully.

202

Development

The probability aspects of this unit are developed further in D4.

Links

The work in this unit links to statistical project work in Science, Geography and PSHE.

Writing a report links to similar report writing in English.

Mental starters

Objectives covered in this unit:
- ▶ Visualise, describe and sketch 2-D and 3-D shapes.
- ▶ Visualise symmetries of 2-D and 3-D shapes.
- ▶ Use metric units for calculations.
- ▶ Convert between metric units.
- ▶ Recall and use formulae for areas.
- ▶ Calculate volumes of cuboids and prisms.
- ▶ Add, subtract, multiply and divide integers.
- ▶ Estimate angles and bearings.

Resources needed

* means class set needed

Essential:
R16 – 3-D shapes
Set of solids
Multilink cubes
Rulers*
Protractors*
Squared paper*
Different-shaped boxes for plenary, some not cuboids

Useful:
S4.2OHP – kite pattern
S4.6OHP – 3-D kite
S3.6OHP – a map
R13 – spotty isometric grid*
R14 – special triangles
R15 – special quadrilaterals
R22 – angles in parallel lines
S4.3ICT* – constructing nets
Maps

S4 Applying geometrical reasoning

This unit will show you how to:
- ▶ Solve problems using properties of angles, of parallel and intersecting lines, and of triangles and other polygons.
- ▶ Visualise 2-D representations of 3-D objects.
- ▶ Analyse 3-D shapes through 2-D projections.
- ▶ Use and interpret maps and scale drawings.
- ▶ Calculate the surface area and volume of right prisms.
- ▶ Solve increasingly demanding problems and evaluate solutions.
- ▶ Represent problems and synthesise information in geometric form.
- ▶ Present a concise, reasoned argument, using symbols, diagrams and explanatory text.
- ▶ Give solutions to problems to an appropriate degree of accuracy.

You can use properties of shapes to help you design your own kite.

Before you start

You should know how to ...
1 Identify the angle and symmetry properties of triangles and quadrilaterals.
2 Draw nets.
3 Calculate with ratios.

Check in
1 Sketch and describe these shapes:
  a equilateral triangle
  b parallelogram c kite
  Include angle and symmetry properties.
2 Sketch the net of a cuboid.
3 Reduce these ratios to their simplest terms, without units:
  a 3 kg : 600 g b 2 hours : 40 minutes
  c 50 cm : 3 km d 75 cl : 4 l

203

Unit commentary

Aim of the unit
The unit aims to develop students' geometric reasoning skills in a practical context, using the idea of designing a kite. Students are encouraged to apply all their previous knowledge to use appropriate notation and justify their reasoning.

Introduction
Discuss shapes of kites and what makes them successful fliers – one important aspect is that they have symmetry otherwise they can be unbalanced. Encourage students to suggest suitable shapes for kites.
Emphasise that kits can be 3-D as well as 2-D.

Framework references
This unit focuses on:
Teaching objectives pages:
81, 185–187, 191, 199, 201, 217, 239–241.
Problem solving pages:
5, 17, 21, 27, 29, 31.

Differentiation

Support tier
Focuses on plan and elevation, tessellations and nets, related to area and volume of a cuboid.

Extension tier
Focuses on revising angle properties, Pythagoras, plan and elevation and then introduces trigonometrical ratios.

Check in activity

Ask students to draw as many different triangles and quadrilaterals as they can.
They should draw each diagram on an A4 piece of paper and clearly mark any side, angle and symmetry properties.
Students should work in pairs or small groups and swap shapes with other groups who should write the name of the shape on the paper.

S4.1 Properties of 2-D shapes

Mental starter

What's my shape?
Students work in pairs, taking turns.
One student describes a shape using its geometric properties.
The other student sketches the shape showing its features, and names the shape.
R14 and **R15** may be useful.

Useful resources

R14 – special triangles
R15 – special quadrilaterals

Introductory activity

Refer to the mental starter.
Emphasise that to uniquely define a shape you must fully describe its side, angle and symmetry properties.

Discuss the difference between a kite and a parallelogram or a rhombus. Use **R15**.

Discuss the side, angle and symmetry properties of a kite.
Discuss the properties of the diagonals.
Emphasise that they meet at 90° and bisect each other.

Draw a kite ABCD on the board or OHP.
Mark one of the equal angles as 120° and the base angle as 40°.
Draw in the diagonals. Mark the intersection M.
Discuss how to find the other angles of the kite, including the angles formed by the diagonals.
Encourage students to give reasons for any assumptions they make.
Encourage students to use correct terminology for angles: ABM etc.

Emphasise that:
▸ the diagonals form two pairs of right-angled triangles, and
▸ the line of symmetry creates two congruent triangles.

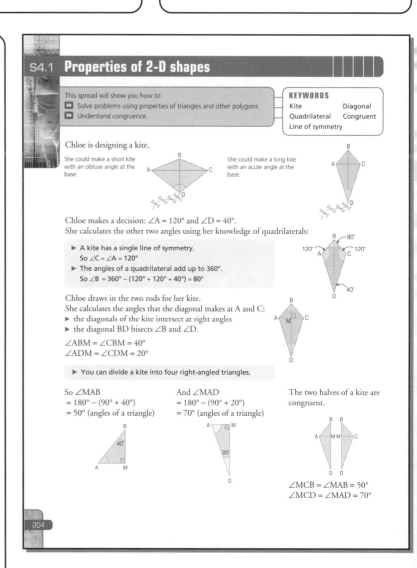

S4.1 Properties of 2-D shapes

This spread will show you how to:
▶▶ Solve problems using properties of triangles and other polygons.
▶▶ Understand congruence.

KEYWORDS
Kite   Diagonal
Quadrilateral   Congruent
Line of symmetry

Chloe is designing a kite.

She could make a short kite with an obtuse angle at the base.

She could make a long kite with an acute angle at the base.

Chloe makes a decision: ∠A = 120° and ∠D = 40°.
She calculates the other two angles using her knowledge of quadrilaterals:

▶ A kite has a single line of symmetry.
  So ∠C = ∠A = 120°
▶ The angles of a quadrilateral add up to 360°.
  So ∠B = 360° − (120° + 120° + 40°) = 80°

Chloe draws in the two rods for her kite.
She calculates the angles that the diagonal makes at A and C:
▶ the diagonals of the kite intersect at right angles
▶ the diagonal BD bisects ∠B and ∠D.

∠ABM = ∠CBM = 40°
∠ADM = ∠CDM = 20°

▶ You can divide a kite into four right-angled triangles.

So ∠MAB
= 180° − (90° + 40°)
= 50° (angles of a triangle)

And ∠MAD
= 180° − (90° + 20°)
= 70° (angles of a triangle)

The two halves of a kite are congruent.

∠MCB = ∠MAB = 50°
∠MCD = ∠MAD = 70°

204

Plenary

Draw a kite with one angle (not an equal angle) showing 120°.
Discuss whether you can find out the other three angles given this information. (You can't.)
Discuss what the equal angles could be – the smallest possible angle and the largest possible.
Discuss what other information you need to be able to work out the other angles – you need one more angle.

Further activities

Students could investigate tessellations involving two or more regular polygons, or irregular polygons, on paper or using ICT.

Differentiation

Core questions:
▸ Question 1 focuses on congruent triangles.
▸ Questions 2–4 focus on using properties of shapes to solve angle problems.
▸ Question 5 involves investigating which shapes will tessellate.

Extension tier: focuses on using angle properties to solve problems.

Support tier: focuses on tessellations.

Exercise S4.1

1 The diagram shows a regular hexagon ABCDEF which is drawn inside a circle with diameter BE.

  a Find a triangle which is congruent to triangle AEF.
  b Find a triangle which is congruent to triangle BED.
  c Calculate:
    i ∠AFE **ii** ∠AEF **iii** ∠BDE.

2 ABCD is a kite.

Work out ∠BAD.

3 These triangles are congruent.

Find the size of:
  a angle *a*
  b side *b*.

4 Work out all the labelled angles in this kite pattern.
It will help to work them out in order.

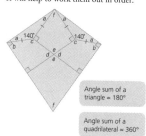

Angle sum of a triangle = 180°

Angle sum of a quadrilateral = 360°

5 Investigation
  a Explain why a regular pentagon does not tessellate.
    This diagram should help ...

Interior angle of a pentagon

  b A square tessellates because the four interior angles marked add to 360°.

Which other regular polygons tessellate? Explain your answers.
  c Do all quadrilaterals tessellate?
  d Do all triangles tessellate?
    Use clear diagrams and angle calculations to explain your answers.
  e Investigate tessellations made using two different regular polygons.

205

Exercise commentary

The questions assess objectives on Framework Pages 185–187 and 191.

Problem solving

The exercise assesses objectives on Framework Page 17.

Question 5 assesses Page 31.

Group work

Question 5 is particularly suitable for paired work.

Misconceptions

Students need to be able to remember the angle and side properties of 2-D shapes in order to be able to answer these questions effectively.

It is worth taking some time to ensure students are confident which facts relate to which shape before starting the exercise.

When using kites, students tend to assume that the opposite angles are equal but only one pair are equal.

The discussion in the introductory activity will help.

Encourage students to design their own kite to give them direct experience.

Links

Geometrical language: Framework Page 179.

Homework

S4.1HW gives more practice in using properties of 2-D shapes and angles to solve problems.

Answers

1 a Triangle BDC **b** Triangle EBA
  c i 120° **ii** 30° **iii** 90°
2 46° **3 a** 60° **b** 8 cm
4 $a = 20°$, $b = 70°$, $c = 130°$, $d = 70°$, $e = 110°$, $f = 70°$
5 a 108° is not a factor of 360°. **b** Equilateral triangle, regular hexagon
  c No **d** No **e** Student's own investigation, for example, square and octagon.

S4.2 Properties of angles

Mental starter

Angles in a pentagon
Ask students to find the size of an interior angle of a regular pentagon.
Discuss methods.
Emphasise that the angle sum is 3 × 180° (3 triangles).
Encourage the use of exterior angles too: 360° ÷ 5 = 72°.
So an interior angle is 180° − 72° = 108°.

Useful resources

R22 – angles in parallel lines
S4.2OHP – the kite pattern from the Students' Book

Introductory activity

Refer to the previous lesson.
Use S4.2OHP to introduce the pattern on the kite.
Discuss any features of the pattern.
Emphasise that the horizontal lines are parallel and mark them on the OHP.
Discuss what aspects can vary this pattern – the angle chosen.
Encourage students to suggest an angle to start with.
Discuss how to find the other angles.
Encourage students to give reasons for their answers.
Emphasise the use of alternate and corresponding angles.
R22 shows these and vertically opposite angles for you to revise with students – mark one angle and ask students to work out the others with reasons.

Discuss which shapes other than a kite might make a good kite to fly.
Encourage students to give reasons for their answers.
Emphasise that a kite would usually have line symmetry as that would keep the shape in balance.
Discuss angle properties of each shape.

Refer to the mental starter.
Discuss the general formula for the interior and exterior angle of a regular polygon.
Discuss how to find the exterior and interior angle of a non-regular polygon.
Emphasise that the angle sum is the same as for a regular polygon.

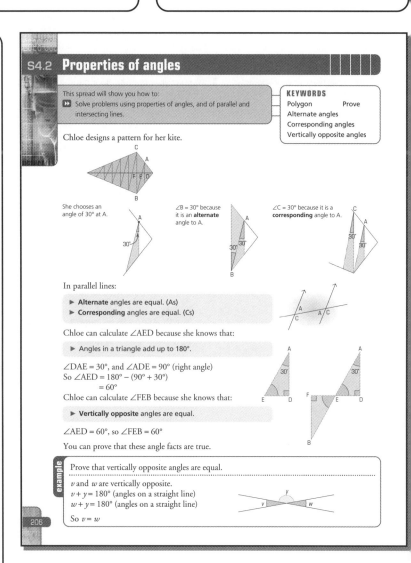

S4.2 Properties of angles

This spread will show you how to:
▶▶ Solve problems using properties of angles, and of parallel and intersecting lines.

KEYWORDS
Polygon   Prove
Alternate angles
Corresponding angles
Vertically opposite angles

Chloe designs a pattern for her kite.

She chooses an angle of 30° at A.

∠B = 30° because it is an **alternate** angle to A.

∠C = 30° because it is a **corresponding** angle to A.

In parallel lines:

▶ **Alternate** angles are equal. (As)
▶ **Corresponding** angles are equal. (Cs)

Chloe can calculate ∠AED because she knows that:

▶ Angles in a triangle add up to 180°.

∠DAE = 30°, and ∠ADE = 90° (right angle)
So ∠AED = 180° − (90° + 30°)
= 60°

Chloe can calculate ∠FEB because she knows that:

▶ **Vertically opposite** angles are equal.

∠AED = 60°, so ∠FEB = 60°

You can prove that these angle facts are true.

example
Prove that vertically opposite angles are equal.

v and w are vertically opposite.
$v + y = 180°$ (angles on a straight line)
$w + y = 180°$ (angles on a straight line)
So $v = w$

Plenary

Discuss questions 4 and 5.
Emphasise the use of diagrams for each part of the question – make them large and mark any known facts.
Encourage students to give reasons for any stages in their working.

Further activities

Students could find the interior and exterior angles of a regular nonagon and a regular decagon.

Differentiation

Core questions:

The exercise is a review of Year 8 work.
▶ Question 1 revises angle properties of shapes and parallel lines.
▶ Questions 2–5 focus on angles in parallel lines and in polygons.
▶ Question 6 is an extended task allowing students to apply a wide range of angle properties.

Extension tier: focuses on using Pythagoras' theorem.

Support tier: focuses on plans and elevations of 3-D shapes.

Exercise S4.2

1 Find the angles marked with letters. Give reasons for your answers.

a 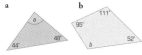　**b**

c　**d**

e　**f**

g　**h**

i　**j**

2 Find the **sum** of the interior angles of these polygons.

a　**b**

3 Find the interior angle and exterior angle of:
  a a regular octagon
  b a regular dodecagon (12 sides).

4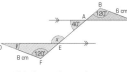

  a Calculate angles *x* and *y*.
  b Show that triangle ABC is similar to triangle DEF.

5 These two polygons are regular.

Calculate the angle *y*.

6 Design a kite with a pattern like the one on page 206.
You will need to work out any angles.

Exercise commentary

The questions assess objectives on Framework Pages 185–187 and 191.

Problem solving
The exercise assesses objectives on Framework Pages 27 and 31.

Group work
Questions 5 and 6 are particularly suitable for paired work.

Misconceptions
Students often mix up angle facts. Encourage them to start from first principles: angles in a triangle add to 180°. Encourage them to draw their own diagrams clearly marking facts they know for each part of a problem.
Students find working with angles in parallel lines difficult as the diagrams often do not make them obvious.
Encourage them to draw large diagrams and clearly mark parallel sides, extending lines where necessary, and then equal angles.
Emphasise that the small (large) angles formed are all the same.

Links
Polygons: Framework Page 183.

Homework

S4.2HW provides practice in finding missing angles using angle properties.

Answers

1 a $a = 88°$　**b** $b = 102°$　**c** $c = 47°$, $d = 133°$　**d** $e = 45°$　**e** $f = 57°$, $g = 123°$, $h = 57°$, $i = 123°$　**f** $j = 100°$　**g** $k = 56°$, $l = m = 87°$, $n = 93°$, $p = 124°$
  h $q = r = 54°$, $s = 86°$　**i** $t = 52°$, $u = v = 128°$　**j** $t = 35°$, $v = 110°$, $w = 35°$
2 a 540°　**b** 900°
3 a Interior = 135°, exterior = 45°　**b** Interior = 150°, exterior = 30°
4 a $x = 140°$, $y = 20°$　**b** Angle BAC = 40° (vertically opposite angles) and angle BCA = 20°, so both triangles have the same angles and must be similar.
5 105°　**6** Student's own kite design.

207

S4.3 2-D representation of 3-D objects

Mental starter

Give me your views

Give students a 3-D shape such as a triangular prism.

Ask them to draw the views and elevation of the shape.

Ask students to draw the net.

Discuss any difficulties. **R16** or a box of solids may be useful.

Repeat for other 3-D shapes such as a square-based pyramid.

Useful resources

R16 – 3-D shapes

R13 – spotty isometric grid

Set of solids

Multilink cubes for the plenary

Introductory activity

Refer to the mental starter.

Discuss how to draw a 3-D version of each shape.

Emphasise that isometric paper (**R26**) makes it easier to give perspective.

Discuss how to use isometric paper.

Emphasise that there is a right way and a wrong way up.

Emphasise that you draw vertical lengths upright.

Check students know the right way.

Ask them to draw the 3-D shapes from the starter on isometric paper.

Discuss results.

Encourage students to give an exact description of their shapes, including the shapes of the faces and the dimensions.

Encourage students to draw the views of their shapes and to mark known lengths.

Use students' views to challenge the class to describe their 3-D shape.

Discuss why the views of a shape are useful – it is difficult to draw 3-D shapes so that you can see them from all angles easily.

Discuss 3-D shapes that students think will make good kites.

Emphasise that you make the kite out of the net.

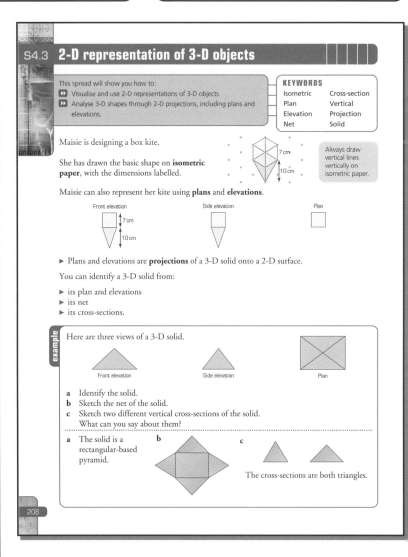

Plenary

Encourage students to work in pairs.

They make a design using six multilink cubes.

They draw the plan, side and front views.

The pair challenges another pair to make the shape with those views.

Further activities

S4.3ICT provides practice at constructing the nets of cuboids, prisms and pyramids.

Alternatively

Challenge students to sketch the plan, front and side elevation of this building:

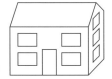

Differentiation

Core questions:

▶ Question 1 focuses on drawing 3-D shapes on isometric paper.

▶ Questions 2–5 focus on drawing nets and elevations for 3-D shapes.

▶ Question 6 is an open-ended challenge.

Extension tier: focuses on 2-D representations of 3-D shapes, plans and elevations.

Support tier: focuses on calculating volumes of cuboids.

Exercise S4.3

1 Draw these solids on isometric paper:
   a A cube of side 2 cm.
   b A cuboid with sides 4 cm, 3 cm and 2 cm.
   c A hexagonal prism of length 4 cm and cross-section a regular hexagon of side 2 cm.
   d A triangular prism of length 5 cm and cross-section an isosceles triangle of base 2 cm and height 4 cm.
   e A triangular prism of length 6 cm and cross-section an equilateral triangle of side 2 cm.

2 Sketch nets for the 3-D objects in question 1.
   Show all the lengths on your sketches.

3 Use the descriptions in the table to identify the 3-D shapes.

	Plans and elevations		
	Front	Side	Plan
a	circle	circle	circle
b	triangle	triangle	square
c	circle	rectangle	rectangle
d	triangle	triangle	circle

4 You need a box of solids.
   Choose a solid from the box.
   a Name the solid.
   b Draw a front view.
   c Draw a side view.
   d Draw a plan view.
   Repeat for other solids.

   > You can choose a solid from memory if you have no box of solid shapes.

5 These diagrams show the same model from different views.

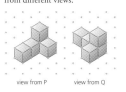

view from P   view from Q

The model is made from 5 cubes.

a One cube is added:

view from Q

Draw the view from P.

b Now start with the original model (5 cubes).
   Add a cube to a different position.
   i Draw the view from P.
   ii Draw the view from Q.

c Now add two cubes to the original model and draw the views from P and Q.

6 A polyhedron is a 3-D shape with straight edges and flat faces.
   Investigate which polyhedra could have a triangle as a front elevation.

209

Exercise commentary

The questions assess objectives on Framework Pages 199 and 201.

Problem solving

The exercise assesses objectives on Framework Page 27.

Group work

Questions 5 and 6 are particularly suitable for group work.

Misconceptions

Students may find using isometric paper difficult.

Encourage them to practise drawing basic shapes first so they get a feel for the sort of construction they need to make before adding the complexity of specific lengths. Looking at finished shapes that are similar will help.

Students often add in extra lines in views, particularly the plan view.

These lines can help students to draw the views but you need to emphasise that the answer is just the outline shape.

Links

Properties of shapes: Framework Pages 185–187.

Homework

S4.3HW focuses on drawing 2-D representations, and plans and elevations. Students will need spotty isometric paper (**R13**).

Answers

1 Drawings of solids on isometric paper.
2 Nets for the solids in question 1.
3 a Sphere   b Square-based pyramid   c Cylinder   d Cone
4 Descriptions of solids and views.
5 a As original view from Q, one cube added to left section.
   b, c New views of solid from P and Q
6 For example, triangular prism or pyramid.

S4.4 Scale drawings and ratio

Mental starter

Journey

Ask students to draw this journey:

▶ Straight ahead for 5 km
▶ Turn right then straight for 3 km
▶ Turn through 60° then straight for 2 km
▶ Turn right then straight for 6 km.

Discuss diagrams.

Useful resources

Protractors
Squared paper
Rulers

Introductory activity

Refer to the mental starter.

Discuss whether you will get back to the beginning on this route.

Emphasise that you can draw an accurate diagram to be sure.

Discuss how to draw such a diagram.

Emphasise that you need to use a scale.

Discuss a sensible scale to use:

▶ 1 cm to 1 km is simple.
▶ 2 cm to 1 km would give a larger diagram and so it would be easier to construct the 60° angle accurately.

Discuss how to work out the distances using the second scale.

Emphasise that every 1 km in real life would be 2 cm on the map.

Encourage students to construct the diagram accurately using this scale.

Challenge them to add a last instruction to take them back to the beginning.

Emphasise that they need to give a direction (angle) and a distance.

Discuss other uses of scales.

Emphasise that you make scale drawings of large objects such as a kite, or plans of large areas.

Discuss how to express a scale such as 1 cm to 3 m.

Emphasise that you can write it as a ratio once the units are the same.

Discuss how to convert between various lengths on the plan and in real life using the scale.

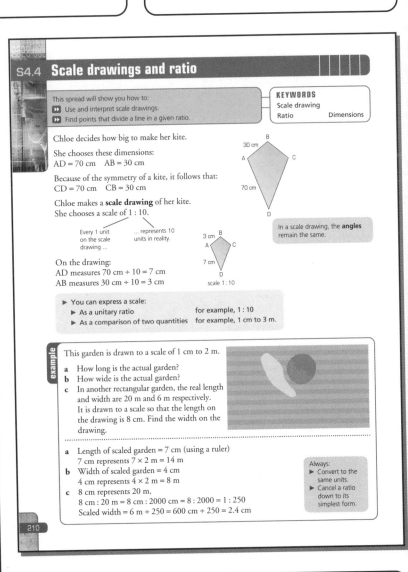

S4.4 Scale drawings and ratio

This spread will show you how to:
▶▶ Use and interpret scale drawings.
▶▶ Find points that divide a line in a given ratio.

KEYWORDS
Scale drawing
Ratio   Dimensions

Chloe decides how big to make her kite.

She chooses these dimensions:
AD = 70 cm   AB = 30 cm

Because of the symmetry of a kite, it follows that:
CD = 70 cm   CB = 30 cm

Chloe makes a **scale drawing** of her kite.
She chooses a scale of 1 : 10.

Every 1 unit on the scale drawing ... ... represents 10 units in reality.

In a scale drawing, the **angles** remain the same.

On the drawing:
AD measures 70 cm ÷ 10 = 7 cm
AB measures 30 cm ÷ 10 = 3 cm

scale 1 : 10

▶ You can express a scale:
  ▶ As a unitary ratio   for example, 1 : 10
  ▶ As a comparison of two quantities   for example, 1 cm to 3 m.

example

This garden is drawn to a scale of 1 cm to 2 m.
a   How long is the actual garden?
b   How wide is the actual garden?
c   In another rectangular garden, the real length and width are 20 m and 6 m respectively. It is drawn to a scale so that the length on the drawing is 8 cm. Find the width on the drawing.

a   Length of scaled garden = 7 cm (using a ruler)
    7 cm represents 7 × 2 m = 14 m
b   Width of scaled garden = 4 cm
    4 cm represents 4 × 2 m = 8 m
c   8 cm represents 20 m.
    8 cm : 20 m = 8 cm : 2000 cm = 8 : 2000 = 1 : 250
    Scaled width = 6 m ÷ 250 = 600 cm ÷ 250 = 2.4 cm

Always:
▶ Convert to the same units.
▶ Cancel a ratio down to its simplest form.

210

Plenary

Ask students to suggest suitable scales in ratio form for a scale drawing of:

▶ Your classroom   ▶ Their desk
▶ The school hall   ▶ A cinema
▶ The school field

Emphasise that the scale must be easy to use and produce a suitably sized diagram.

Further activities

Students could investigate the dimensions and markings of a tennis court, football pitch or similar, and make an accurate scale drawing.

Differentiation

Core questions:

▶ Question 1 focuses on using a simple scale.
▶ Questions 2–4 focus on using scales and ratios. Question 4 is a typical Key Stage 3 style question.
▶ Question 5 requires students to split a line in a given ratio.

Extension tier: focuses on finding sin, cos and tan ratios for triangles.

Support tier: focuses on calculating the surface areas of cuboids.

Exercise S4.4

1 a On the plan of a house, a door measures 4 cm by 10 cm.
      The plan is drawn to a scale of 1 : 20.
      Find the actual dimensions of the door.
   b Another plan of the same house is made to a
      scale of 1 : 25.
      On the plan, a rectangular window measures 10 cm
      by 5 cm.
      Find the actual dimensions of the window.

2 A dolls' house is an exact replica of a real house,
   on a scale of 1 : 12.
   The dolls' house is 84 cm long, 66 cm wide and 54 cm high.
   Find the dimensions of the real house.

3 A school playground has dimensions of 40 m by 24 m.
   Devlin draws a plan of the playground to a scale of 1 : 200.
   Find the dimensions of the playground in Devlin's plan.

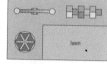

4 The diagram shows an area to be tiled.
   It can be tiled with the blue tiles, or the green tiles.
   a Show that the ratio of blue to green tiles used
      is 1 to 5.
   b Change the measurements of the blue tile so
      that the ratio of blue to green is:
      i   2 : 5
      ii 1 : 8
      iii 1 : 4

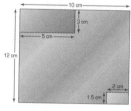

5 The point X divides the line AB in the ratio 1 : 2.
   The ratio has 1 + 2 = 3 parts altogether.
   You divide the horizontal and vertical distance into 3 parts.

   Work out the coordinates of the points which divide:
   a AC in the ratio of 1 : 1
   b AC in the ratio of 1 : 2   Dividing in the ratio 1 : 1 gives
   c CB in the ratio of 1 : 2   the midpoint.
   d CD in the ratio of 1 : 1
   e AE in the ratio of 1 : 2

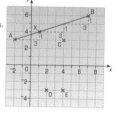

211

Exercise commentary

The questions assess objectives on Framework Page 217.

Problem solving

The exercise assesses objectives on Framework Page 21.

Group work

The exercise is suitable for paired work.

Misconceptions

Students may mix up the units, using m for lengths on a scale drawing or cm for a real-life length.

Encourage them to think carefully about which units are appropriate: scale drawings use small units, real life uses large units.

In choosing an appropriate scale, students often think 1 : 10 is a larger scale than 1 : 5.

Encourage them to draw the longest length in each scale so they can see whether the drawing will fit on the page.

Links

Ratio and proportion: Framework Page 81.

Homework

S4.4HW gives practice in calculating distances using scales, and drawing a scale diagram.

Answers

1 a 80 cm by 200 cm   b 250 cm by 125 cm
2 10.08 m long, 7.92 m wide, 6.48 m high
3 20 cm by 12 cm
4 a No. of blue tiles to cover whole area = 8,
      No. of green tiles = 40, 8 : 40 = 5 : 1
   b i blue: 3×2.5 ii blue: 12 cm × 2 cm   iii blue: 6 cm × 2 cm
5 a (1, 3)   b (0, 3)   c (5, 4)   d (3, 0)   e (0, 1)

211

S4.5 Maps and ratio

Mental starter

What's my length?
Give students a scale in ratio form, such as 1 : 50.
Ask for distances in real life given the scale drawing distance.
Ask for scale drawing distances given the real-life distance.
Use m for real-life distances and cm for scale-drawing distances.

Useful resources

S3.6OHP – a map
A variety of **maps** would be useful for students to see how scales are used.

Introductory activity

Refer to the mental starter.
Discuss how to write the scale using units.
Emphasise that 1 : 50 means 1 cm to 50 cm or 1 m to 50 m.
Encourage students to express the scale in the form 1 cm to 0.5 m or 2 cm to 1 m.
Discuss why this form might be useful – it can be simpler to change between the distances.

Discuss map scales in general.
Encourage students to suggest the scale of a map of their local area (or use **S3.6OHP** with the scale covered up).
Emphasise that many maps use a scale of 1 cm to 2 km.
Discuss how to write this as a ratio:
1 : 200 000
Emphasise that you convert km to m then to cm.

Discuss how to use the scale 1 : 80 000 to find real-life distances.
Emphasise the unitary method:
1 cm = 80 000 cm
so 3 cm = 3 × 80 000 cm
Encourage students to convert the answer into appropriate units: 2.4 km
Discuss how to find map distances.
Emphasise that you divide instead of multiply.
Encourage students to consider whether their answers are sensible.

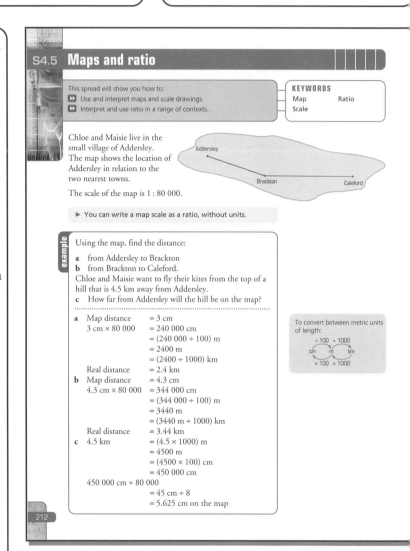

S4.5 Maps and ratio

This spread will show you how to:
- Use and interpret maps and scale drawings.
- Interpret and use ratio in a range of contexts.

KEYWORDS
Map   Ratio
Scale

Chloe and Maisie live in the small village of Addersley. The map shows the location of Addersley in relation to the two nearest towns.

The scale of the map is 1 : 80 000.

▶ You can write a map scale as a ratio, without units.

example

Using the map, find the distance:
a from Addersley to Brackton
b from Brackton to Caleford.
Chloe and Maisie want to fly their kites from the top of a hill that is 4.5 km away from Addersley.
c How far from Addersley will the hill be on the map?

a Map distance   = 3 cm
   3 cm × 80 000   = 240 000 cm
                 = (240 000 ÷ 100) m
                 = 2400 m
                 = (2400 ÷ 1000) km
   Real distance   = 2.4 km
b Map distance   = 4.3 cm
   4.3 cm × 80 000 = 344 000 cm
                 = (344 000 ÷ 100) m
                 = 3440 m
                 = (3440 m ÷ 1000) km
   Real distance   = 3.44 km
c 4.5 km   = (4.5 × 1000) m
                 = 4500 m
                 = (4500 × 100) cm
                 = 450 000 cm
   450 000 cm ÷ 80 000
                 = 45 cm ÷ 8
                 = 5.625 cm on the map

To convert between metric units of length:
÷ 100   ÷ 1000
cm   m   km
× 100   × 1000

212

Plenary

Give students a map scale such as 1 : 500.
Ask them to find the actual length shown by a distance of 6 cm on the map.
Repeat for other scales such as
1 : 1000, 1 : 5000 and 1 : 250 000
Challenge them to find the length on the scale drawing of an actual length of 7.5 km.

Students could use an Ordnance Survey map of their local area. They could measure the distance on the map for journeys such as home to school, and use the scale to work out the distance in km.

Differentiation

Core questions:

▶ Question 1 focuses on using a map and interpreting its scale.
▶ Questions 2–5 focus on using scales to finding distances.
▶ Question 6 involves choosing an appropriate scale and making a scale drawing.

Extension tier: focuses on using trigonometrical ratios to find angles.

Support tier: focuses on making scale drawings of nets.

Exercise S4.5

1   This map of Ireland is drawn to a scale of 1 cm to 65 km.

Scale 1:6 500 000 (1 cm = 65 km)

0	100	200	300	400 km

The numbers on the map indicate the distances between major towns.
For example, the distance from Dublin to Belfast is 102 km.
For the following:
i   find the distance given by the map.
ii estimate the distance in cm and use the scale to check the numbers given by the map. Are they correct?
a   Belfast to Dublin   b   Limerick to Dublin
c   Limerick to Sligo   d   Londonderry to Cork.

2   The scale of a map is 1 : 20 000.
Find the actual length in metres of 4 cm on the map.

3   The scale of a map is 1 cm to 50 m.
The length of a field is 79.4 m.
What length will the field be on the map?

4   A map is drawn to a scale of 1 : 2000.
Find the actual distance in metres between two farms which are 5.7 cm apart on the map.

5   Copy and complete this table.

	Map scale	Actual length	Map length
a	1 : 20 000	12.5 km	☐ cm
b	1 : 5000	4 km	☐ cm
c	1 : 20 000	☐ km	6.3 cm
d	1 : 5000	☐ km	37 cm
e	1 : 250 000	37 km	☐ cm
f	1 : 250 000	☐ km	12 cm

6   Make an accurate scale drawing of a room in your school, such as your classroom.

213

Exercise commentary

The questions assess objectives on Framework Pages 81 and 217.

Problem solving
The exercise assesses objectives on Framework Pages 5 and 31.

Group work
Question 6 is particularly suitable for small group work.

Misconceptions
Students will often use the wrong units, quoting real-life lengths in cm and scale lengths in km.
Emphasise that real-life lengths use the bigger units.
Many students find using ratios for scales confusing and tend to multiply or divide depending on the numbers rather than whether it is right to do so.
Encourage students to check their answers, considering whether they are appropriate.
Emphasise that you can start from first principles: 1 : 20 000 means 1 cm to 20 000 cm which is 1 cm to 200 m.

Links
Metric units: Framework Pages 229–231.

Homework

S4.5HW gives practice in reading maps and using scale to convert distances.

Answers

1 i a 102 km   b 124 km   c 154 km   d 365 km
  ii a 150 km   b 175 km   c 250 km   d 450 km
     Map numbers not correct, all underestimates.
2 800 m   3 1.6 cm   4 114 m
5 a 62.5 cm   b 80 cm   c 1.26 km   d 1.85 km
  e 14.8 cm   f 30 km
6 Student's own scale drawing.

Mental starter

Cuboids

Ask students to sketch a cuboid measuring 2 m by 3 m by 4 m and to draw its net.

Challenge them to work out the volume and surface area of the cuboid.

Encourage them to use the correct units.

Repeat with another cuboid using decimal lengths.

Useful resources

S4.6OHP – diagrams from the Students' Book

Introductory activity

Refer to the mental starter.

Discuss how to find the volume of the cuboid.

Encourage students to explain why the formula works.

Emphasise that the units are cubic: cm^3.

Discuss an appropriate degree of accuracy.

Discuss how to find the surface area of the cuboid.

Encourage students to work out the area of the faces in pairs so they only need find three areas.

Emphasise that the units are squared: cm^2.

Refer back to **S4.4** and the 3-D kites.

S4.6OHP shows the 3-D kite from the Students' Book.

Discuss why you might want to find the surface area of the kite – so you know how much material you need.

Encourage students to draw the net to help them work out the areas of the faces.

Emphasise that the end faces are not used so you just need to find one area.

Discuss how to find the volume of the kite – that would show you how much air the kite would hold.

Emphasise that the kite is a prism.

Encourage students to explain the formula.

Discuss how to find the area of the end-face: you find the area of one triangle.

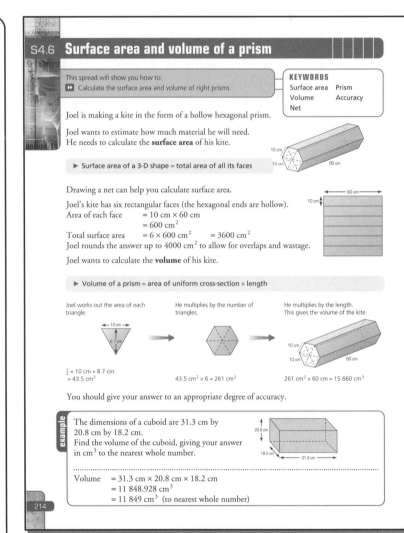

S4.6 Surface area and volume of a prism

This spread will show you how to:
▸▸ Calculate the surface area and volume of right prisms.

KEYWORDS
Surface area Prism
Volume Accuracy
Net

Joel is making a kite in the form of a hollow hexagonal prism.

Joel wants to estimate how much material he will need.
He needs to calculate the **surface area** of his kite.

▸ Surface area of a 3-D shape = total area of all its faces

Drawing a net can help you calculate surface area.

Joel's kite has six rectangular faces (the hexagonal ends are hollow).
Area of each face $= 10 \text{ cm} \times 60 \text{ cm}$
  $= 600 \text{ cm}^2$
Total surface area $= 6 \times 600 \text{ cm}^2$ $= 3600 \text{ cm}^2$
Joel rounds the answer up to 4000 cm^2 to allow for overlaps and wastage.

Joel wants to calculate the **volume** of his kite.

▸ Volume of a prism = area of uniform cross-section × length

Joel works out the area of each triangle.

$\frac{1}{2} \times 10 \text{ cm} \times 8.7 \text{ cm}$
$= 43.5 \text{ cm}^2$

He multiplies by the number of triangles.

$43.5 \text{ cm}^2 \times 6 = 261 \text{ cm}^2$

He multiplies by the length. This gives the volume of the kite.

$261 \text{ cm}^2 \times 60 \text{ cm} = 15\,660 \text{ cm}^3$

You should give your answer to an appropriate degree of accuracy.

example

The dimensions of a cuboid are 31.3 cm by 20.8 cm by 18.2 cm.
Find the volume of the cuboid, giving your answer in cm^3 to the nearest whole number.

Volume $= 31.3 \text{ cm} \times 20.8 \text{ cm} \times 18.2 \text{ cm}$
  $= 11\,848.928 \text{ cm}^3$
  $= 11\,849 \text{ cm}^3$ (to nearest whole number)

214

Plenary

Discuss question 4.

Encourage students to suggest an appropriate degree of accuracy.

Discuss what the volume and surface area would be if you converted all the lengths to cm.

Encourage students to check by calculating.

Discuss which is easier to use: cm or m.

Students could calculate the volume of air in the classroom, or school hall, in m³.

Differentiation

Core questions:
▶ Question 1 revises volume and surface area of a cuboid.
▶ Questions 2–4 focus on volume and surface area of prisms.
▶ Questions 5 and 6 involve investigating volumes.

Extension tier: focuses on surface area and volume of prisms, where lengths have to be calculated first.

Support tier: focuses on making and designing boxes, using nets.

Exercise S4.6

1 Find the volume and the surface area of these cuboids.
Use appropriate units for your answers.

a

b

2 Find the volume of these shapes.

a

b

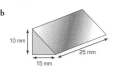

c

d

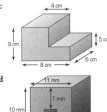

3 Here is a sketch of a swimming pool. Calculate the volume of water the swimming pool holds.

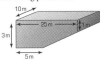

4 Find the surface area of this triangular prism.

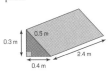

5 This cuboid has a surface area of
(2×8) cm² + (2×6) cm² + (2×12) cm²
= $(16 + 12 + 24)$ cm² = 52 cm²

Find another cuboid with the same surface area.

6 **Investigation**
This cube has a volume of 1000 cm³.

Find other prisms with a volume of 1000 cm³.

215

Exercise commentary

The questions assess objectives on Framework Pages 239–241.

Problem solving
The exercise assesses objectives on Framework Pages 27 and 31. Question 6 assesses Page 29.

Group work
Questions 5 and 6 are suitable for paired or group work.

Misconceptions
Students need to be able to work out compound areas.
The process for finding the surface area already involves many steps in working and it is important that students work systematically through these questions. Encourage them to draw diagrams at each stage to help them structure their working, marking known lengths.
In question 3, students may need to be prompted that the cross-section of the swimming pool is a trapezium.

Links
Metric units: Framework Pages 229–231.

Homework

S4.6HW provides practice in finding surface area and volume of cuboids and prisms.

Answers

1 a Volume = 105 cm³, surface area = 142 cm²
 b Volume = 10.8 m³, surface area = 33.8 m²
2 a 120 cm³ **b** 1875 mm³ **c** 336 cm³ **d** 606 mm³
3 12 300 m³
4 $1.2 + 0.96 + 0.72 + 2 \times (0.06) = 3$ m²
5 Example: 2 cm × 2 cm × 5.5 cm
6 Example: 4 cm × 25 cm × 10 cm

Summary

The key objectives for this unit are:

▶ Solve problems using properties of angles, of parallel and intersecting lines, and of triangles and other polygons. (185–187)

▶ Present a concise and reasoned argument using symbols and explanatory text. (31)

▶ Give solutions to an appropriate degree of accuracy. (31)

Check out commentary

1 This is a multi-stage question that many students will find difficult.
Encourage students to draw diagrams at each stage of working and mark on known facts.
Students may need reminding about the formula for the area of a circle, and in particular that they use the radius not the diameter.
In part **b** students may be tempted to round their answers too early, leading to rounding errors.
Encourage students to round when appropriate.
Emphasise that rounding at the end of a calculation gives a more precise answer.

2 Emphasise the importance of measuring distances and angles carefully to make the scale drawing, or students will not be able to measure the distance accurately for part **b**.
Discuss an appropriate level of accuracy for the measurement.
Encourage students to state the scale as a ratio 1 : *n* and use this in their calculation.

3 Students need to measure AB and draw it on their squared grid.
Encourage students to sketch each shape first and work out the dimensions for the given area. They should show their working clearly and mark all measurements clearly on their sketches.

Plenary activity

Show the students boxes of different shapes.
Encourage them to sketch nets, plans and elevations for the boxes and calculate the surface area and volume.
Include non-cuboid boxes if possible.

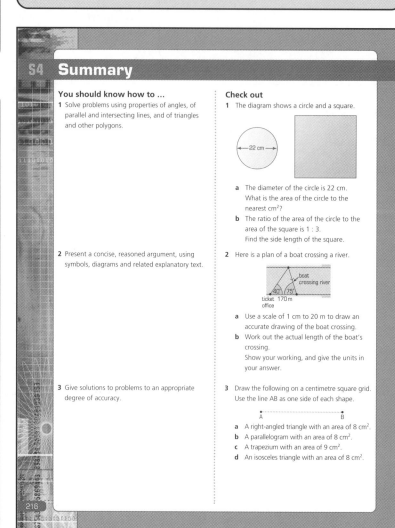

S4 Summary

You should know how to ...

1 Solve problems using properties of angles, of parallel and intersecting lines, and of triangles and other polygons.

2 Present a concise, reasoned argument, using symbols, diagrams and related explanatory text.

3 Give solutions to problems to an appropriate degree of accuracy.

Check out

1 The diagram shows a circle and a square.

— 22 cm

a The diameter of the circle is 22 cm. What is the area of the circle to the nearest cm²?

b The ratio of the area of the circle to the area of the square is 1 : 3. Find the side length of the square.

2 Here is a plan of a boat crossing a river.

boat crossing river
40° 75°
ticket 170 m
office

a Use a scale of 1 cm to 20 m to draw an accurate drawing of the boat crossing.

b Work out the actual length of the boat's crossing.
Show your working, and give the units in your answer.

3 Draw the following on a centimetre square grid. Use the line AB as one side of each shape.

A — — — B

a A right-angled triangle with an area of 8 cm².

b A parallelogram with an area of 8 cm².

c A trapezium with an area of 9 cm².

d An isosceles triangle with an area of 8 cm².

216

Development

This work is a summary of all the geometrical reasoning students have met at Key Stage 3 and will form the basis for much of the shape work at GCSE.

Links

The work on maps and scales can be practically applied in everyday life and in other subjects, particularly Geography. The design work has links to Technology where students will apply properties of shapes.

Mental starters

Objectives covered in this unit:

▶ Find fractions and percentages of quantities.
▶ Convert between fractions, decimals and percentages, and between improper fractions and mixed numbers.
▶ Solve simple problems involving probabilities.

Resources needed

* means class set needed

Essential:
Red, green and blue counters*

Useful:
D4.1OHP – sample space diagram
D4.3OHP – tree diagrams
D4.4OHP – more tree diagrams
D4.5OHP – tree diagram for spinner
D4.6OHP – probability experiments
Mini-whiteboards*
Coins*
D4.6ICT* – simulation

D4 Theoretical and experimental probability

This unit will show you how to:

▶▶ Use the vocabulary of probability in interpreting results involving uncertainty and prediction.
▶▶ Identify all the mutually exclusive outcomes of an experiment.
▶▶ Know that the sum of probabilities of all mutually exclusive outcomes is 1 and use this when solving problems.
▶▶ Estimate probabilities from experimental data.

▶▶ Compare experimental and theoretical probabilities in a range of contexts.
▶▶ Appreciate the difference between mathematical explanation and experimental evidence.
▶▶ Solve increasingly demanding problems in the context of probability and evaluate solutions.
▶▶ Represent problems and synthesise information in graphical form.

There are two ways, let's flip a coin.

Which way shall we go?

You can estimate the probability of a particular outcome when events are random.

Before you start

You should know how to ...
1 Find probabilities based on equally likely outcomes.

2 Calculate with fractions, decimals and percentages.

Check in
1 Find the probability of:
  a choosing a King from an ordinary pack of playing cards.
  b throwing a 5 or a 6 with an ordinary dice.

2 Find:
  a $\frac{1}{3}$ of 45   b 0.3 × 70   c 15% of 80

217

Unit commentary

Aim of the unit
This unit aims to consolidate and extend students' understanding of theoretical and experimental probability. Tree diagrams are introduced, and practical work is used to investigate the relationship between theoretical and experimental probabilities.

Introduction
Discuss the possible routes the boat can take in the student book illustration and methods of choosing randomly between the four choices. (For example, pick a card: one suit for each outcome.) What is the probability of going over the waterfall? Discuss examples where probability is used in 'real life'. They can include: weather forecasting, insurance premiums, games and sport.

Framework references
This unit focuses on:
Teaching objectives pages: 277–285.
Problem solving objectives pages: 23, 27, 29, 31.

Differentiation

Support tier
Focuses on understanding of theoretical and experimental probability. Tree diagrams are used to represent combined events.

Extension tier
Focuses on extending knowledge of theoretical probability to combined events. The unit includes a probability experiment.

Check in activity

Ask students how many 'heads' they would expect if they threw a coin 20 times.
Give pairs of students a coin and ask them to throw the coin and record the result.
Pool the class results.
Discuss their findings.

D4.1 Combined events

Mental starter

Ask questions on multiplication of decimals and fractions. For example:

$\frac{2}{3} \times \frac{1}{4}$

$\frac{5}{3} \times \frac{3}{4}$

0.3×0.7

1.2×0.9

Students can respond using mini-whiteboards.

Useful resources

Mini-whiteboards for the mental starter

D4.1OHP – sample space diagram from the Students' Book

Introductory activity

Recap how to find theoretical probabilities using equally likely outcomes.

Start by referring to a single event, such as the probability of obtaining a triangular number when you toss a fair coin once.

Extend to two events.

Introduce the fruit machine example in the Student's book. Show how you can use a sample space diagram to show all possible outcomes. **D4.1OHP** contains the table in the Student's Book.

Emphasise that:

▸ To use a sample space diagram, all the outcomes must be equally likely.

▸ You can use the diagram to count how many outcomes there are.

▸ You can use the probability formula even when there is more than one event.

Show the multiplication method for calculating probabilities connected with combined events.

Demonstrate how the probability of two stars can be obtained simply by multiplying the probabilities of getting a star in each window.

Discuss independent events.

Emphasise that probabilities can only be multiplied in this way for independent events, and ask for situations where this might not be the case (such as picking counters from a bag without replacement).

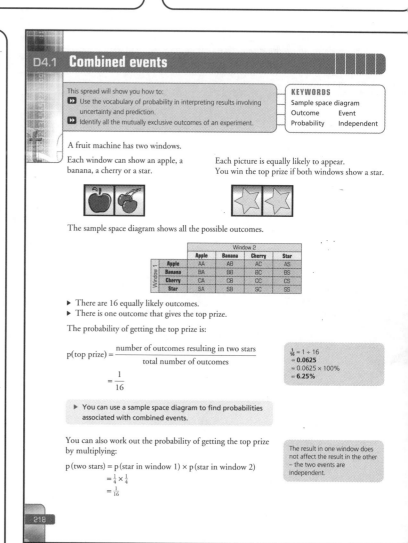

D4.1 Combined events

This spread will show you how to:
▸▸ Use the vocabulary of probability in interpreting results involving uncertainty and prediction.
▸▸ Identify all the mutually exclusive outcomes of an experiment.

KEYWORDS
Sample space diagram
Outcome   Event
Probability   Independent

A fruit machine has two windows.

Each window can show an apple, a banana, a cherry or a star.

Each picture is equally likely to appear.
You win the top prize if both windows show a star.

The sample space diagram shows all the possible outcomes.

		Window 2			
		Apple	Banana	Cherry	Star
Window 1	Apple	AA	AB	AC	AS
	Banana	BA	BB	BC	BS
	Cherry	CA	CB	CC	CS
	Star	SA	SB	SC	SS

▸ There are 16 equally likely outcomes.
▸ There is one outcome that gives the top prize.

The probability of getting the top prize is:

$$p(\text{top prize}) = \frac{\text{number of outcomes resulting in two stars}}{\text{total number of outcomes}}$$

$$= \frac{1}{16}$$

$\frac{1}{16} = 1 \div 16$
$= 0.0625$
$\approx 0.0625 \times 100\%$
$= 6.25\%$

▸ You can use a sample space diagram to find probabilities associated with combined events.

You can also work out the probability of getting the top prize by multiplying:

$p(\text{two stars}) = p(\text{star in window 1}) \times p(\text{star in window 2})$

$= \frac{1}{4} \times \frac{1}{4}$

$= \frac{1}{16}$

The result in one window does not affect the result in the other – the two events are independent.

218

Plenary

Discuss the advantages of finding the probability of combined events by multiplication rather than using a sample space diagram:

▸ It is quicker, easier and needs less space.

▸ It works even when you are not dealing with equally likely outcomes.

For example, if two independent events have probabilities of 0.4 and 0.7, what will the combined probability be? [0.28]

Further activities

Students could discuss how the situation in question 4 would change if the marble picked were not put back into the bag.

Differentiation

Core questions:

▶ Question 1 involves using a sample space diagram to find the probability of combined events.
▶ Questions 2–4 focus on finding the probability of combined events without necessarily using a sample space diagram.
▶ Question 5 focuses on the criteria for independence.

Extension tier: focuses on drawing and using tree diagrams to find probabilities of combined events.

Support tier: focuses on drawing tree diagrams and calculating probabilities.

Exercise D4.1

1 Jenny goes to the theatre. She wants to buy a souvenir sweatshirt for her dad as a birthday present.
There are three colours available, and four different pictures.
Jenny cannot decide what to pick, so she decides to choose a colour and a design at random.

Colours	Pictures
Black	Large logo
Red	Small logo
Green	Large photo
	Small photo

  a Draw a sample space diagram to show all the combinations of colour and picture that Jenny could pick.
  b Use your diagram to find the probability that Jenny's dad will get a red sweatshirt with a small logo.
  Give your answer as a fraction, a decimal and a percentage.

2 A fair coin is tossed twice.
Show how you can work out the probability of getting two heads.

3 An ordinary dice is rolled twice.
Find the probability of each of these events without using a sample space diagram.
  a The score is 1 both times.
  b Both scores are even numbers.
  c The first score is an odd number, and the second score is a prime number.

4 A bag contains 3 red marbles, 2 green marbles and 5 blue marbles.
Ken picks a marble at random, notes the colour, and puts it back.
He then picks another marble.
Find the probability that:
  a both marbles are red
  b both marbles are blue
  c the first marble is green, and the second one is blue.

5 Explain whether or not the probabilities of success in each pair of trials are independent. The first one is done for you.

	First trial	Second trial
a	Tossing a coin to try to get 'heads'.	Tossing a coin to try to get 'tails'.
	These events are independent because the probability of getting heads or tails with the second coin does not depend on the outcome of the first toss.	
b	Rolling a fair dice to try to get a 6.	Rolling the same dice again, trying to get a 4.
c	Trying to burst a balloon with one shot from a peashooter.	Trying to burst the same balloon with another shot from the same peashooter.
d	Trying to pick an even-numbered card at random from a pack marked 1–10.	Trying to pick an even-numbered card from the same pack, after the first card is replaced.
e	Trying to pick an even-numbered card at random from a pack marked 1–10.	Trying to pick an even-numbered card from the same pack, if the first card chosen is not put back in the pack.

Exercise commentary

The questions assess the objectives on Framework Pages 277 and 281.

Problem solving

Questions 1–4 assess the objectives on Framework Page 23.
Question 5 assesses Page 31.

Group work

Question 5 can be discussed in pairs or small groups.

Misconceptions

Some students may take the total number of outcomes in question 1 as being 7. Encourage the correct use of a sample space diagram, with the columns representing one event and the rows representing the other.

Links

Equivalence of decimals, fractions and percentages: Framework Page 70.

Homework

D4.1HW requires students to give examples to illustrate the methods for calculating theoretical probability.

Answers

1 a BLL, BSL, BLP, BSP; RLL, RSL, RLP, RSP; GLL, GSL, GLP, GSP
  b $\frac{1}{12}$, 0.083, 8.3%
2 $\frac{1}{2} \times \frac{1}{2} = \frac{1}{4}$
3 a $\frac{1}{36}$ b $\frac{1}{4}$ c $\frac{1}{4}$
4 a $\frac{9}{100}$ b $\frac{1}{4}$ c $\frac{1}{10}$
5 b Independent c Not independent d Independent
  e Not independent

D4.2 Mutually exclusive outcomes

Mental starter

Revise addition and subtraction of fractions and decimals. Ask questions such as:

$\frac{1}{3} + \frac{1}{3}$

$1 - \frac{1}{5}$

$0.3 + 0.05 + 0.4$

$1 - 0.35$

Students can respond using mini-whiteboards.

Useful resources

Mini-whiteboards for the mental starter

Introductory activity

Recap the main points of D4.1.

Discuss the multiplication method of calculating the probability of two independent events occurring.

You may need to recap the term 'independence'.

Introduce mutually exclusive outcomes.

Emphasise that they cannot occur at the same time, and illustrate with the pictures in the Students' book.

Encourage students to give more examples.

Discuss the example in the Students' Book.

Establish the key ideas that:

▸ The sum of all mutually exclusive probabilities is 1.

▸ You find the probability of one or another mutually exclusive outcome by adding.

Use the example to illustrate that problems involving mutually exclusive outcomes are always 'either ... or ...' situations.

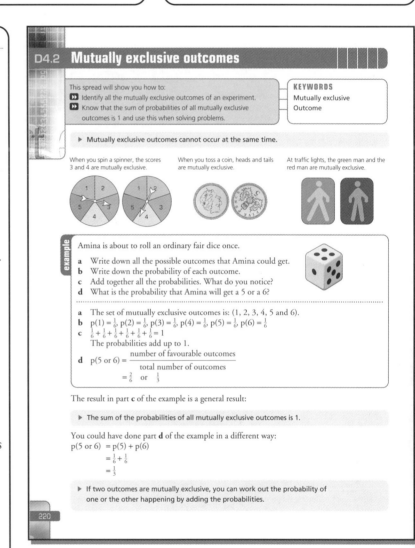

D4.2 Mutually exclusive outcomes

This spread will show you how to:
▸▸ Identify all the mutually exclusive outcomes of an experiment.
▸▸ Know that the sum of probabilities of all mutually exclusive outcomes is 1 and use this when solving problems.

KEYWORDS
Mutually exclusive
Outcome

▸ Mutually exclusive outcomes cannot occur at the same time.

When you spin a spinner, the scores 3 and 4 are mutually exclusive.

When you toss a coin, heads and tails are mutually exclusive.

At traffic lights, the green man and the red man are mutually exclusive.

Amina is about to roll an ordinary fair dice once.
a Write down all the possible outcomes that Amina could get.
b Write down the probability of each outcome.
c Add together all the probabilities. What do you notice?
d What is the probability that Amina will get a 5 or a 6?

a The set of mutually exclusive outcomes is: (1, 2, 3, 4, 5 and 6).
b p(1) = $\frac{1}{6}$, p(2) = $\frac{1}{6}$, p(3) = $\frac{1}{6}$, p(4) = $\frac{1}{6}$, p(5) = $\frac{1}{6}$, p(6) = $\frac{1}{6}$
c $\frac{1}{6} + \frac{1}{6} + \frac{1}{6} + \frac{1}{6} + \frac{1}{6} + \frac{1}{6} = 1$
   The probabilities add up to 1.
d p(5 or 6) = $\dfrac{\text{number of favourable outcomes}}{\text{total number of outcomes}}$
   = $\frac{2}{6}$ or $\frac{1}{3}$

The result in part **c** of the example is a general result:

▸ The sum of the probabilities of all mutually exclusive outcomes is 1.

You could have done part **d** of the example in a different way:
p(5 or 6) = p(5) + p(6)
           = $\frac{1}{6} + \frac{1}{6}$
           = $\frac{1}{3}$

▸ If two outcomes are mutually exclusive, you can work out the probability of one or the other happening by adding the probabilities.

220

Plenary

Discuss questions 5 and 6, emphasising that outcomes need to be mutually exclusive if their probabilities are to be added.

Link to the previous lesson:

▸ You **multiply** to find the probability of two independent events **both** occurring.

▸ You **add** to find the probability of **either** of two mutually exclusive outcomes occurring.

Further activities

Challenge students to give an example set of 10 tickets that would fit the conditions given in question 7.
They could then work in pairs to discuss and suggest everyday examples of mutually exclusive outcomes, for example in the context of weather.

Differentiation

Core questions:
▶ Questions 1 and 2 require students to add simple decimal probabilities, and identify mutually exclusive outcomes.
▶ Questions 3–5 focus on mutually exclusive outcomes in context, and involve percentages and fractions.
▶ Questions 6 and 7 require students to apply logical argument to probability situations.

Extension tier: focuses on sampling without replacement.

Support tier: focuses on tree diagrams.

Exercise D4.2

1 The table shows the probabilities for this five-sided spinner.

Score	1	2	3	4	5
Probability	0.2	0.15	0.15	0.25	0.25

Find the probability that the score is:
a 1 or 2 **b** more than 2
c an odd number.

2 An ordinary dice is rolled.
Explain whether or not these pairs of outcomes are mutually exclusive.
The first one is done for you.

	First outcome	Second outcome
a	The score is 5.	The score is 3.
	These outcomes are mutually exclusive. A dice cannot show a score of 3 and a score of 5 at the same time.	
b	The score is 3.	The score is an even number.
c	The score is an even number.	The score is greater than 4.
d	The score is a prime number.	The score is an even number.
e	The score is a multiple of 5.	The score is a multiple of 3.

3 Every member of a computer club is classified as 'beginner', 'intermediate' or 'expert'.
A member of the club is picked at random.
The table shows the probability of picking each type of member.

Category	Beginner	Intermediate	Expert
Probability	22%		39%

a Copy and complete the table.
b What is the probability of picking a 'beginner' or an 'intermediate' member of the club?

4 A jar contains red marbles, yellow marbles and green marbles. 30% of the marbles are red, and 35% are yellow.
A marble is picked at random.
What is the probability that the marble picked will be yellow or green?
Explain your answer.

5 A set of coloured counters is placed in a bag. The table shows the probability of getting each colour when a counter is picked at random.

Colour	Red	Yellow	Green	Blue	White
Probability	$\frac{1}{3}$	$\frac{1}{6}$	$\frac{1}{4}$	$\frac{1}{6}$	$\frac{1}{12}$

Find the probability of picking:
a a yellow counter or a blue counter
b a yellow counter or a white counter
c a red counter or a green counter
d a yellow counter or a blue counter or a white counter.

6 Martin picks a card at random from this set.

Martin says:

> The probability of picking a yellow card is $\frac{2}{5}$.
> The probability of picking a 3 is $\frac{2}{5}$.
> So the probability of picking a yellow card or a 3 is $\frac{2}{5} + \frac{2}{5} = \frac{4}{5}$

a Explain why Martin is wrong.
b Work out the correct probability of picking a yellow card or a 3.

7 A raffle ticket is picked at random from a box.
The probability of getting a red ticket is 0.6. The probability of getting a ticket with an even number is 0.5.
Explain why you know that the outcomes 'picking a red ticket' and 'picking an even number' cannot be mutually exclusive.

221

Exercise commentary

The questions assess the objectives on Framework Pages 279 and 281.

Problem solving
Questions 1, 3, 4 and 5 assess the objectives on Framework Page 23.
Questions 2, 6 and 7 assess Page 31.

Group work
Students could discuss their responses to questions 2, 6 and 7 in pairs or small groups.

Misconceptions
Students will often multiply when they should add, and vice versa.
Reinforce the distinction between the two as described in the plenary (or = add, and = multiply).

Links
Adding and subtracting fractions: Framework Page 67.

Homework

D4.2HW requires students to give examples to illustrate how to calculate probabilities of mutually exclusive outcomes.

Answers

1 **a** 0.35 **b** 0.65 **c** 0.6
2 **b** Mutually exclusive **c** Not mutually exclusive
  d Not mutually exclusive **e** Mutually exclusive
3 **a** Intermediate 39% **b** 61%
4 70%   5 **a** $\frac{1}{3}$ **b** $\frac{1}{4}$ **c** $\frac{7}{12}$ **d** $\frac{5}{12}$
6 **a** They are not mutually exclusive events. **b** $\frac{3}{5}$
7 The sum of the probabilities is more than one.

D4.3 Tree diagrams

Mental starter

Reinforce multiplication of fractions and decimals, going slightly further than in **D4.1**.

For fractions, use questions like $\frac{1}{2} \times \frac{1}{3}$ and $\frac{2}{3} \times \frac{3}{5}$, encouraging students to cancel the answers down to their lowest terms.

For decimals, do not go beyond simple cases of 1 dp × 2 dp. For example, 0.3×0.7 and 0.8×0.25.

Useful resources

D4.3OHP – tree diagrams from the Students' Book.

Mini-whiteboards may be useful for the mental Starter.

Introductory activity

Recap the key ideas in D4.1 and D4.2, focusing on the distinction between events and outcomes.

You can calculate the probability of **combined events** by either:

▶ Drawing a sample space diagram (if the outcomes are equally likely)

▶ Multiplying the individual probabilities (if the events are **independent**).

You can calculate the probability of **mutually exclusive outcomes** within an event by adding the individual probabilities.

Discuss the situation in the Students' Book.

Show how you can use a tree diagram as an alternative to a sample space diagram for illustrating combined events. **D4.3OHP** contains the tree diagram in the Students' book.

Discuss how using a tree diagram gives you a sense of the sequence of events (first you spin a spinner, then you throw a coin).

Outline the key features of a tree diagram:

▶ You write outcomes at the **ends** of the branches.

▶ You write the probabilities **on** the branches.

▶ You calculate the probability of a combined event by **multiplying** along the branches.

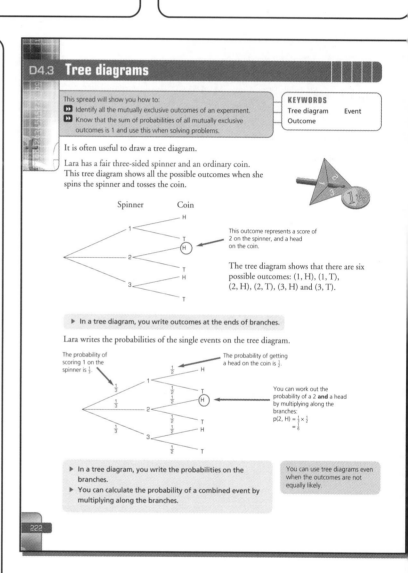

D4.3 Tree diagrams

This spread will show you how to:
- Identify all the mutually exclusive outcomes of an experiment.
- Know that the sum of probabilities of all mutually exclusive outcomes is 1 and use this when solving problems.

KEYWORDS
Tree diagram   Event
Outcome

It is often useful to draw a tree diagram.

Lara has a fair three-sided spinner and an ordinary coin. This tree diagram shows all the possible outcomes when she spins the spinner and tosses the coin.

This outcome represents a score of 2 on the spinner, and a head on the coin.

The tree diagram shows that there are six possible outcomes: (1, H), (1, T), (2, H), (2, T), (3, H) and (3, T).

▶ In a tree diagram, you write outcomes at the ends of branches.

Lara writes the probabilities of the single events on the tree diagram.

The probability of scoring 1 on the spinner is $\frac{1}{3}$.

The probability of getting a head on the coin is $\frac{1}{2}$.

You can work out the probability of a 2 **and** a head by multiplying along the branches:
$p(2, H) = \frac{1}{3} \times \frac{1}{2}$
$= \frac{1}{6}$

▶ In a tree diagram, you write the probabilities on the branches.
▶ You can calculate the probability of a combined event by multiplying along the branches.

You can use tree diagrams even when the outcomes are not equally likely.

222

Plenary

Review question 6, and encourage students to offer solutions. Emphasise that the answers to **b**, **c**, **d** and **e** can be found without having to redraw the tree diagram.

Further activities

Students could work through the example on p. 222 again, changing the probabilities for the first spinner to:
p(Red) = $\frac{1}{3}$, p(Green) = $\frac{1}{2}$, p(Blue) = $\frac{1}{6}$.

Differentiation

Core questions:

▶ Questions 1 and 2 provide practice in drawing simple tree diagrams.

▶ Questions 3 and 4 involve two-stage tree diagrams for repeated and combined events.

▶ Questions 5 and 6 are harder examples of using tree diagrams to solve problems.

Extension tier: focuses on tree diagrams for more than two outcomes.

Support tier: focuses on using tree diagrams.

Exercise D4.3

1 Copy and complete the one-stage tree diagrams to show these situations:
   a A fair coin is tossed.

   b An ordinary dice is rolled.

   A one-stage tree diagram only has a single set of branches.

2 Draw a two-stage tree diagram to show the possible outcomes when a fair coin is tossed twice.

3 When this drawing pin is dropped on a table, the probability that it lands 'point up' is 0.6.
   a Draw a tree diagram to show all of the possible outcomes when the drawing pin is dropped twice.
   Use your diagram to work out the probability that the drawing pin will land:
   b point up both times.
   c point down both times.

4 Marie has two bags, each containing red and blue counters. She picks a counter at random from each bag. The probability of getting a red counter is 0.5 for the first bag, and 0.7 for the second bag.
   a Draw a tree diagram to show all the possible outcomes.
   b Use your diagram to work out the probability that Marie picks two red counters.

5 A four-sided spinner is marked 2, 3, 5 and 7. The probability of each score is shown in the table.

Score, x	2	3	5	7
p(x)	0.4	0.3	0.2	0.1

   The spinner is spun twice.
   a Draw a tree diagram to show the possible outcomes.
   The scores for each spin are multiplied together. Use your tree diagram to work out the probability that the product is:
   b less than 5
   c exactly 25
   d more than 40.

6 These two spinners produce the scores shown with the probabilities in the table.

Score on Spinner 1	1	2	3
Probability	0.5	0.15	0.35

Score on Spinner 2	5	7	9
Probability	0.5	0.25	0.25

   a Draw a tree diagram to show the possible outcomes when both spinners are spun.
   Use your diagram to work out the probability that:
   b the product of the scores will be 15
   c the sum of the scores will be 11
   d the difference between the scores will be 8
   e both scores will be even numbers.

223

Exercise commentary

The questions assess the objectives on Framework Pages 279 and 281.

Problem solving
The questions in this exercise assess the objectives on Framework Pages 23 and 27.

Group work
Questions 5 and 6 can be tackled in pairs.

Misconceptions
Students often find it difficult to fit in all the branches when drawing a tree diagram, so encourage drawing a rough sketch if necessary.
Students may attach incorrect probabilities to the branches. Encourage students to see for themselves that the sum of each set of branches is always 1. They can use this fact as a check.

Links
Multiplying fractions: Framework Page 69.

Homework

D4.3HW gives more practice in drawing a tree diagram and using it to find probabilities.

Answers

1 **a** Tails, $\frac{1}{2}$ **b** 3, 4, 5, 6, $\frac{1}{6}$ each
2 Heads, Tails ($\frac{1}{2}$ each) then Heads, Tails, Heads, Tails ($\frac{1}{2}$ each).
3 **a** Up (0.6), down (0.4) then up, down, up, down.   **b** 0.36   **c** 0.16
4 **a** Red (0.5) Blue (0.5) then Red (0.7) Blue (0.3), Red (0.7) Blue (0.3)   **b** 0.35
5 **a** 2(0.4), 3(0.3), 5(0.2), 7(0.1)   **b** 0.16   **c** 0.04   **d** 0.01
6 **a** 1 + 5(0.25), 1 + 7(0.125), 1 + 9(0.125), 2 + 5(0.075), 2 + 7(0.0375), 2 + 9(0.0375),
      3 + 5(0.175), 3 + 7(0.0875), 3 + 9(0.0875),   **b** 0.175   **c** 0.0375   **d** 0.125   **e** 0

Useful resources

D4.4OHP – tree diagram from the Students' Book
Coins for question 6

Introductory activity

Recap tree diagrams from D4.3.
Emphasise that they are useful in representing combined events, where the outcomes may not necessarily be equal.

Discuss the first example in the Students' Book.
Carefully outline the steps involved in calculating the 'at least one' probability:

▶ Draw a tree diagram.
▶ Calculate the probability of each combined event (this is not always necessary, but it has been done here – encourage students to check by multiplying).
▶ Identify all the (favourable) mutually exclusive outcomes from the diagram.
▶ Add them together.

D4.4OHP contains the tree diagram from the Students' Book.

Discuss how you could solve the 'at least one' problem a quicker way.
Encourage the strategy of finding the probability of not getting a red, and subtracting it from 1.
Emphasise that this is a general result, and can be applied to other 'at least one' situations.

Discuss the second example in the Students' Book.
Use it to illustrate how you can compare a theoretical probability with an experimental probability.

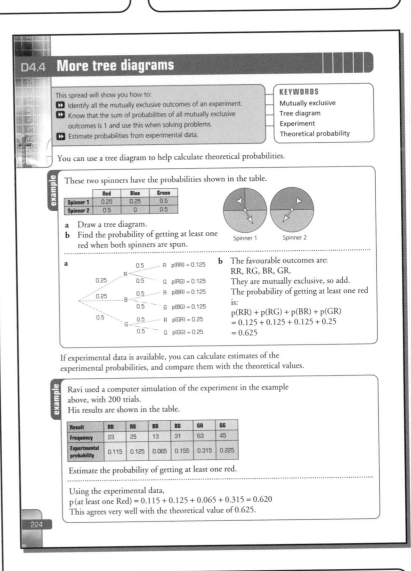

Plenary

Discuss question 5, and encourage students to outline their strategies.
In particular, encourage strategies for part **e** that follow immediately from the answer to part **d**, without having to carry out another multiplication.
Discuss students' comparison of the experimental probability from question 7 with the theoretical probability from question 6.

Further activities

Extend question 7 by conducting more trials.

What happens to the experimental probabilities as you increase the number of trials?

Differentiation

Core questions:
- Question 1 involves using a simple tree diagram to find probabilities.
- Questions 2–5 involve combined events and mutually exclusive outcomes in context.
- Questions 6 and 7 extend to comparing theoretical and experimental probabilities for combined events.

Extension tier: focuses on more that two successive events.

Support tier: focuses on carrying out an experiment and calculating probabilities.

Exercise D4.4

1 Kiran plays two games at a school fair. The probability of winning a prize is 0.3 on the first game, and 0.2 on the second game.
   a Draw a tree diagram to show the possible outcomes.
   Use your diagram to find the probability that Kiran gets:
   b two prizes
   c exactly one prize
   d at least one prize.

2 Maya spins a 50p coin, a 20p coin, and a penny.
   a Draw a tree diagram to show the possible outcomes of the experiment.
   Use your diagram to find the probability that Maya will get:
   b the same result on each coin
   c at least one tail.

3 These two spinners produce the scores shown with the probabilities in the tables.

Spinner 1

Score	1	2
Probability	0.4	0.6

Spinner 2

Score	3	4
Probability	0.3	0.7

   a Draw a tree diagram to show the possible outcomes when both spinners are spun.
   The scores on the two spinners are multiplied together.
   Use your diagram to work out the probability that the product will be:
   b exactly 6   c 3 or 4
   d an even number   e more than 5.

4 Nina has to drive over two level crossings on the way to work each day. The probability that she has to stop is 0.2 at the first one, and 0.3 at the second one.
   a Draw a tree diagram to show the possible outcomes.
   Use your tree diagram to work out the probability that the number of times that Nina has to stop at a level crossing will be:
   b zero
   c exactly 1
   d at least 1
   e 2.

5 Jane drops a cup and a saucer on the floor. The probability that the cup breaks is 0.6, and the probability that the saucer breaks is 0.3.
   a Draw a tree diagram to show the possible outcomes.
   Use your diagram to work out the probability that:
   b The cup and the saucer both break.
   c Just one of the items breaks.
   d At least one of the items breaks.
   e Neither of the items breaks.

6 Andy flips an ordinary coin three times.
   a Draw a tree diagram to show the possible outcomes.
   b Use your tree diagram to work out the probability of getting each number of 'Heads', from 0 to 3.
   c Draw a bar-line chart to show your results.

7 Carry out the experiment described in question 6.
   Estimate the experimental probability for each number of 'Heads'.
   Compare your experimental data with the theoretical values you found in question 6.

225

Exercise commentary

The questions assess the objectives on Framework Pages 279–283.

Problem solving

Questions 1–5 assess the objectives on Framework Pages 23 and 27.

Group work

Question 7 is suitable for group work.

Misconceptions

Students may need some practice before they can use the sum of exclusive probabilities to solve problems efficiently. For example, the answer to question 1d can be found by adding the two previous answers, or by subtracting the probability of winning no prizes from 1.

Links

Adding and multiplying decimals: Framework Pages 95–97.

Homework

D4.4HW focuses on drawing and using tree diagrams and involves students carrying out a coin tossing experiment.

Answers

1 a win (0.3), lose (0.7) then win (0.2), lose (0.8), win (0.2), lose (0.8)   b 0.06   c 0.38
   d 0.44   2 a HHH, HHT, HTT, TTT, THH, HTH, THT, TTH (all 0.125) or
   split into three choices   b $\frac{1}{4}$ c $\frac{7}{8}$ 3 a 1 + 3(0.12), 1 + 4(0.28), 2 + 3(0.18),
   2 + 4(0.42)   b 0.18   c 0.4   d 0.88   e 0.6   4 a Stop (0.2) Go (0.8) then, Stop
   (0.3), Go (0.7), Stop (0.3), Go (0.7)   b 0.56   c 0.38   d 0.44   e 0.06
5 a Cup breaks (0.6), Cup OK (0.4) then saucer breaks (0.3), saucer OK (0.7)   b 0.18
   c 0.54 d 0.72   e 0.28   6 a HHH, etc (all 0.125) or split into 3 levels, H, T
   then H, T then H, T (all 0.5)   b $\frac{1}{8}, \frac{3}{8}, \frac{3}{8}, \frac{1}{8}$ c Appropriate bar-line chart.
7 Student's own experiment.

D4.5 Comparing theoretical and experimental probability

Introductory activity

Briefly consolidate the earlier lessons in D4.
Focus on the common themes:
▶ Combined events
▶ Theoretical probability.

Ask students to describe what they mean by theoretical probability.

Use the scenario in the Students' Book to show how you can use theoretical probability to predict the result of an experiment.
The diagram in the Students' Book is shown on **D4.5OHP**.
Recap how you can work out the probability of A **and** A by **multiplying** (discuss the assumption that they are independent events).

Show how the expected frequency can be found by multiplying the probability by the number of trials.
Emphasise that the actual result of an experiment may be different due to the events being **random**.

Highlight the key points:
▶ Expected frequency = number of trials × probability
▶ The results of an experiment are not always the same as what you expect in theory.

Describe the game 'Less than, more than' shown in the exercise as a bridge to written and practical work.

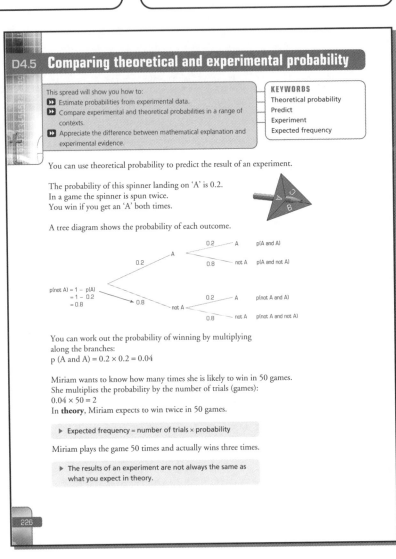

D4.5 Comparing theoretical and experimental probability

This spread will show you how to:
▶▶ Estimate probabilities from experimental data.
▶▶ Compare experimental and theoretical probabilities in a range of contexts.
▶▶ Appreciate the difference between mathematical explanation and experimental evidence.

KEYWORDS
Theoretical probability
Predict
Experiment
Expected frequency

You can use theoretical probability to predict the result of an experiment.

The probability of this spinner landing on 'A' is 0.2.
In a game the spinner is spun twice.
You win if you get an 'A' both times.

A tree diagram shows the probability of each outcome.

p(not A) = 1 – p(A)
= 1 – 0.2
= 0.8

You can work out the probability of winning by multiplying along the branches:
p (A and A) = 0.2 × 0.2 = 0.04

Miriam wants to know how many times she is likely to win in 50 games.
She multiplies the probability by the number of trials (games):
0.04 × 50 = 2
In **theory**, Miriam expects to win twice in 50 games.

▶ Expected frequency = number of trials × probability

Miriam plays the game 50 times and actually wins three times.

▶ The results of an experiment are not always the same as what you expect in theory.

226

Plenary

Discuss the answers obtained in the exercise.
Calculate the expected number of wins for a particular card in 200 trials, and combine data from several students to generate an experimental result.

Discuss the results.

Further activities

Students could attempt variations of the 'Less than, more than' game.
They could choose different numbers on the cards, or different numbers of cards.

Differentiation

Core questions:

‣ Questions 1–3 focus on calculating theoretical probability and expected frequency.

‣ Questions 4 and 5 require students to conduct a statistical experiment.

‣ Question 6 involves discussing the results of an experiment.

Extension tier: focuses on an investigation using relative frequency.

Support tier: focuses on students' own experiments.

Exercise D4.5

'Less than, more than' is a dice game.
You start by picking one of these number cards.

You then roll an ordinary dice twice.

To win the game:
‣ your first dice score must be **less** than the number on the card
‣ your second dice score must be **more** than the number on the card

1 Select the card marked '2'.
Copy the tree diagram, and complete it by filling in the probabilities on each branch.

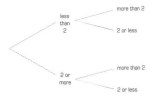

2 Use your tree diagram to work out the theoretical probability of winning the game when you choose the card marked '2'.

3 Use your answer to question 2 to predict how many times you would win if you played the game 50 times, choosing the card marked '2' each time.

4 Now test your prediction by playing the game 50 times, using an ordinary dice.
You can record your results in a tally chart like this.

Result	Tally	Total
Win		
Lose		

In each game you only need to roll a second time if the first roll lands on 1. If it is anything else, you have already lost!

5 Repeat questions 1 to 4 with a different choice of number card.

6 Which card would you choose?
Give a reason for your choice.

Exercise commentary

The questions assess the objectives on Framework Pages 283 and 285.

Problem solving
Question 6 requires students to present a concise reasoned argument, assessing the objectives on Framework Page 31.

Group work
The practical activities in this exercise should be conducted in a small group.

Misconceptions
Some students may have difficulty in understanding that the results of an experiment are relatively closer to the predicted values for larger data sets. Emphasise that larger numbers of trials should give frequencies that are **proportionately** closer to the expected values, although the **absolute** differences between the actual and expected values may increase.

Links
Planning an experiment and collecting data: Framework Pages 253–255.

Homework

D4.5HW focuses on predicting theoretical probability and comparing it with experimental probability.

Answers

1 First dice: $\frac{1}{6}$, $\frac{5}{6}$; second dice: $\frac{2}{3}$, $\frac{1}{3}$; $\frac{2}{3}$, $\frac{1}{3}$

2 $\frac{1}{9}$

3 6 times

4 Student's own experiment

5 Cards 3 or 4: probability $= \frac{1}{6}$ and 8 wins; card 5: probability $= \frac{1}{9}$ and 6 wins

6 3 and 4 give equal best chance of winning.

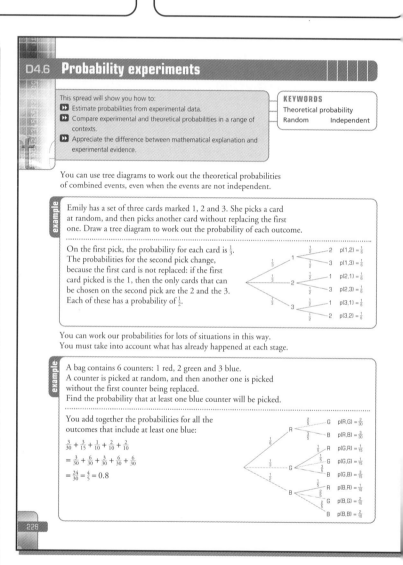

Mental starter

Draw a set of cards numbered 1–5 on the board.
Ask for probabilities when a card is picked at random, for example
p(3), p(even), p(>3).
Now ask for probabilities for combined events, for example
p(3, then 5), first with, then without replacement.
Discuss answers and agree upon an effective approach.

Useful resources

Red, green and blue counters preferably in bags or boxes
D4.6OHP – tree diagrams from the Students' Book

Introductory activity

Recap independent events.
Describe how the previous work in this unit has focused on combined events where the probabilities are independent. Tree diagrams have been used to find theoretical probabilities, and to compare theoretical and experimental results.

Extend to situations where probabilities are not independent.
Use the first example in the Students' Book to illustrate how the same techniques as before can be applied.
D4.6OHP shows both of the tree diagrams in the Students' Book.
Emphasise that the probabilities on the branches representing the second selection need to be adjusted to take into account the result of the first selection.

Now discuss the second example in the Students' Book.
Ensure that the class understands the use of common denominators in adding the fractions.

Progress to discussing how you can use probability experiments to check theoretical probabilities.

Distribute the counters that students will need to perform the experiments. They can be in small bags or boxes, provided the counters cannot be seen.

Plenary

Some groups may have collected together large data sets. Either discuss these, or collate the results of several groups on the board. Compare the results from large and small data sets. With only 50 trials, theoretical and experimental values will typically differ by up to 6% to 8%. With 1000 trials, values will seldom differ by more than 1% or 2%.

Further activities

D4.6ICT uses a random number generator on a spreadsheet to simulate experiments, so students can calculate experimental probabilities.

Alternatively

Encourage students to write up their probability experiment into a report, and make conclusions.

Differentiation

Core questions:

▸ Question 1 requires students to calculate probabilities as percentages.
▸ Question 2 involves conducting a probability experiment.
▸ Question 3 requires students to combine data and compare results.

Extension tier: focuses on an investigation using relative frequency and probability.

Support tier: focuses on finding experimental and theoretical probabilities for an experiment.

Exercise D4.6

1 The table shows the possible outcomes for the experiment described in the second example on page 228, along with the probabilities for each one.

Outcome	RG	RB	GR	GG	GB	BR	BG	BB
Probability	$\frac{2}{30}$	$\frac{3}{30}$	$\frac{1}{15}$	$\frac{1}{15}$	$\frac{3}{15}$	$\frac{1}{10}$	$\frac{3}{10}$	$\frac{2}{10}$
Probability %	6.7%							

  a Copy and complete the table, to show the probabilities as percentages (to one decimal place) in the bottom row.
  b Draw a bar-line chart to show the theoretical probability of each outcome.

2 a Carry out an experiment to estimate the experimental probability of each outcome in question 1.
    ▸ Collect counters of the correct colours.
    ▸ Pick one of the counters at random.
    ▸ Pick another counter, without replacing the first one.
    Repeat the experiment at least 50 times – the more the better!
    Record the results in a tally chart:

Outcome	Tally	Frequency
RG		
RB		
GR		

  b Work out the experimental probability of each outcome as a percentage.

Divide the frequency for the outcome by the total, and convert this to a percentage.

  c Plot a bar chart to show the experimental probability for each outcome.

3 Collect together some data for question 2 from several other groups, and combine them into a single large data set.
   Use a table like this to collect the data:

Outcome	Frequencies				Total
	Group 1	Group 2	Group 3	Group 4	
RG					
RB					
GR					

This example uses data from 4 different groups, but you could use more if you have time.

  a Work out a new set of experimental probabilities, based on this large data set.
  b Draw a bar chart to show your new estimates for the experimental probability of each outcome.

229

Exercise commentary

The questions assess the objectives on Framework Pages 283 and 285.

Problem solving

The exercise forms a substantial problem that can be broken into smaller tasks, assessing the objectives on Page 29.

Group work

The practical activity and data collation are suitable for group work.

Misconceptions

Students may assume that if their value of experimental probability is different to the theoretical value, they have made a mistake. Emphasise that this is to be expected with random events.

Links

Constructing graphs and diagrams: Framework Page 263.

Homework

D4.6HW focuses on calculating experimental probabilities from data, and how these change as more trials are conducted.

Answers

1 a 10%, 6.7%, 6.7%, 20%, 10%, 20%, 20%
   b Appropriate bar-line chart
2, 3 Student's own experiment.
     Question 3 values should be nearer the theoretical probabilities in question 1.

Summary

The key objectives for this unit are:

▶ Know that the sum of the probabilities of all mutually exclusive outcomes is 1 and use this when solving problems. (279–281)

Another objective is:

▶ Compare experimental and theoretical probabilities in a range of contexts. (285)

Check out commentary

1 In part **a** emphasise that the outcomes 'win' and 'lose' are mutually exclusive, so their probabilities sum to 1.

In part **b** students need to recognise that the event 'exactly one win' corresponds to the outcomes, 'win, lose' and 'lose, win'.

Students may confuse how to calculate probabilities from the tree diagram. Emphasise that we multiply along the branches to find the probability of a combined event. They then need to add the probabilities for (win, lose) and (lose, win).

In part **c** students need to remember to multiply probabilities of the combined events.

2 Emphasise that a sample space diagram is a clear way of setting out all the outcomes.

A tree diagram for these outcomes is possible but it would be quite large. Students may assume that if the experimental and theoretical probabilities do not exactly match, the dice are not fair.

Emphasise that they should look at the distribution of probabilities to see if they generally match. Random results may not tally exactly.

Plenary activity

Discuss key vocabulary and ideas, such as theoretical and experimental probability, events and outcomes, sample space and tree diagrams and independent events.

Encourage students to give examples of these ideas and discuss their use.

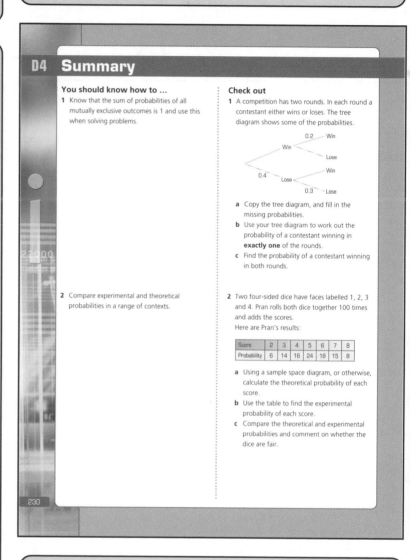

D4 Summary

You should know how to ...

1 Know that the sum of probabilities of all mutually exclusive outcomes is 1 and use this when solving problems.

2 Compare experimental and theoretical probabilities in a range of contexts.

Check out

1 A competition has two rounds. In each round a contestant either wins or loses. The tree diagram shows some of the probabilities.

a Copy the tree diagram, and fill in the missing probabilities.

b Use your tree diagram to work out the probability of a contestant winning in **exactly one** of the rounds.

c Find the probability of a contestant winning in both rounds.

2 Two four-sided dice have faces labelled 1, 2, 3 and 4. Pran rolls both dice together 100 times and adds the scores.
Here are Pran's results:

Score	2	3	4	5	6	7	8
Probability	6	14	16	24	18	15	8

a Using a sample space diagram, or otherwise, calculate the theoretical probability of each score.

b Use the table to find the experimental probability of each score.

c Compare the theoretical and experimental probabilities and comment on whether the dice are fair.

Development

The theoretical and experimental probability techniques from this unit will be developed in GCSE work, particularly in coursework.

Links

Experimental probability techniques can be applied to other situations where experiments have to be designed, and to predict results, for example in Science.

Mental starters

Objectives covered in this unit:
▶ Recall multiplication and division facts to 10×10.
▶ Solve equations.
▶ Know and use squares, cubes, roots and index notation.

Resources needed

* means class set needed

Essential:
B1.1OHP – triangles in a circle
2 mm graph paper*
Scientific calculators*

Useful:
B1.2OHP – right-angled triangles
B1.3OHP – opposite and adjacent
B1.4OHP – tangents
B1.5OHP – Pythagoras' theorem
B1.6OHP – trigonometrical ratios
B1.1ICT* – constructions
R9 – 2 mm grid

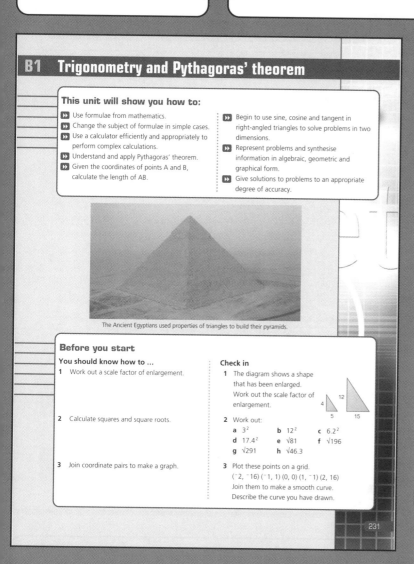

B1 Trigonometry and Pythagoras' theorem

This unit will show you how to:

▶▶ Use formulae from mathematics.
▶▶ Change the subject of formulae in simple cases.
▶▶ Use a calculator efficiently and appropriately to perform complex calculations.
▶▶ Understand and apply Pythagoras' theorem.
▶▶ Given the coordinates of points A and B, calculate the length of AB.

▶▶ Begin to use sine, cosine and tangent in right-angled triangles to solve problems in two dimensions.
▶▶ Represent problems and synthesise information in algebraic, geometric and graphical form.
▶▶ Give solutions to problems to an appropriate degree of accuracy.

The Ancient Egyptians used properties of triangles to build their pyramids.

Before you start

You should know how to ...
1 Work out a scale factor of enlargement.

2 Calculate squares and square roots.

3 Join coordinate pairs to make a graph.

Check in
1 The diagram shows a shape that has been enlarged. Work out the scale factor of enlargement.

2 Work out:
  a 3^2 b 12^2 c 6.2^2
  d 17.4^2 e $\sqrt{81}$ f $\sqrt{196}$
  g $\sqrt{291}$ h $\sqrt{46.3}$

3 Plot these points on a grid.
  ($^-$2, $^-$16) ($^-$1, 1) (0, 0) (1, $^-$1) (2, 16)
  Join them to make a smooth curve.
  Describe the curve you have drawn.

231

Unit commentary

Aim of the unit

This unit aims to provide an accessible introduction to trigonometry and Pythagoras' theorem. The approach used includes practical work on drawing and measuring, and problem solving in a range of contexts.

Introduction

Discuss how the Ancient Egyptians could have used properties of triangles to create such huge pyramids. For example, you can use Pythagoras' theorem to check that a triangle is right-angled, by checking that $a^2 = b^2 + c^2$.

Emphasise that this unit focuses on other useful properties of triangles.

Framework references

This unit focuses on:
▶ Teaching objectives pages: 189, 243, 245, 247.
▶ Problem solving objectives pages: 17, 27, 31, 33.

Differentiation

Support tier

Focuses on carrying out a mathematical investigation, systematically breaking the work down into manageable steps.

Extension tier

Focuses on applying Pythagoras' theorem and trigonometry in real-life contexts.

Check in activity

Draw some right-angled triangles on the board with 'missing' information and encourage students to estimate the side lengths using scale drawing.

Emphasise that this unit will help them calculate exact solutions to these types of questions.

B1.1 Triangles in a circle

Mental starter

Missing angles

Draw a range of triangles on the board.

For each triangle, mark the size of two angles and ask the students to find the missing angle. Include triangles that are acute-angled, isosceles, right-angled and obtuse-angled.

Useful resources

B1.1OHP – diagram from the Students' Book

2 mm graph paper

Introductory activity

Discuss right-angled triangles.

Ask for any facts that students know about them, and where they have encountered them both in maths and in real life.

Say that the aim of the lesson is to investigate lengths and angles in right-angled triangles.

Introduce the diagram in the Students' Book, which is reproduced on **B1.1OHP**.

Ask the class to imagine that the dot at the top of the triangle is a bead that can slide along a circular wire. For all positions of the 'bead', the black radius, and the green and red lines will form a right-angled triangle.

Ask which lengths and angles in the triangle will change as the bead moves, and which will stay the same.

Focus on quantifying the change in each length and angle, between 0° and 90°.

Ensure that the class understand how the scale works, and show how the lengths of the green and red lines are measured.

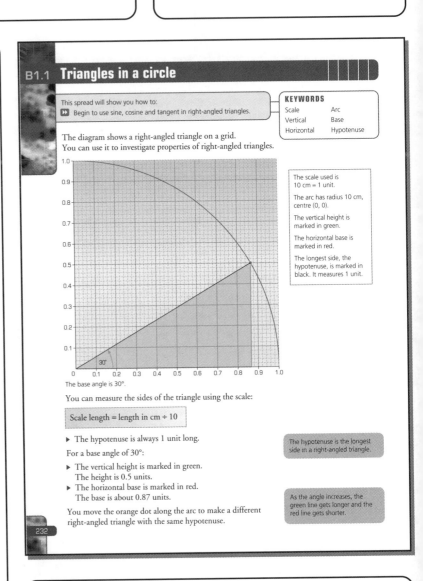

B1.1 Triangles in a circle

This spread will show you how to:
▶▶ Begin to use sine, cosine and tangent in right-angled triangles.

KEYWORDS
Scale — Arc
Vertical — Base
Horizontal — Hypotenuse

The diagram shows a right-angled triangle on a grid.
You can use it to investigate properties of right-angled triangles.

The scale used is 10 cm = 1 unit.

The arc has radius 10 cm, centre (0, 0).

The vertical height is marked in green.

The horizontal base is marked in red.

The longest side, the hypotenuse, is marked in black. It measures 1 unit.

The base angle is 30°.

You can measure the sides of the triangle using the scale:

Scale length = length in cm ÷ 10

▶ The hypotenuse is always 1 unit long.

For a base angle of 30°:

▶ The vertical height is marked in green.
The height is 0.5 units.
▶ The horizontal base is marked in red.
The base is about 0.87 units.

You move the orange dot along the arc to make a different right-angled triangle with the same hypotenuse.

The hypotenuse is the longest side in a right-angled triangle.

As the angle increases, the green line gets longer and the red line gets shorter.

232

Plenary

Sketch the graph from question 4 on the board. Discuss what would happen to the lines if the angles could be larger than 90°.

Ask students to justify their responses both by using the shape of the graphs and by considering what would happen to the diagram on page 232 as the angle continues past 90°.

Further activities

B1.1ICT provides practice for students in constructing right-angled triangles and relevant graph.

Alternatively

Challenge students to use their tables and graphs to predict what will happen to the horizontal and vertical lengths as the angle increases above 90°. Encourage them to relate their predictions back to the diagram.

Differentiation

Core questions:

▸ Question 1 simply involves reproducing the graph shown on page 232.
▸ Questions 2 and 3 involve drawing and measuring a range of lines on the diagram.
▸ Question 4 extends to plotting results on line graphs.

Extension tier: focuses on Pythagorean triples.

Support tier: focuses on an investigation into costs of making rectangles.

Exercise B1.1

1. To make an accurate copy of the grid on page 232:
   ▸ Copy the grid on squared paper, and mark the axes as shown.
   ▸ Draw a circular arc with a radius of 10 cm, centre (0, 0), using compasses.
   ▸ Construct a base angle of 30° as shown, using a protractor.
   ▸ Draw the hypotenuse (black) and vertical (green) height of the triangle. The horizontal (red) base of the triangle will lie along the horizontal axis.
   ▸ Check that the vertical height is 5 cm, and the horizontal base is about 8.7 cm.

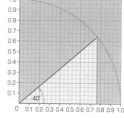

2. **a** Draw a line with a base angle of 40° on your diagram from question 1.
   Draw the line as far as the arc.
   Draw the vertical side of this triangle.
   b Work out the scale length of the vertical height.
   Scale length = (length in centimetres) ÷ 10
   c Work out the scale length of the horizontal base.

3. Draw more lines on your diagram, for every angle from 0° to 90° in steps of 10°.
   For each line, work out (to 2 decimal places) the scale lengths of the horizontal base and vertical height.
   Record your results in a copy of this table:

Angle	0°	10°	20°	30°	40°	50°	60°	70°	80°	90°
Horizontal	1.00			0.87						0
Vertical	0			0.50						1.00

4. **a** Copy this grid.
   ▸ Plot the values for the horizontal base for each angle in question 3:
   (0, 1) (30, 0.87) (90, 0)
   and so on.
   ▸ Join the points with a smooth curve.
   ▸ Comment on your graph.
   b On a new copy of the grid, plot the values for the vertical height.
   Join them with a smooth curve.
   Comment on your graph.

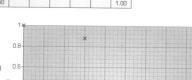
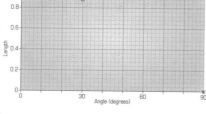

Exercise commentary

The questions assess the objectives on Framework Pages 243 and 245.

Problem solving

Question 4 requires students to synthesise information in graphical form, assessing the objectives on Framework Page 27.

Group work

Students can compare the shapes of their diagrams and graphs.

Misconceptions

Students may have difficulty in finding scale length from their diagram. Encourage students to work out how much one square on the grid is worth. Emphasise also that they should take care not to mix up horizontal and vertical measurements.

Links

Constructing triangles: Framework Page 223.

233

Homework

B1.1HW provides further investigations into the relationship between ratio of lengths and the angle.

Answers

1. Accurate copy of diagram on p. 232.
2. **a** Diagram as shown **b** 0.64 units **c** 0.77 units
3. Horizontal: 1.00, 0.98, 0.94, 0.87, 0.77, 0.64, 0.50, 0.34, 0.17, 0; Vertical: 0, 0.17, 0.34, 0.50, 0.64, 0.77, 0.87, 0.94, 0.98, 1.00
4. Graphs of sin and cos from 0° to 90°.

B1.2 Sines and cosines

Draw a pair of similar right-angled triangles on the board (different sizes). Mark the right angle and corresponding acute angles on each one.

Now mark the length of the hypotenuse as 1 unit on the smaller triangle and 5 units on the enlargement. Label another side of the smaller triangle as 0.8 units. Encourage students to give the corresponding length on the larger triangle.

Repeat with other scale factors, and other side lengths.

Useful resources

B1.2OHP – sequence of right-angled triangles
Scientific calculators

Introductory activity

Draw a variety of right-angled triangles on the board, with the hypotenuse being 1 unit in each case.

Ask students how the horizontal base and the vertical height are changing as the angle changes.

B1.2OHP shows a sequence of right-angled triangles, with increasing angle.

Ensure that all students have access to a scientific calculator, in degree mode.
Describe how the calculator can tell you the horizontal and vertical lengths when the hypotenuse is 1 unit. Discuss why this would be useful – it means that you don't have to draw the triangles.

Introduce sine and cosine.
Refer to the first example in the Students' Book, and ensure that students know how to use their calculators to find the required values.

Refer to the measured values found in B1.1 to confirm the calculator values.
Discuss discrepancies – some students will have had more accurate drawings than others.
Extend to angles other than 30°.

Now progress to situations where the hypotenuse is not 1 unit.
Link to the concept of enlargement, where the length of the hypotenuse gives the scale factor.

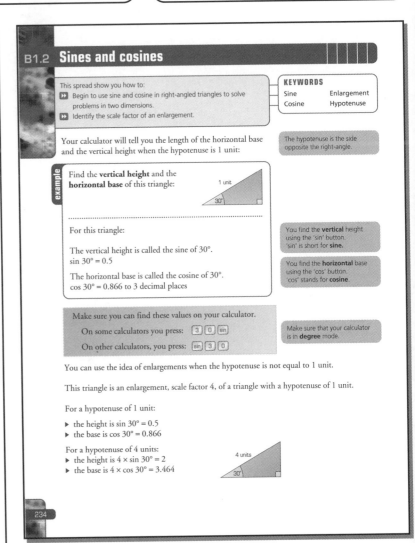

B1.2 Sines and cosines

This spread show you how to:
▶▶ Begin to use sine and cosine in right-angled triangles to solve problems in two dimensions.
▶▶ Identify the scale factor of an enlargement.

KEYWORDS
Sine   Enlargement
Cosine   Hypotenuse

The hypotenuse is the side opposite the right-angle.

Your calculator will tell you the length of the horizontal base and the vertical height when the hypotenuse is 1 unit:

example
Find the **vertical height** and the **horizontal base** of this triangle:

1 unit
30°

For this triangle:

The vertical height is called the sine of 30°.
sin 30° = 0.5

The horizontal base is called the cosine of 30°.
cos 30° = 0.866 to 3 decimal places

You find the **vertical** height using the 'sin' button. 'sin' is short for **sine**.

You find the **horizontal** base using the 'cos' button. 'cos' stands for **cosine**.

Make sure you can find these values on your calculator.
On some calculators you press: 3 0 sin
On other calculators, you press: sin 3 0

Make sure that your calculator is in **degree** mode.

You can use the idea of enlargements when the hypotenuse is not equal to 1 unit.

This triangle is an enlargement, scale factor 4, of a triangle with a hypotenuse of 1 unit.

For a hypotenuse of 1 unit:
▶ the height is sin 30° = 0.5
▶ the base is cos 30° = 0.866

For a hypotenuse of 4 units:
▶ the height is 4 × sin 30° = 2
▶ the base is 4 × cos 30° = 3.464

4 units
30°

234

Plenary

Review questions 5 and 6.
Draw attention to the use of scale factors in question 5, and the changed orientation of some of the triangles in question 6.

Further activities

Students could confirm some of their calculations in the exercise by constructing the triangles and measuring.

Differentiation

Core questions:
▸ Question 1 requires students to use a calculator to find sines and cosines.
▸ Questions 2–4 involve finding missing lengths in triangles with unit hypotenuse.
▸ Questions 5 and 6 extend to triangles with non-unit hypotenuses.

Extension tier: focuses on using trigonometry to find angles, sides and hence area.

Support tier: focuses on tabulating students' results.

Exercise B1.2

1 **a** Use a calculator to copy and complete this table. Give lengths to 2 dp.

Angle	Cosine	Sine
0°		
10°		
20°		
30°		
40°		
50°		
60°		
70°		
80°		
90°		

   b Compare your results with the table you compiled in question 3 on page 233. What do you notice?

2 Find the lengths of the sides marked with letters.

3 Find the lengths of the sides marked with letters.
   Remember to include the units.

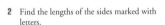

4 Find the lengths marked with letters.

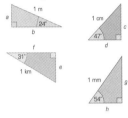

5 Find the lengths marked with letters.

6 Find the lengths marked with letters.

235

Exercise commentary

The questions assess the objectives on Framework Page 247.

Problem solving
The exercise contains problems involving angle, assessing Framework Page 17.

Group work
The exercise is best suited to an individual approach, though some students may wish to share a calculator.

Misconceptions
Students may not appreciate that any discrepancy between calculator values and measured values of sine and cosine are most likely due to errors in measurement. Emphasise that a measured value will not be as accurate as a calculator value.

Links
Similarity: Framework Page 193.

Homework

B1.2HW provides further practice at using sin and cos.

Answers

1 **a** Cosine: 1.00, 0.98, 0.94, 0.87, 0.77, 0.64, 0.50, 0.34, 0.17, 0; sine: 0, 0.17, 0.34, 0.50, 0.64, 0.77, 0.87, 0.94, 0.98, 1.00 **b** Cosine gives the horizontal distance, sine gives the vertical distance. **2** $a = 0.47$ units, $b = 0.33$ units, $c = 0.75$ units, $d = 0.47$ units
3 $a = 0.36$ cm, $b = 0.93$ cm, $c = 0.96$ mm, $d = 0.29$ mm, $e = 0.56$ m, $f = 0.83$ m, $g = 0.78$ km, $h = 0.63$ km   **4** $a = 0.41$ m, $b = 0.91$ m, $c = 0.73$ cm, $d = 0.68$ cm, $e = 0.52$ km, $f = 0.86$ km, $g = 0.81$ mm, $h = 0.59$ mm   **5** $a = 0.62$ cm, $b = 1.90$ cm, $c = 2.39$ km, $d = 2.56$ km, $e = 7.55$ cm, $f = 9.33$ cm, $g = 23.76$ mm, $h = 16.63$ mm   **6** $a = 2.65$ m, $b = 4.24$ m, $c = 8.24$ km, $d = 14.87$ km, $e = 7.02$ cm, $f = 6.55$ cm, $g = 35.63$ mm, $h = 15.86$ mm

Mental starter

Draw a triangle like this:

Say that the number in the top space is the product of the two numbers in the base. (Use the example of 48, 6 and 8.) Now cover each number in turn, and ask students to write down a calculation at each stage. For example, cover the 6, then students should write down $48 \div 8 = 6$.

Move on to examples involving one, two or three algebraic symbols.

Useful resources

B1.3OHP – right-angled triangles in different orientations
Scientific calculators

Introductory activity

Recap the meanings of sine and cosine from B1.2.

Describe how you can use a calculator to find the 'vertical' and 'horizontal' sides in any right-angled triangle.

Show a triangle drawn at an angle, and ask which is the vertical and which is the horizontal. Encourage students to appreciate that these terms are inadequate.

Introduce the terms 'opposite' and 'adjacent'.

Use the diagrams in the Students' Book to show how opposite and adjacent sides can be identified for any orientation.

B1.3OHP shows a variety of triangles, each with a nominated angle. Engage the class in identifying the opposite and adjacent side in each case.

Introduce the formulae for sine and cosine.

Illustrate the use of the formulae with the example in the Students' Book. Emphasise that this example uses sine, rather than cosine, because of the information given.

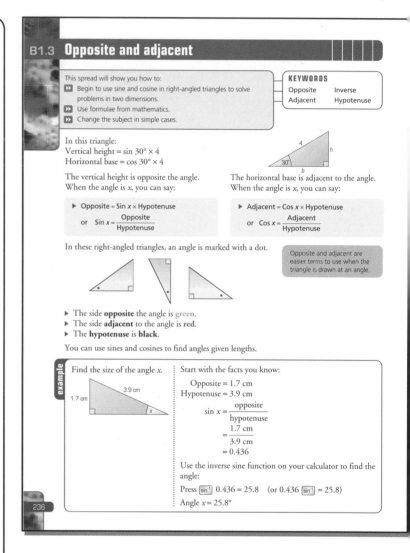

B1.3 Opposite and adjacent

This spread will show you how to:
▶▶ Begin to use sine and cosine in right-angled triangles to solve problems in two dimensions.
▶▶ Use formulae from mathematics.
▶▶ Change the subject in simple cases.

KEYWORDS
Opposite · Inverse
Adjacent · Hypotenuse

In this triangle:
Vertical height = sin 30° × 4
Horizontal base = cos 30° × 4

The vertical height is opposite the angle.
When the angle is x, you can say:

▶ Opposite = Sin x × Hypotenuse
or Sin x = $\dfrac{\text{Opposite}}{\text{Hypotenuse}}$

The horizontal base is adjacent to the angle.
When the angle is x, you can say:

▶ Adjacent = Cos x × Hypotenuse
or Cos x = $\dfrac{\text{Adjacent}}{\text{Hypotenuse}}$

In these right-angled triangles, an angle is marked with a dot.

Opposite and adjacent are easier terms to use when the triangle is drawn at an angle.

▶ The side **opposite** the angle is green.
▶ The side **adjacent** to the angle is red.
▶ The **hypotenuse** is black.

You can use sines and cosines to find angles given lengths.

example

Find the size of the angle x.

Start with the facts you know:

Opposite = 1.7 cm
Hypotenuse = 3.9 cm

$\sin x = \dfrac{\text{opposite}}{\text{hypotenuse}}$
$= \dfrac{1.7 \text{ cm}}{3.9 \text{ cm}}$
$= 0.436$

Use the inverse sine function on your calculator to find the angle:
Press [sin⁻¹] 0.436 = 25.8 (or 0.436 [sin⁻¹] = 25.8)
Angle x = 25.8°

236

Plenary

Discuss questions 2, 4, 5 and 6.
Ask volunteers to give their answers to a particular question, and encourage students to write down each stage of their working. Identify any errors in working or presentation, and identify misconceptions.

Further activities

Encourage students to work in pairs to make up and solve their own examples based on those in questions 2, 4, 5 and 6.

Differentiation

Core questions:
▶ Question 1 provides practice in labelling sides in a right-angled triangle.
▶ Questions 2–4 focus on finding unknown lengths.
▶ Questions 5 and 6 extend to using inverse functions to find angles.

Extension tier: focuses on bearings and trigonometry.

Support tier: focuses on finding patterns and rules in investigation results.

Exercise B1.3

1 Sketch these right-angled triangles.
▶ Mark each hypotenuse with an H.
▶ Mark the side opposite the angle marked • with an O.
▶ Mark the side adjacent to the angle marked • with an A.
The first one is done for you.

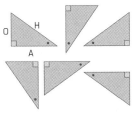

2 Sketch these right-angled triangles. Work out the length of the sides marked with letters.

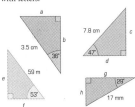

3 Write down a formula you could use to work out the hypotenuse of a right-angled triangle, when you know:
a the size of an angle and the length of the opposite side
b the size of an angle and the length of the adjacent side.

4 Use the formulae you found in question 3 to work out these missing lengths.

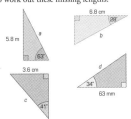

5 Use the inverse sine function ($\sin^{-1}$) on your calculator to find the size of the angles marked with letters. The first one is done for you.

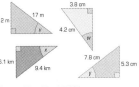

$\sin v = 12 \div 17 = 0.7059$
so $v = \sin^{-1} 0.7059 = 44.9°$

6 Use the inverse cosine function ($\cos^{-1}$) on your calculator to find the size of the angles marked with letters in these right-angled triangles.

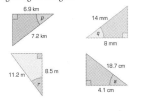

Exercise commentary

The questions assess the objectives on Framework Pages 245 and 247.

Problem solving

Question 3 requires students to generalise, assessing Framework Page 33.

Group work

Students could work in pairs to compare and check some of their answers, for example in questions 1 and 3.

Misconceptions

Students may be unsure as to which ratio to use. Encourage them to write out all the given information on a copy of the triangle, and label the sides as opposite, adjacent and hypotenuse. Then use the formula for which they have two out of the three pieces of information.

Links

Pythagoras' theorem: Framework Pages 187–189.

Homework

B1.3HW gives further practice at explaining and using sin and cos.

Answers

1 Triangles marked appropriately.
2 $a = 2.06$ cm, $b = 2.83$ cm, $c = 5.70$ cm, $d = 5.32$ cm, $e = 47.12$ m, $f = 35.51$ m, $g = 14.87$ mm, $h = 8.24$ mm
3 a Opposite $\div \sin x$ **b** Adjacent $\div \cos x$
4 $a = 6.5$ m, $b = 7.7$ cm, $c = 5.5$ cm, $d = 76$ mm
5 $w = 64.8°$, $x = 40.5°$, $y = 42.8°$
6 $p = 16.6°$, $q = 55.2°$, $r = 40.6°$, $s = 77.3°$

B1.4 Tangents

Mental starter

Write a variety of formulae on the board.

For example, $a = bc$; $w = \frac{x}{y}$, $f = np^2$.

Challenge students to transform each into a formula that gives b in terms of a and c, for example.

Encourage students to check by substitution that their answers are correct.

Useful resources

B1.4OHP – right-angled triangles on a 2 mm grid

Scientific calculators

2 mm graph paper

OHP of R9 – 2 mm grid

Introductory activity

Recap sine and cosine.

Discuss how to find missing angles and lengths in right-angled triangles.

Discuss why this is better than drawing the triangles:

▶ It is quicker and easier.

▶ It is more accurate.

Introduce the tangent, and describe how it links O and A.

Emphasise that sine links O and H, whereas cosine links A and H.

Using a 2 mm grid on an OHP (**R9**), show different right-angled triangles where the angle and opposite both change, but the adjacent is fixed as 1 unit.

B1.4OHP shows a variety of triangles, including 30°.

Emphasise how the opposite changes, and describe this as a measure of the tangent.

The last diagram on **B1.4OHP** shows the diagram in the Students' Book, which includes the arc of the circle. This illustrates why it is called a tangent, as it just touches the circle.

Ask students to verify the estimated values by using the [tan] **key on a calculator.**

Show how the opposite side can be found by enlargement when the adjacent side is not 1 unit.

Introduce the general formula for tangent of an angle.

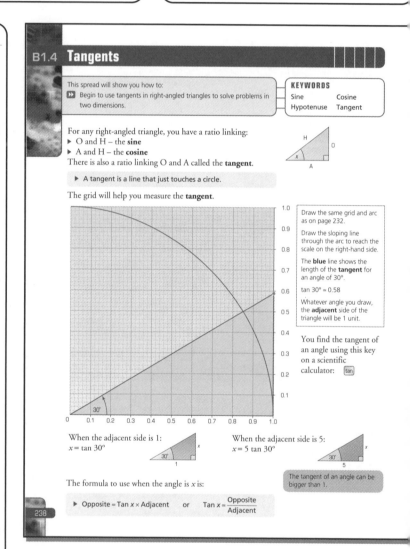

B1.4 Tangents

This spread will show you how to:

▶▶ Begin to use tangents in right-angled triangles to solve problems in two dimensions.

KEYWORDS
Sine Cosine
Hypotenuse Tangent

For any right-angled triangle, you have a ratio linking:
▶ O and H – the **sine**
▶ A and H – the **cosine**
There is also a ratio linking O and A called the **tangent**.

▶ A tangent is a line that just touches a circle.

The grid will help you measure the **tangent**.

Draw the same grid and arc as on page 232.

Draw the sloping line through the arc to reach the scale on the right-hand side.

The **blue** line shows the length of the **tangent** for an angle of 30°.

tan 30° ≈ 0.58

Whatever angle you draw, the **adjacent** side of the triangle will be 1 unit.

You find the tangent of an angle using this key on a scientific calculator: [tan]

When the adjacent side is 1:
$x = \tan 30°$

When the adjacent side is 5:
$x = 5 \tan 30°$

The tangent of an angle can be bigger than 1.

The formula to use when the angle is x is:

▶ Opposite = Tan x × Adjacent   or   Tan $x = \dfrac{\text{Opposite}}{\text{Adjacent}}$

238

Plenary

Discuss answers to question 2, establishing that the tangent increases without limit as the angle approaches 90°.

By comparing the diagrams on pages 238 and 232, establish the idea that for small angles, the tangent will be similar in size to the sine.

Calculate some values of sine and tangent for angles of different sizes.

Further activities

Challenge students to work out the values of tan for angles from 0° to 360° in 10° intervals, then plot them on a graph. Encourage them to draw the corresponding triangles to make sense of their results.

Differentiation

Core questions:

▶ Question 1 provides practice at using a calculator to find tangents.
▶ Questions 2–5 focus on finding opposite sides and tangents of angles.
▶ Questions 6 and 7 extend to using a formula.

Extension tier: focuses on problem solving, using Pythagoras' theorem and trigonometry.

Support tier: focuses on drawing graphs for students' data.

Exercise B1.4

1 Copy and complete the table for the tangents of angles from 0° to 90°. Use a calculator, giving values correct to 3 decimal places.

Angle	Tangent
0°	0
10°	
20°	
30°	
40°	
50°	
60°	
70°	
80°	
90°	–

2 You will not be able to work out the tangent of 90°.
  a Use the diagram on page 238 to explain why it is not possible.
  b Make a table like the one in question 1, to show the tangents of angles from 80° to 89°, in steps of 1°.
  c Use your calculator to work out the tangent of 89.9°.

3 Draw a line graph to show the value of the tangents of angles from 0° to 80° in steps of 10°.

4 Use your calculator to work out the lengths marked with letters.

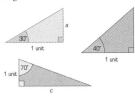

5 Use your calculator to work out the lengths marked with letters.

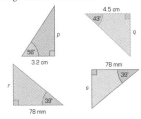

6 Write a formula you could use to work out:
  a the size of an angle, if you know the lengths of the adjacent and opposite sides
  b the length of the adjacent side, if you know the size of an angle and length of the opposite side.

7 Use the formulae you wrote down in question 6 to find the lengths and angles marked with letters.

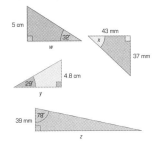

239

Exercise commentary

The questions assess the objectives on Framework Pages 243–247.

Problem solving

Question 2 assesses the objectives on Framework page 31.
Question 6 assesses Page 33.

Group work

Students could work in pairs on questions 1–3.

Misconceptions

Students may confuse the diagrams on pages 232 and 238. The essential difference is that in the first diagram (to illustrate sine and cosine) the hypotenuse is always 1 unit, whereas in the second diagram (to illustrate tangent) the adjacent side is 1 unit.
Encourage correct presentation of work – sin, cos and tan are not quantities in themselves, but only exist in relation to an angle.

Links

Pythagoras' theorem: Framework Pages 187–189.

Homework

B1.4HW gives practice in explaining and using tan.

Answers

1 0.176, 0.364, 0.577, 0.839, 1.192, 1.732, 2.747, 5.671
2 a The hypotenuse of the triangle would be vertical, so it would not reach the scale on the right-hand side. b 5.671, 6.314, 7.115, 8.144, 9.514, 11.430, 14.301, 19.081, 28.636, 57.290 c 572.957
3 Line graph of tan x 4 $a = 0.577$ unit, $b = 0.839$ unit, $c = 2.747$ units
5 $p = 4.7$ cm, $q = 4.2$ cm, $r = 63$ mm, $s = 63$ mm
6 a $x = \tan^{-1}\left(\frac{O}{A}\right)$ b $A = O \div \tan x$ 7 $w = 8$ cm, $x = 40.7°$, $y = 8.7$ cm, $z = 183.5$ mm

B1.5 Pythagoras' theorem

Introductory activity

Recap knowledge of right-angled triangles.
Use the first diagram in the Students' Book to recap how you can work out the opposite and adjacent if you know one angle (with a unit hypotenuse).

Encourage students to:
▸ Calculate sin 39° and cos 39°, writing down all the digits on their calculator display.
▸ Square these lengths.
▸ Add them together (they should get 1).

Extend to a non-unit hypotenuse.
Again, ask students to use their knowledge of sine and cosine to find the two shorter lengths, square them and add them together. Encourage students to comment on their result.

Establish Pythagoras' theorem for a right-angled triangle with lengths a, b and c.
Use the example in the Students' book to illustrate the use of the theorem.

B1.5OHP shows visually how the squares of the two shorter sides add together to make the square of the hypotenuse.

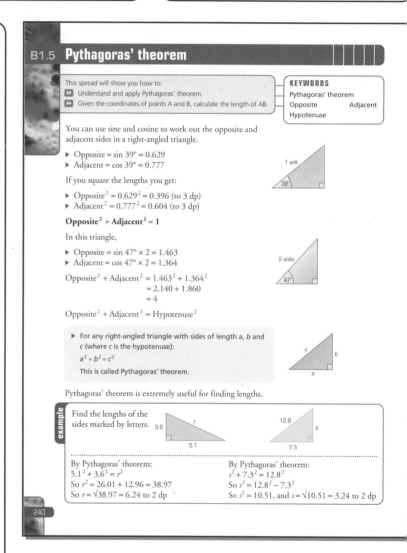

B1.5 Pythagoras' theorem

This spread will show you how to:
▸ Understand and apply Pythagoras' theorem.
▸ Given the coordinates of points A and B, calculate the length of AB.

KEYWORDS
Pythagoras' theorem
Opposite   Adjacent
Hypotenuse

You can use sine and cosine to work out the opposite and adjacent sides in a right-angled triangle.
▸ Opposite = sin 39° = 0.629
▸ Adjacent = cos 39° = 0.777

If you square the lengths you get:
▸ $\text{Opposite}^2 = 0.629^2 = 0.396$ (to 3 dp)
▸ $\text{Adjacent}^2 = 0.777^2 = 0.604$ (to 3 dp)

$\text{Opposite}^2 + \text{Adjacent}^2 = 1$

In this triangle,
▸ Opposite = sin 47° × 2 = 1.463
▸ Adjacent = cos 47° × 2 = 1.364

$\text{Opposite}^2 + \text{Adjacent}^2 = 1.463^2 + 1.364^2$
$= 2.140 + 1.860$
$= 4$

$\text{Opposite}^2 + \text{Adjacent}^2 = \text{Hypotenuse}^2$

▸ For any right-angled triangle with sides of length a, b and c (where c is the hypotenuse):
$a^2 + b^2 = c^2$
This is called Pythagoras' theorem.

Pythagoras' theorem is extremely useful for finding lengths.

example
Find the lengths of the sides marked by letters.

By Pythagoras' theorem:
$5.1^2 + 3.6^2 = r^2$
So $r^2 = 26.01 + 12.96 = 38.97$
So $r = \sqrt{38.97} = 6.24$ to 2 dp

By Pythagoras' theorem:
$s^2 + 7.3^2 = 12.8^2$
So $s^2 = 12.8^2 - 7.3^2$
So $s^2 = 10.51$, and $s = \sqrt{10.51} = 3.24$ to 2 dp

240

Plenary

Emphasise the idea that Pythagoras' theorem is often useful when there is no 'obvious' triangle to start with.
Use question 4 to illustrate this – the triangle is constructed as a means of finding the distance between the points.

Further activities

Students could verify Pythagoras' theorem by constructing right-angled triangles (using compasses), measuring the sides and substituting them into the formula.

Differentiation

Core questions:
▸ Question 1 requires students to check whether triangles are right-angled.
▸ Questions 2 and 3 focus on using Pythagoras' theorem to find missing lengths.
▸ Question 4 extends to finding the distance between points specified by coordinates.

Extension tier: focuses on sines of angles greater than 90°.

Support tier: focuses on variations of students' investigations.

Exercise B1.5

1 To check that a triangle with sides of length 3, 4 and 5 is right-angled:
▸ Put $a = 3$, $b = 4$ and $c = 5$ into the equation $a^2 + b^2 = c^2$.
▸ Work out the left-hand side of the equation:
$a^2 + b^2 = 3^2 + 4^2 = 9 + 16 = 25$
▸ Work out the right-hand side of the equation: $c^2 = 5^2 = 25$
▸ If the two sides of the equation are equal then the triangle must be right-angled.
Follow these steps to check whether these lengths give right-angled triangles:
a $a = 4$, $b = 5$, $c = 6$
b $a = 6$, $b = 8$, $c = 10$
c $a = 5$, $b = 10$, $c = 12$
d $a = 5$, $b = 12$, $c = 13$

2 Find the length of the hypotenuse in each triangle.

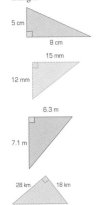

3 Find the length of the sides marked with letters.

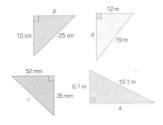

4 To find the distance, d, between two points, draw a right-angled triangle:

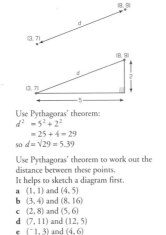

Use Pythagoras' theorem:
$d^2 = 5^2 + 2^2$
$= 25 + 4 = 29$
so $d = \sqrt{29} = 5.39$

Use Pythagoras' theorem to work out the distance between these points.
It helps to sketch a diagram first.
a (1, 1) and (4, 5)
b (3, 4) and (8, 16)
c (2, 8) and (5, 6)
d (7, 11) and (12, 5)
e (⁻1, 3) and (4, 6)
f (⁻3, ⁻2) and (7, 5)

Exercise commentary

The questions assess the objectives on Framework Page 189.

Problem solving
Question 1 assesses the objectives on Framework Page 17.

Group work
Students may attempt the further activity in pairs.

Misconceptions
Students may substitute numbers into the formula incorrectly. Emphasise the correct order of operations (square then add, not add then square).
Students may also be caught out by situations where one of the shorter sides is required. Encourage labelling of the sides before applying the formula. Emphasise that when you are finding the hypotenuse you 'square, square, add, square root', but when finding a shorter side you 'square, square, subtract smaller from larger, square root'.

Links
Trigonometry: Framework Pages 243–247.

Homework

B1.5HW asks students to explain Pythagoras' theorem using drawings, text and areas of squares.

Answers

1 a No **b** Yes **c** No **d** Yes
2 9.43 cm, 19.21 mm, 9.49 m, 33.29 km
3 $p = 22.91$ cm, $q = 14.73$ m, $r = 62.68$ mm, $s = 8.05$ m
4 a 5 **b** 13 **c** 3.61 **d** 7.81
e 5.83 **f** 12.21

241

B1.6 Triangle problems

Mental starter

Draw a right-angled triangle on the board.
Indicate two quantities by marking them with a cross (for example, a side and an angle), then ask the class how they would work out a specified third quantity (either a side or an angle).
Repeat for other combinations of quantities.

Useful resources

B1.6OHP – diagram from the Students' Book example
Scientific calculators

Introductory activity

Refer to the mental starter.
Consolidate right-angled triangles, and identify the techniques that students should know:
▸ Angle sum of a triangle
▸ Trigonometry
▸ Pythagoras' theorem

Emphasise that students should:
▸ Use **Pythagoras' theorem** when they know two sides of a triangle and they want to find the third one.
▸ Use **trigonometry** for problems involving lengths **and** angles.

The formula triangles in the Students' Book summarise which trigonometric ratio should be used, depending on what information is provided.

Bring the techniques together in the context of a problem.
Use the example in the Students' Books to illustrate how a problem may require more than one of the procedures introduced in this unit.
B1.6OHP shows the diagram from the example.

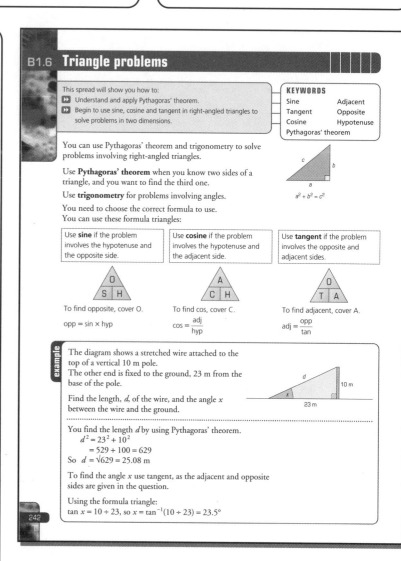

B1.6 Triangle problems

This spread will show you how to:
▸ Understand and apply Pythagoras' theorem.
▸ Begin to use sine, cosine and tangent in right-angled triangles to solve problems in two dimensions.

KEYWORDS
Sine   Adjacent
Tangent   Opposite
Cosine   Hypotenuse
Pythagoras' theorem

You can use Pythagoras' theorem and trigonometry to solve problems involving right-angled triangles.

Use **Pythagoras' theorem** when you know two sides of a triangle, and you want to find the third one.

Use **trigonometry** for problems involving angles.

You need to choose the correct formula to use.
You can use these formula triangles:

$a^2 + b^2 = c^2$

Use **sine** if the problem involves the hypotenuse and the opposite side.

Use **cosine** if the problem involves the hypotenuse and the adjacent side.

Use **tangent** if the problem involves the opposite and adjacent sides.

To find opposite, cover O.
$opp = \sin \times hyp$

To find cos, cover C.
$\cos = \dfrac{adj}{hyp}$

To find adjacent, cover A.
$adj = \dfrac{opp}{tan}$

example

The diagram shows a stretched wire attached to the top of a vertical 10 m pole.
The other end is fixed to the ground, 23 m from the base of the pole.

Find the length, d, of the wire, and the angle x between the wire and the ground.

You find the length d by using Pythagoras' theorem.
$d^2 = 23^2 + 10^2$
$\quad = 529 + 100 = 629$
So $d = \sqrt{629} = 25.08$ m

To find the angle x use tangent, as the adjacent and opposite sides are given in the question.

Using the formula triangle:
$\tan x = 10 \div 23$, so $x = \tan^{-1}(10 \div 23) = 23.5°$

242

Plenary

Discuss question 2, asking students to explain their choice of technique for each part.

Further activities

Challenge students in pairs to use all the trigonometry facts they have learnt, including Pythagoras' theorem, to make up some examples of their own, then solve them.

Differentiation

Core questions:

▸ Questions 1 and 2 involve using trigonometry and Pythagoras' theorem to find lengths and angles in right-angled triangles.
▸ Questions 3 and 4 use Pythagoras' theorem to check whether triangles are right-angled.
▸ Questions 5 and 6 use Pythagoras' theorem and trigonometry to solve problems.

Support tier: focuses on writing a report of the investigation.

Extension tier: focuses on the graph of $y = \sin x$.

Exercise B1.6

1 Find the angles marked with letters.

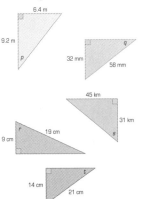

2 Find the lengths of the sides marked with letters.

3 A triangle has sides with lengths 6 cm, 8 cm and 10 cm. Without drawing the triangle, prove that it has a right angle.

4 These are the lengths of the sides of some triangles. For each set of lengths, explain whether or not the triangle is right-angled.
 a 7 m, 8 m, 15 m
 b 7 cm, 24 cm, 25 cm
 c 1.5 m, 2 m, 2.5 m

5 A ladder of length 4.5 m leans against a wall of a house so that the top just reaches a windowsill that is 3.7 m above the ground. Work out:
 a The distance, d, between the bottom of the ladder and the base of the wall.
 b The angle, x, between the ladder and the ground.

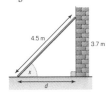

6 A radar station measures the distance to an aeroplane as 9.4 km, and the angle of elevation as 21°. Find the height, h, of the aeroplane above the ground.

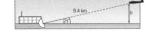

Exercise commentary

The questions assess the objectives on Framework Pages 189, 245 and 247.

Problem solving

Questions 3–6 assess the objectives on Framework Page 17.
Questions 5 and 6 assess the objectives on Page 31.

Group work

Students could work in pairs on questions 1 and 2, to discuss their choice of technique.

Misconceptions

In multi-step problems, students may compound errors by using an inappropriate ratio.
Encourage students to select the ratio that uses numbers that have been given, rather than numbers that students have derived.

Links

This topic links to trigonometric problems at GCSE.
Also trigonometry: Framework Pages 243–247

243

Homework

B1.6HW gives further practice at triangle problems using trigonometry.

Answers

1 $p = 34.8°$, $q = 33.5°$, $r = 61.7°$, $s = 55.4°$, $t = 41.8°$
2 $v = 3.71$ cm, $w = 6.33$ m, $x = 8.33$ cm, $y = 19.43$ mm, $z = 14.25$ km
3 $6^2 + 8^2 = 100 = 10^2$
4 a No **b** Yes **c** Yes
5 a 2.56 m **b** 55.3°
6 3.37 km

The key objectives for this unit are:

▸ Understand and apply Pythagoras' theorem. (189)
▸ Begin to use sine, cos and tangent in right-angled triangles. (243–247)
▸ Give solutions to problems to an appropriate degree of accuracy. (31)

Plenary activity

Discuss some final examples of trigonometry problems involving sin, cos, tan and Pythagoras' theorem.
Encourage students to use all the facts they know to find angles and lengths in turn to label every part of a triangle.

Check out commentary

1 Encourage students to visualise triangles carefully to establish which side is the hypotenuse before they start.
In part **c**, encourage a sketch to work out the lengths of the two shorter sides of the imaginary triangle.

2 Encourage students to consider carefully which ratio to use. It may be helpful for them to sketch a triangle, label the three sides O, A and H and then use the formula for which they have two of the three pieces of information.

3 Encourage students to think sensibly about what measurements mean and how useful this level of accuracy is. Discuss what an appropriate level of accuracy would be, for example, to draw the triangle exactly.

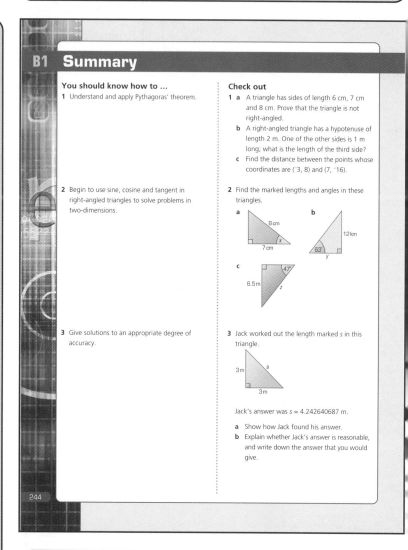

B1 Summary

You should know how to ...

1 Understand and apply Pythagoras' theorem.

2 Begin to use sine, cosine and tangent in right-angled triangles to solve problems in two-dimensions.

3 Give solutions to an appropriate degree of accuracy.

Check out

1 a A triangle has sides of length 6 cm, 7 cm and 8 cm. Prove that the triangle is not right-angled.
   b A right-angled triangle has a hypotenuse of length 2 m. One of the other sides is 1 m long; what is the length of the third side?
   c Find the distance between the points whose coordinates are ($^-$3, 8) and (7, $^-$16).

2 Find the marked lengths and angles in these triangles.
   a [triangle with 8 cm, 7 cm, angle x]
   b [triangle with 12 km, 63°, y]
   c [triangle with 6.5 m, 47°, z]

3 Jack worked out the length marked s in this triangle.
   [triangle with 3 m, s, 3 m]

   Jack's answer was $s = 4.242640687$ m.

   a Show how Jack found his answer.
   b Explain whether Jack's answer is reasonable, and write down the answer that you would give.

244

Development

Trigonometrical ratios and Pythagoras' theorem are used and developed in Key Stage 4 work.

Links

Trigonometry and Pythagoras' theorem link to work in design drawing, ICT, Design and Technology and Art.

accuracy
S4.6

You can round numbers to any degree of accuracy, for example, to the nearest power of 10 or to a given number of decimal places. The degree of accuracy of an answer depends on the information given in the question.

adjacent
B1.3, N2.8, B1.5, B1.6

Adjacent means 'next to'. The side adjacent to the angle in a right-angled triangle is the side next to the angle that is not the hypotenuse.

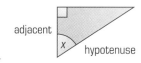

alternate angles
S1.4, S4.2

A pair of alternate angles are formed when a line crosses a pair of parallel lines. Alternate angles are equal.

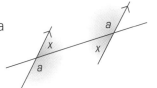

angles in a triangle
P1.5

Angles in a triangle add up to 180°.

angles on a straight line
P1.5

Angles on a straight line add up to 180°.

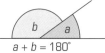

anomaly
D1.4

An anomaly is an exceptional case – a piece of the data which doesn't fit into the general pattern.

approximate, approximation
N2.6, N2.7, P1.4, P1.6

An approximate value is a value that is close to the actual value.

approximately equal to (≈)
N2.6

Approximately equal to means almost the same size.

arc
S1.6, S1.7, B1.1

An arc is a part of a curve.

area: square millimetre, square centimetre, square metre, square kilometre
S2.1, S2.4, S2.5, P1.1

The area of a surface is a measure of the space it covers.

assumed mean
D1.2

An assumed mean is used to simplify the arithmetic when calculating the mean. The assumed mean is subtracted from all the data and added back on once the mean of the smaller numbers has been calculated.

average
D1.2

An average is a representative value of a set of data.

axis, axes
A2.2, D1.6

An axis is one of the lines used to locate a point in a coordinate system.

Glossary

bar chart
D1.3

A bar chart is a diagram that uses rectangles of equal width to display data. The frequency is given by the height of the rectangle.

bar-line chart
D3.5

A bar-line chart is a diagram that uses lines to display data. The lengths of the lines are proportional to the frequencies.

base
A4.3

In index notation, the base is the number which is to be raised to a power, for example, in 5^3, 5 is the base.

base (of plane shape or solid)
B1.1

The lower horizontal edge of a plane shape is called the base. Similarly, the base of a solid is its bottom face.

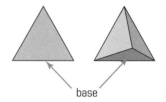

base

best estimate
A3.6

The best estimate of a value is the closest you can achieve.

bias
D2.4

An experiment is biased if not all outcomes are equally likely. A selection is biased if not all the members of the population from which it comes have an equal chance of being chosen

bisect, bisector
S1.9

A bisector is a line that divides an angle or another line in half.

brackets
N1.9, A3.3, N2.8

Operations within brackets should be carried out first.

calculate, calculation
P1.1

Calculate means work out using a mathematical procedure.

cancel, cancellation
N1.1, N2.5, A5.4

A fraction is cancelled down by dividing the numerator and denominator by a common factor,

for example, $\frac{24}{40} = \frac{3}{5}$ (÷ 8)

capacity: litre
S2.5

Capacity is a measure of the amount of liquid a 3-D shape will hold.

centre (of a circle)
S1.6, S2.2

The centre of a circle is the point in the middle.

centre

centre of enlargement
S3.5

The centre of enlargement is the point from which an enlargement is measured.

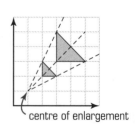

centre of enlargement

centre of rotation
3.1

The centre of rotation is the fixed point about which a rotation takes place.

certain
)2.1

An event that is certain will definitely happen.

chord
1.6

A chord is a line joining two points on the circumference of a circle.

chord

circle
1.8, S2.2, S2.3, S2.4

A circle is a set of points that are the same distance from a fixed point, the centre.

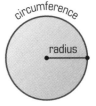

circumference
1.6, S2.2, S2.3, S2.4, P1.1

The circumference is the distance around the edge of a circle. You calculate it using the formula: $C = 2\pi r$ where r is the radius.

class interval
)3.4

A class interval is a group that you put data into to make it easier to handle.

common denominator
)2.3, A5.4

A common denominator is an integer that is exactly divisible by all the denominators in a set of fractions, for example, the common denominator of $\frac{2}{3}$ and $\frac{1}{2}$ is 6.

common factor
N2.5

A common factor is a factor of two or more numbers. For example, 2 is a common factor of 4 and 10.

compare
N1.1, N1.7, D1.5

Compare means to assess the similarity of.

compasses (pair of)
S1.7

Compasses are used for constructions and drawing circles.

compensation
N2.4, N2.5

The method of compensation makes some calculations easier, for example, some multiplications are easier if you double one of the numbers and then compensate by halving the answer.

conclude, conclusion
D3.6

To come to a decision after a series of logical steps.

congruent, congruence
S3.2, S4.1

Congruent shapes are exactly the same shape and size.

construct
A3.2, S1.7

To form an equation from given facts or to draw a line, angle or shape accurately.

construction lines
S1.7

Arcs and lines drawn during the construction of bisectors of angles and lines with a straight edge and compasses.

continuous (data)
D1.2, D3.2

Continuous data can take any value between given limits, for example, less than 1 m.

convention
S1.1, S3.1, S3.2

A convention is an agreed way of describing a situation. For example, this line is AB:

A   B

Glossary

convert
S2.1

To change.

coordinate pair
A4.5

A coordinate pair is a pair of numbers that give the position of a point on a coordinate grid, for example, (3, 2) means 3 units across and 2 units up.

coordinates
B1.5

Coordinates are the numbers that make up a coordinate pair.

correlation
D3.3

Correlation is a measure of the relationship between pairs of variables.

corresponding angles
S1.4, S3.2, S4.2

A pair of corresponding angles are formed when a straight line crosses a pair of parallel lines. Corresponding angles are equal.

corresponding sides
S3.2, S3.5

Corresponding sides in congruent shapes are equal in length.

cosine
B1.2, B1.4, B1.6

The cosine of an angle in a right-angled triangle is the ratio of the adjacent side a, to the hypotenuse h.

$$\cos x = \frac{a}{h}$$

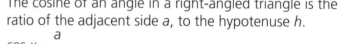

cost price
N1.5

The price that an item costs to produce.

cross-section
S2.6, S3.4, S4.3

The cross-section of a solid is the 2-D shape you get when you slice the solid perpendicular to its length.

cube, cube number
N1.9, N2.1

A cube number is the product of three equal integers, for example, $27 = 3 \times 3 \times 3$, so 27 is a cube number.

cube root
N1.9, N2.1

The cube root of a number is the value that gives the number when multiplied by itself twice.
For example, $2 \times 2 \times 2 = 8$, so 2 is the cube root of 8, or $2 = \sqrt[3]{8}$.

cubed
A4.3

A number is cubed if it is multiplied by itself twice.
For example, 2 cubed, written 2^3, is $2 \times 2 \times 2 = 8$.

data
D2.4

Data are pieces of information.

data collection sheet
D3.1

A data collection sheet is used to collect data. It is sometimes a list of questions with tick boxes for answers.

decimal place (dp)
N2.3, A3.6

Each column after the decimal point is called a decimal place, for example, 0.65 has two decimal places (2 dp).

decrease
N1.4

To decrease means to make or become smaller.

definition
S1.1

A definition is a set of conditions that uniquely specify something.

degree (°)
S1.1

A degree is a measure of turn. There are 360° in a full turn.

denominator
N1.1

The denominator is the bottom number in a fraction. It shows how many parts there are in total.

derived property
1.1

A derived property is a consequence of a definition.

diagonal
4.1

A diagonal of a polygon is a line joining two vertices but not forming a side.

This is a diagonal.

diameter
1.6, S2.2, S2.3, P1.1

A diameter is the distance across a circle through the centre.

diameter

difference
A1.3

The difference between the terms of a linear sequence is constant (always the same).

digit
N2.2, N2.3, A4.4

A digit is any of the numbers 0, 1, 2, 3, 4, 5, 6, 7, 8, 9.

dimensions
S2.5, S4.4

Flat 2-D shapes have two dimensions:

length and width   or   base and height

height

base

Solid 3-D shapes have three dimensions:

length, width and height.

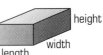

height

width

length

direct proportion
A3.4

Two quantities are in direct proportion if they are always in the same ratio.

direction
S3.1

The direction is the course, clockwise or anticlockwise, an object takes when it is rotated.

discrete (data)
D1.2, D3.2

Discrete data can only take certain definite values, for example, shoe sizes.

distance axis
A2.2

The distance axis is the vertical axis on a distance–time graph.

distance–time graph
A2.2, A2.3, A4.9

A graph showing distance on the vertical axis and time on the horizontal axis.

distribution
D1.5, D3.4, D3.5

Distribution describes the way data is spread out.

dividend, divisor
N2.7

In this division sum: $6.25 \div 5 = 1.25$

this is the dividend   this is the divisor   this is the quotient

elevation
S4.3

An elevation is an accurate drawing of the side or front view of a solid.

enlarge, enlargement
A3.4, S3.5, B1.2

An enlargement is a transformation that multiplies all the sides of a shape by the same scale factor.

Glossary

equally likely
D2.1

Events are equally likely if they have the same probability.

equation
A3.1, A3.2, P1.3, A5.1, A5.3

An equation is a statement linking two expressions that are equal in value.

equidistant
S1.6

Equidistant means the same distance from a point or line.

equivalent, equivalence
N1.1, A3.1, N2.5, N2.6, P1.2

Equivalent fractions are fractions with the same value, for example, $\frac{12}{20} = \frac{3}{5}$.

estimate
A3.5, N2.3, N2.6

An estimate is an approximate answer.

evaluate

Evaluate means find the value of an expression.

event
D2.1, D4.1, D4.3

An event is an activity or the result of an activity.

exact, exactly
A3.6

Exact means completely accurate.
For example, three divides into six exactly.

exception
D1.4

An exception is a case which disproves a rule or hypothesis.

expand
A5.2

You expand brackets by multiplying them out,
for example, $3(2x - 5) = 6x - 15$.

expected frequency
D2.2, D2.3, D4.5

The expected frequency of an event is the number of times it is expected to occur.

Expected frequency = probability × number of trials

experiment
D2.2, D4.4, D4.5

An experiment is a test or investigation to gather evidence for or against a theory.

experimental probability
D2.4

Experimental probability is calculated from the results of an experiment.

explain
P1.2

To explain your answer, you give the reasons why you chose that answer. An explanation may consist of a description of your method or a diagram to illustrate the reason.

expression
A3.1, A3.2, P1.6, A5.2

An expression is a collection of numbers and symbols linked by operations that does not include an equals sign.

exterior angle
S1.2, S1.3

An exterior angle is made by extending one side of a shape.

face
S2.6

A face is a flat surface of a solid.

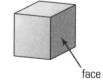
face

factor
N2.5, A4.1

A factor is a number that divides exactly into another number. For example, 3 and 7 are factors of 21.

factorise
A5.2

A number or expression is factorised when it is written as a product of its factors, for example, $4a + 6 = 2(2a + 3)$.

fair
1.6

In a fair experiment there is no bias towards any particular outcome.

favourable outcome
2.1

A favourable outcome is a successful result of doing something. For example, throwing a 'six' with a fair dice.

formula, formulae
3.1, S2.4, A5.1, A5.5

A formula is a statement that links variables.

fraction
1.4, N1.5, N2.4, A5.4

A fraction is a way of describing a part of a whole. For example, $\frac{2}{5}$ of the shape shown is shaded.

frequency
3.2

Frequency is the number of times something occurs.

frequency diagram
1.3

A frequency diagram uses bars to display grouped data. The height of each bar gives the frequency of the group, and there is no space between the bars.

frequency table
3.2

A frequency table shows how often each event or quantity occurs.

function
2.1, A3.1, A5.1, A5.6

A function is a rule. For example, $+2$, -3, $\times 4$ and $\div 5$ are all functions.

function machine
2.1

A function machine links an input value to an output value by performing the function.

general term
A1.1, A1.2, A1.3, A2.1

The general term of a sequence is an expression which relates its value to its position in the sequence.

generate
A1.1

Generate means produce.

gradient, steepness
A4.5, A4.6, A4.7, A5.6

A gradient is a measure of the steepness of a line.

graph
D1.3, A2.2, A5.6

A graph is a diagram that shows a relationship between variables.

greater than or equal to ($\geqslant$)
N2.3

Greater than or equal to means equal to or more than, for example, $x \geqslant 3$ means x can have any value from 3 upwards.

grouped data
D3.2

When there is a lot of data it is often easier to collect it into groups to see trends more easily. The end of one group must not overlap with the start of the next group:

$$0 < x \leqslant 10 \qquad\qquad 10 < x \leqslant 20$$

This group includes 10.   This group doesn't.

hectare
S2.1

A hectare is a unit of area equal to $10\,000$ m^2.

highest common factor (HCF)
N1.1, A4.2

The highest common factor is the largest factor that is common to two or more numbers, for example, the HCF of 12 and 8 is 4.

horizontal
S1.1, A4.8, A4.9

Horizontal means level with the flat ground.

Glossary

hypotenuse
S1.7, B1.1, B1.2, B1.3, B1.4,
B1.5, B1.6

The hypotenuse is the longest side in a
right-angled triangle.
It is opposite the right-angle.

hypotenuse

hypothesis, hypotheses
D3.1, D3.6

A hypothesis is an unproved theory.

**identity, identically
equal to (≡)**
A3.1, A5.1

The expressions on either side of an identity are always equal,
for example, $3(x + 2) \equiv 3x + 6$ for all values of x.

image
S3.1, S3.2, S3.3

An image is the position of an object following a transformation.

impossible
D2.1

An event is impossible if it cannot happen.

improper fraction
N1.2

In an improper fraction the numerator is greater than the
denominator, for example, $\frac{8}{5}$ is an improper fraction.

increase
N1.4, A4.6

To increase means to make or become larger.

independent events
D4.1, D4.6

Two events are independent when one does not affect the
outcome of the other.
For example, the outcome from flipping a coin has no
effect on the outcome from rolling a dice.
The two events are independent.

index form
N2.1

A number is in index form when it is written as a power:
5^3 is in index form.

index, indices
N1.9, N2.1, N2.2, A4.3

The index of a number tells you how many of the number must be
multiplied together. When a number is written in index notation,
the index or power is the raised number.
For example, the index of 4^2 is 2. The plural of index is indices.

index laws
A4.3

The rules that tell you how to multiply and divide powers of the
same base:
$a^m \times a^n = a^{m+n}$
$a^m \div a^n = a^{m-n}$

index notation
N2.1

A number is written in index notation when it is expressed as a
power of another number. For example, 9 in index notation is 3^2.

inference
D1.4

An inference is a conclusion based on evidence.

inspection
A4.7

Inspection is by looking.

integer
N1.2, N1.3, N2.4, A4.4

An integer is a positive or negative whole number (including zero).
The integers are: ..., ⁻3, ⁻2, ⁻1, 0, 1, 2, 3, ...

intercept
A4.5, A4.6, A5.6

The intercept is the length between the origin and the point where
a line crosses the axis.

interior angle
S1.2, S1.3

An interior angle is inside a shape, between two adjacent sides.

interpret, interpretation
A2.3, D1.1, D1.6, A4.8, D3.6

You interpret data whenever you make sense of it.
What you write is your interpretation of the data.

intersect, intersection
A5.6

Two lines intersect at the point where
they cross.

intersection

interval
D3.4

An interval is the size of a class or group in a frequency table.

inverse
N1.6, B1.3

An inverse operation has the opposite effect to the original
operation, for example, multiplication is the inverse of division.

inverse function
A2.1

An inverse function undoes the effect of a function, for example
the function $x \rightarrow 2x - 1$, maps 3 onto 5 and the inverse function
$x \rightarrow \dfrac{x + 1}{2}$ maps 5 onto 3.

isometric
S4.3

Isometric grids are designed to make it easier to draw shapes.

justify
P1.2

To justify is to explain or to prove right.

length: millimetre, centimetre, metre, kilometre
S2.1, S2.5

Length is a measure of distance. It is often used to describe one
dimension of a shape.

less than or equal to (≤)
D3.2

Less than or equal to means equal to or smaller than, for example,
$x \leqslant 2$ means that x can have any value from 2 downwards.

line graph
D1.3

On a line graph points are joined by straight lines.

line symmetry
S4.1

A shape has line symmetry if it has a line of
symmetry.

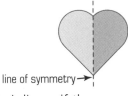

line of symmetry →

linear equation, linear expression, linear function, linear relationship
A4.5, A4.7

An equation, expression, function or relationship is linear if the
highest power of any variable it contains is 1.
For example, $y = 3x - 4$ is a linear equation, and its graph is a
straight line.

linear sequence
A1.3

The terms of a linear sequence increase by the same amount each
time.

locus, loci
S1.8, S1.9

A locus is the position of a set of points, usually a line, that satisfies
some given condition. Loci is the plural of locus.

lowest common multiple (LCM)
N1.1, A4.2, A5.4

The lowest common multiple is the smallest multiple that is common
to two or more numbers, for example, the LCM of 4 and 6 is 12.

map
S3.3, S3.6, S4.5

To map is to follow the rule of a mapping that links two sets of
numbers.

Glossary

mapping
A2.1

A mapping is a rule that can be applied to a set of numbers to give another set of numbers.

mean
D1.2, P1.6

The mean is an average value found by adding all the data and dividing by the number of pieces of data.

median
D1.2

The median is an average found by taking the middle value when the data is arranged in size order.

mirror line
S3.1

A mirror line is a line or axis of symmetry.

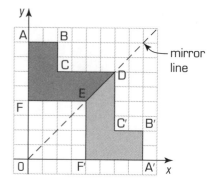

modal class
D1.2, D1.5

The modal class is the most commonly occurring class when the data is grouped. It is the class with the highest frequency.

mode
D1.2

The mode is an average and is the data value that occurs most often.

multiplicative inverse
N1.3, N1.6

You can always get from one number to another by multiplying: $2 \times 3 = 6$.

$$2 \xrightarrow{\times 3} 6$$
$$\times \tfrac{1}{3}$$

To get back to the original number you can multiply by the multiplicative inverse:

$6 \times \tfrac{1}{3} = 2$.

$\tfrac{1}{3}$ is the multiplicative inverse of 3.

multiply out (expressions)
A5.2

To multiply out a bracket you multiply each term inside by the term outside.
For example, $3(x + 1)$ multiplied out is $3x + 3$.

mutually exclusive
D2.2, D4.2, D4.4

Mutually exclusive events cannot both occur in one trial, for example, if you toss a coin once, you cannot get a Head and a Tail.

nearest
N2.3

Nearest means the closest value.

negative
A3.3

A negative number is a number less than zero.

net
S4.3, S4.6

A net is a 2-D arrangement that can be folded to form a solid shape.

numerator
N1.2

The numerator is the top number in a fraction. It shows how many parts you are dealing with.

object
3.2

The object is the original shape before a transformation.

operation
2.1

An operation is a rule for processing numbers or objects. The arithmetic operations are addition, subtraction, multiplication and division.

opposite (sides, angles)
1.3, B1.5, B1.6

Opposite means across from.

This side is opposite the shaded angle.

order of operations
N1.9, N2.8

The conventional order of operations is:
brackets first, then powers,
then division and multiplication,
then addition and subtraction.

outcome
D2.1, D4.1, D4.2, D4.3

An outcome is the result of a trial.

parallel
G1.4

Two lines that always stay the same distance apart are parallel. Parallel lines never cross or meet.

partition, part
N2.4, N2.5

To partition means to split a number into smaller amounts, or parts. For example, 57 could be split into 50 + 7, or 40 + 17.

percentage (%)
N1.4, N1.5, P1.4

A percentage is a fraction expressed as the number of parts per hundred.

perimeter
S2.2, P1.3

The perimeter of a shape is the distance around it. It is the total length of the edges.

perpendicular
G1.7

Two lines are perpendicular to each other if they meet at a right angle.

perpendicular bisector
G1.8

The perpendicular bisector of a line crosses the line at right angles and cuts it in half.

pi (π)
S2.2, S2.3, S2.4

In a circle, the ratio of the circumference to the diameter is constant. This ratio is called pi, written π.
It doesn't have an exact value – the decimal places go on forever without a pattern.
π is a little over 3.
Good approximations are $\pi = 3.14$ or $\pi = \frac{22}{7}$.

pie chart
D1.3

A pie chart is a circle used to display data. The angle at the centre of a sector is proportional to the frequency.

plan
S4.3

A plan of a solid is the view from directly overhead.

Glossary

plane of symmetry
S3.4

A plane of symmetry is a cross-section through a 3-D shape that divides the shape into two identical halves. All prisms have at least one plane of symmetry.

p(n)
D2.1

p(*n*) stands for the probability of event *n* occurring.

polygon: pentagon, hexagon, octagon
S1.2, S4.2

A polygon is a closed shape with three or more straight edges.

A pentagon has five sides.

A hexagon has six sides.

An octagon has eight sides.

population pyramid
D1.5

A population pyramid is a back-to-back bar chart comparing two populations.

position-to-term rule
A1.1, A1.3

The position-to-term rule links the value of a term to its position in the sequence.

positive
A3.3

A positive number is greater than zero.

power, index, indices
N1.9, N2.1, N2.2, A4.3, A4.4

When a number is written in index notation, the power or index is the raised number, for example, the power of 3^2 is 2.

predict, prediction
D4.5

Predict means forecast.

primary (data)
D1.1, D3.1

Data you collect yourself is primary data.

prime number
N1.1, A4.1

A prime number is a number that has exactly two different factors.

prime factor
A4.2

A prime factor is a factor that is prime.

prime factor decomposition
A4.1

Expressing a number as the product of its prime factors is prime factor decomposition.
For example, $12 = 2 \times 2 \times 3 = 2^2 \times 3$.

prism
S2.6, S3.4, S4.6

A prism is a 3-D shape with a constant cross-section.

  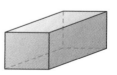

You name a prism by its cross-section.

probability
P1.2, D4.1

Probability is a measure of how likely an event is.

probability scale
D2.1

A probability scale is a line numbered 0 to 1 or 0% to 100% on which you place an event based on its probability.

product
2.8

The product is the result of a multiplication.

projection
4.3

When you look at a 3-D shape from different angles you can see 2-D shapes, called projections.
The projections of this shape are:

Front　　　Side　　　Plan

proof, prove
4.2

A proof is a chain of reasoning that establishes the truth of a proposition.

proportion
N1.5, N1.8, S3.5, P1.4

Proportion compares the size of a part to the size of a whole. You can express a proportion as a fraction, decimal or percentage.

proportional to
N1.8, S3.6

Quantities are proportional to one another when they increase or decrease in the same proportion.

pyramid
S3.4

A pyramid is a 3-D shape that tapers to a point called the apex.

You name a pyramid by its base.

Pythagoras' theorem
B1.5, B1.6

In any right-angled triangle, Pythagoras' theorem gives the relationship between the lengths of the sides:

$$a^2 + b^2 = c^2$$

where c is the hypotenuse.

quadrilateral: kite, parallelogram, rectangle, rhombus, square, trapezium
S1.2, S1.5, S2.1, S4.1

A quadrilateral is a polygon with four sides.

rectangle　　　　　　　parallelogram　　　　　　kite

All angles are right angles. Opposite sides equal.　　Two pairs of parallel sides.　　Two pairs of adjacent sides equal. One line of symmetry.

rhombus　　　　　　　square　　　　　　　trapezium

 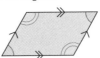 

All sides the same length. Opposite angles equal.　　All sides and angles equal.　　One pair of parallel sides.

questionnaire
D3.1

A questionnaire is a list of questions used to gather information in a survey.

Glossary

radius
S1.6, S2.2, S2.3, S2.4

The radius of a circle is the distance from the centre to the circumference.

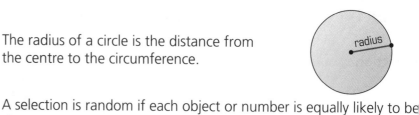

random
D2.3, D4.6

A selection is random if each object or number is equally likely to be chosen.

range
D1.2, D1.5, D3.5

The range is the difference between the largest and smallest values in a set of data.

ratio
N1.7, N1.8, A3.4, S3.5, P1.4, S4.4, S4.5

Ratio compares the size of one part with the size of another part.

raw data
D1.6, D3.2, D3.4, D3.5

Raw data is data that has been collected but not ordered in any way.

rearrange
A5.5

You rearrange a formula by making the subject a different variable, for example, $A = l \times w$ and $w = \dfrac{A}{l}$.

recurring decimal
N1.5, N2.8

A recurring decimal has an unlimited number of digits, which form a repeating pattern, after the decimal point, for example, $\frac{1}{3} = 0.333...$

reflect, reflection
S3.1

A reflection is a transformation in which corresponding points in the object and the image are the same distance from the mirror line.

regular polygon
S1.3

A regular polygon has equal sides and equal angles.

relationship
D3.3

A relationship is a link between objects or numbers.

remainder
N2.7

A remainder is the amount left over when one quantity is divided by another. For example, $9 \div 4 = 2$ remainder 1.

represent
D1.1

You represent data when you display it in the form of a diagram.

rotate, rotation
S3.1

A rotation is a transformation in which every point in the object turns through the same angle relative to a fixed point.

rotational symmetry
P1.5

A shape has rotational symmetry if, when turned, it fits onto itself more than once during a full turn.

round
A3.6, N2.3, N2.6, N2.7

You round a number by expressing it to a given degree of accuracy. For example, 639 is 600 to the nearest 100 and 640 to the nearest 10.
To round to one decimal place means to round to the nearest tenth, for example, 12.47 is 12.5 to 1 dp.

rule
A1.2

A rule describes the link between objects or numbers, for example, the rule linking 2 and 6 might be +4 or ×3.

ample
1.1, D1.6

A sample is part of a population.

ample space (diagram)
2.1, D4.1

A sample space diagram records all the outcomes of an experiment.

cale, scale factor
1.7, N1.8, A3.4, S3.5, S3.6
4.5, B1.1

A scale gives the ratio between the size of the object and its diagram. A scale factor is the multiplier in an enlargement.

cale drawing
1.7, S3.6, S4.4

A scale drawing of an object has every part reduced or enlarged by the same amount, the scale factor.

catter graph
1.3, D3.3

A scatter graph is a graph on which pairs of observations are plotted.

econdary (data)
D3.1

Data already collected is secondary data.

ector
1.6, S2.3

Any two radii (plural of radius) will split a circle into two sectors.

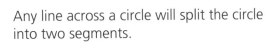

egment
1.6

Any line across a circle will split the circle into two segments.

selling price
N1.5

The price at which an item is sold.

semicircle
S1.6

A diameter splits a circle into two equal halves called semicircles.

sequence
A1.1, A1.2, A2.1, A4.4

A sequence is a set of numbers or diagrams that follow a rule.

similar
S3.5

Two shapes are similar if the angles are the same and corresponding lengths are in proportion.

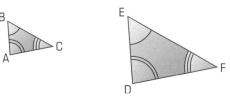

These triangles are similar.
The angles are equal.
DE = 2AB, DF = 2AC, EF = 2BC

simplest form
N1.2

A fraction (or ratio) is in its simplest form when the numerator and denominator (or parts of the ratio) have no common factors.
For example, $\frac{3}{5}$ is expressed in its simplest form.

Glossary

simplify
N1.1, A3.1, A5.2

To simplify a fraction, you divide the numerator and denominator by their highest common factor.
To simplify an expression, you gather all like terms together into a single term.

simulation
D4.4

A simulation is a mathematical model.

sine
B1.2, B1.4, B1.6

The sine of an angle in a right-angled triangle is the ratio of the opposite side o to the hypotenuse h.

$$\sin x = \frac{o}{h}$$

sketch
S1.1

A sketch shows the general shape of a graph or diagram.

skew
D3.4

A distribution is skew if most of the data are at one end of the range.

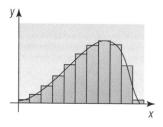
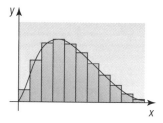

solid (3-D) shape: cube, cuboid, prism, pyramid, square-based pyramid, tetrahedron
S4.3

A solid is a shape formed in three-dimensional space.

cube

six square faces

cuboid

six rectangular faces

prism

the cross section is constant

pyramid

the faces meet at a common vertex

tetrahedron

all the faces are equilateral triangles

square-based pyramid

the base is a square

solution (of an equation)
A3.3, A3.4, A3.6, A5.3

The solution of an equation is the value of the variable that makes the equation true.

solve
A3.2, A5.3

To solve an equation you need to find the value of the variable that will make the equation true.
To solve a problem you need to find the correct answer.

specify
D1.1

You specify a problem by setting it down in detail.

square number, squared
N1.9, A4.1, A4.3

If you multiply a number by itself the result is a square number, for example, 25 is a square number because $5^2 = 5 \times 5 = 25$.

square root
N1.9, A3.3, N2.1

A square root is a number that when multiplied by itself is equal to a given number. For example √25 = 5, because 5 × 5 = 25.

statistics
D1.6

Statistics is the collection, display and analysis of information.

stem-and-leaf diagram
D1.3

A stem-and-leaf diagram is a way of displaying grouped data. For example, the numbers 29, 16, 18, 8, 4, 16, 27, 19, 13 and 15 could be displayed as:

0	4 8
1	3 5 6 6 8 9
2	7 9

Key: | 0 | 4 | means 4

straight-line graph
A4.5

When coordinate points lie in a straight line they form a straight-line graph. It is the graph of a linear equation.

This is the graph of the equation
y = x + 1.

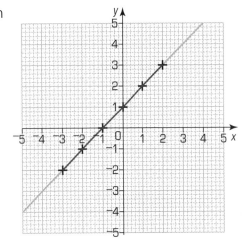

subject
A5.5

The subject of a formula is the term on its own on the left of the equals sign.

substitute
A3.2, A5.1

When you substitute you replace part of an expression with a particular value.

success, successful
D2.3, D2.4

A trial is a success if its result is the required outcome.

sum
S1.3

The sum is the total and is the result of an addition.

surface, surface area
S2.6, S4.6

The surface area of a solid is the total area of its faces.

survey
D3.1

A survey is an investigation to find information.

symmetric, symmetrical
D3.4, D3.5

A shape is symmetrical if a line divides it into two equal parts. The line is a line of symmetry.

systematic
A3.5

A systematic approach to a problem means you start with the simplest case and gradually build up to more complicated ones, one step at a time.

T(n)
A1.1, A1.2, A1.3

T(n) is the notation for the general, nth, term of a sequence. For example, T(3) is the third term.

Glossary

tangent (of an angle)
B1.4, B1.6

The tangent of an angle in a right-angled triangle is the ratio of the opposite side o to the adjacent side a.

$$\tan x = \frac{o}{a}$$

tangent (to a circle)
S1.6

A tangent to a circle is a line that touches the circle in one place.

tenth
N2.3

A tenth is 1 out of 10 or $\frac{1}{10}$.
For example, 0.5 has 5 tenths.

term
A1.1, A1.2, A2.1

A term is a number or object in a sequence or part of an expression.

tessellate, tessellation
S1.2, S1.5

A tessellation is a tiling pattern with no gaps. Shapes will tessellate if they can be put together to make such a pattern.

theoretical probability
D4.4, D4.5, D4.6

A theoretical probability is worked out without an experiment by considering all the possible outcomes.

term-to-term rule
A1.1, A1.3

A term-to-term rule links a term in a sequence to the previous term.

thousandth
N2.3

A thousandth is 1 out of 1000 or $\frac{1}{1000}$.
For example, 0.002 has 2 thousandths.

three-dimensional (3-D)
S3.4

Any solid shape is three-dimensional.

time axis
A2.2

The time axis is the horizontal axis on a distance–time graph.

transformation
S3.3

A transformation moves a shape from one place to another.

translate, translation
S3.1

A translation is a transformation in which every point in an object moves the same distance and direction. It is a sliding movement.

tree diagram
D4.3, D4.4

A tree diagram shows all the possible outcomes of one or more events.
This tree diagram shows the possible outcomes of flipping a coin twice.

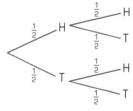

You write the outcomes at the end of branches and the probabilities on the branches.

trend
A4.8

A trend is a relationship between observed data and an independent variable such as time.

rial
2.2, D2.4

A trial is a single observation in an experiment.

rial and improvement
3.5, P1.3, P1.4

To find the answer to a complex calculation it is sometimes easier to estimate the answer then improve the estimate.
This is called trial and improvement.

riangle: equilateral, sosceles, scalene, ight-angled
1.5

A triangle is a polygon with three sides.

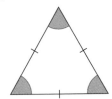
equilateral

three equal sides

isosceles

two equal sides

scalene

no equal sides

right-angled

one angle is 90°

triangular number
A1.1

The triangular numbers form the sequence 1, 3, 6, 10, 15, 21, 28, ...
They are the number of dots in a triangular pattern.

two-way table
D3.2

A two-way table links two independent variables, for example, the result when you toss two dice and add the scores.

		Dice 1					
		1	2	3	4	5	6
Dice 2	1	2	3	4	5	6	7
	2	3	4	5	6	7	8
	3	4	5	6	7	8	9
	4	5	6	7	8	9	10
	5	6	7	8	9	10	11
	6	7	8	9	10	11	12

unit fraction
N1.2, N1.3

A unit fraction has 1 as the numerator, for example, $\frac{1}{2}, \frac{1}{7}, \frac{1}{23}$.

unitary method
N1.4, N1.6, S3.6

In a unitary method you first work out the size of a single unit and then scale it up or down.

unknown
A5.3

An unknown is a variable. You can often find the value of an unknown by solving an equation.

value
P1.6

The value is the amount an expression or variable is worth.

variable
A5.1, D3.3

A variable is a symbol that can take a range of values.

Glossary

vector
S3.1

You can use a vector to specify a translation. For example, $\binom{3}{4}$ means you move the object 3 units to the right and 4 units up.

To move left or down you use negative numbers in the vector.

vertex, vertices
S1.2

A vertex of a solid is a point at which two or more edges meet.
A vertex of a 2-D shape is where two sides meet.

vertex

vertical
S4.3, A4.8, A4.9, B1.1

Vertical means straight up and down, at right angles to the horizontal.

vertically opposite angles
S1.4, S4.2

When two straight lines cross they form two pairs of equal angles called vertically opposite angles.

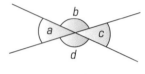
$a = c$ $b = d$

volume: cubic millimetre, cubic centimetre, cubic metre
S2.5, S4.6

The volume of an object is a measure of how much space it occupies.

A1 Check in

1 a 13, 16
   b 3, 6
   c $^-9$, $^-13$
   d 2.7, 2.9, 3.1
2 a 7
   b 14
   c 4
   d 1

A1 Check out

1 a 9, 13, 19
   b $^-3$, 7, 22
   c 8, 4, $^-2$
   d $^-17$, $^-11$, $^-2$
   e 0.5, $^-4.5$, $^-12$
2 a Start at 4 and add 3; $3n + 1$
   b Start at 9 and add 2; $2n + 7$
   c Start at 20 and subtract 2; $22 - 2n$
   d Start at 8 and add 5; $5n + 3$
3 a 6, 8, 10, 12
   b $T(10) = 24$, $T(25) = 54$
   c $6 + (24 \times 2)$
   d $T(n) = 2(n - 1) + 6 = 2n + 4$

A2 Check in

1 $3n + 4$

2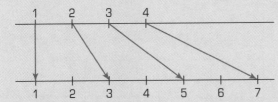

3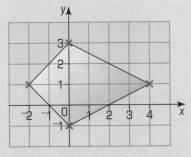

Kite

A2 Check out

1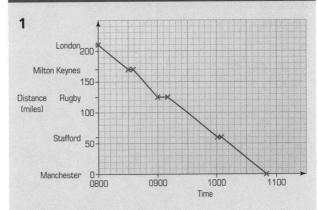

2 a 100 miles
   b 40 miles, 30 minutes
   c 80 mph

N1 Check in

1 HCF = 4, LCM = 120

2 $\frac{1}{2} = \frac{12}{24}$, $\frac{24}{40} = \frac{6}{10}$, $\frac{2}{3} = \frac{24}{36}$, $\frac{15}{60} = \frac{3}{12}$

3 a $\frac{1}{5}$
   b 45%
   c 0.15
   d 44%

4 a 1 : 3
   b 10 : 3
   c 3 : 5
   d 200 : 1

N1 Check out

1 a $\frac{23}{24}$
   b i $\frac{3}{10}$
      ii
   c 22
   d $4\frac{2}{5}$

2 a 238 g   b 17.8%

3 a i Smaller   ii Larger
      iii Larger   iv Smaller
   b i $10 \times \frac{1}{2} = 5$ ii $10 \div \frac{1}{2} = 20$
      iii $10 \times 1\frac{1}{2} = 30$ iv $10 \div 2 = 5$
   c i 4   ii 25   iii 35   iv $7\frac{1}{7}$

4 a $200\text{ g} \times \frac{300}{200} = 300$ g, $\frac{40}{200} = 20\%$
   b Students' own answers

5 a The answer should be less than £340.
   b £289
   c John divided by $\frac{85}{100}$ when he should have multiplied.

A3 Check in

1 a ^-y
   b $p - r + 7$

2 a $p = 5$
   b $n = 2$

3 $y = ^-5, ^-3, ^-1, 1, 3$

4 a $2t - 6y$
   b $24 - 3x$

A3 Check out

1 a i $x = 10$
      ii $x = 2.5$
   b $11y = 220$, $y = 20$
   c $x = 12.5$ cm

2 a

Estimate	$2x^2$	$3x$	$2x^2 - 3x$	Too small / too big
8	128	24	104	too small
8.1	131.22	24.3	106.92	correct

   b $6x^2 + x = 84$, $x = 3.7$ to 1 dp

S1 Check in

1 $a = 25°$, $b = 120°$

2 a Isosceles triangle: two equal sides, two equal angles.

  b Parallelogram: opposite sides parallel and equal, opposite angles equal.

S1 Check out

1 a 30° because $x + 60° + 90° = 180°$

  b 60° because $y + 30° + 90° = 180°$

  c 10 cm because triangle ABC is equilateral.

  d 10 cm because triangle ABC is equilateral.

  e Gill is correct. Paul should have used the vertical height, which will be less than 10 cm, and halved the result.

2 No, the total of the two shorter sides needs to be greater than the length of the longest side.

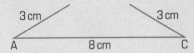

D1 Check in

1 a 1, 2, 3, 6, 7, 7, 8

  b 0.6, 0.8, 1.2, 1.2, 1.3, 1.4, 1.5, 1.9

2

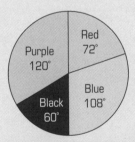

Shows proportions clearly.

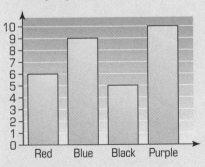

Shows actual values.

D1 Check out

1 Data you collect yourself is primary data for example, a survey of classmates. Data that is already available is secondary data, for example, nationally gathered statistics on the internet.

2 a Small sample size, possibly mostly boys, holiday timing so more TV watched. Primary data so more accurate, large variety of detail available.

  b Expensive, time-consuming, too detailed. Larger sample size so possibly more accurate, more detailed results.

3 a Questions that don't work as expected can be changed as a result of the pilot survey. New questions could also be added.

  b Sample survey question with range of options.

4 a 3-D charts look attractive. However, they can be misleading.

  b Scales that don't start at zero, for example, can be used to make results look more dramatic than they are.

S2 Check in

1 Perimeter = 28 m, Area = 28 m^2

2 a 1.2 m

b 26 100 m

c 3.7 cm

d 1920 cm

3 a 20 cm^2

b 10 cm^2

4 a 15 m^3

b 6.3 cm^3

S2 Check out

1 a 13 people

b 16 people

c 17 people

2 57°

3 No, they would have less than 38 cm of space each.

N2 Check in

1 a $^-7$

b $^-3$

c $^-10$

d 10

e 1

2 $\frac{18}{36}, \frac{24}{36}, \frac{27}{36}, \frac{30}{36}. \frac{5}{6}$ is largest

3 a 1114

b 1719

c 9594

d 23

N2 Check out

1 a £1200

b £21

2 a $4 \times (3.9 \div 1.3) = 12$

b $100 \times 0.8 \div 5 = 16$

3 24.457 m

4 a £12.85

b 230 bags

A4 Check in

1 a 3^4

b m^4

c f^7

2 a $2 \times 2 \times 5$

b $2 \times 2 \times 5 \times 3$

c $2 \times 2 \times 2 \times 2 \times 2$

d $2 \times 2 \times 5 \times 5$

3 $^-11, ^-3, 1, 5$

A4 Check out

1 a i A: gradient 2, intercept $^+3$

B: gradient 2, intercept $^-2$

ii A: $y = 2x + 3$

B: $y = 2x - 2$

b i A: gradient 3, intercept $^-2$

B: gradient 1, intercept $^-2$

ii $(0, ^-2)$

2

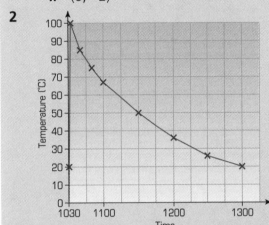

3 a 1220   **b** 1055

c 1120   **d** 2 h 28 min

D2 Check in

1

2 C, R, O, D, I, L, E

3 a 75%

b 40%

c 35%

d 35%

D2 Check out

1 $p(\text{orange}) = 1 - p(\text{red}) - p(\text{green})$

$= 1 - 0.2 - 0.35$

$= 0.45$

2 Game A:

Chance of winning $= \frac{3}{36} = \frac{1}{12}$

Game B:

Chance of winning $= \frac{6}{36} = \frac{1}{6}$

There is a greater chance of winning on Game B.

S3 Check in

1

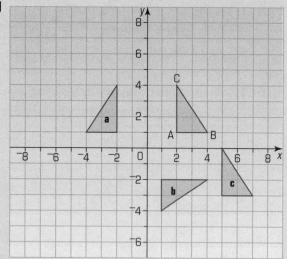

2 a Cuboid
b Tetrahedron
c Pentagonal prism

3 a 1 : 4   **b** 2 : 5
  c 5 : 8   **d** 6 : 23

S3 Check out

1 a and **b**

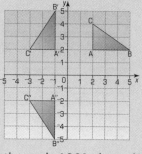

c Rotation through 180° about (0, 0)

2 a–d

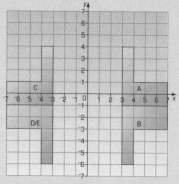

e D and E are in the same place.

3 No. Any hexagon drawn on four mirror lines ends up with six lines of symmetry.

P1 Check out

1 96 cm by 72 cm

2 The longer side is (12 – p) cm, so the area is
$p(12 - p) = 12p - p^2$.

3 275 ml

4 The man walks at a steady pace to the park, which is 2 km away. He then stays at the park for about an hour. He walks most of the way home very quickly, and the last 0.5 km very slowly.

5 $x = 55°$ (angles on a straight line)
$y = 30°$ (vertically opposite angles)
$z = 95°$ (angles in a triangle sum to 180°)

A5 Check in

1 11, 5, 2, ⁻1

2 a $t + 7 = {}^-5$

 b $7m - 12 - 2t = 17$

 c $6 - 5y = 7$

A5 Check out

1 a $18 - 2x + (3y - 7) = 0$

 $18 - 2x + (6x - 5) = 23$

 $x = 2.5, y = {}^-2$

 b ⁻10.5

2 a $l = \frac{2V}{bh}$

 b 75 cm

3 a

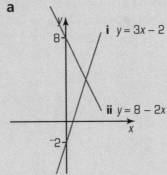

 i $y = 3x - 2$

 ii $y = 8 - 2x$

 b (2, 4)

 c $y = 3x - 2$

D3 Check in

1 For example:

Time (t seconds)	Frequency
$16 \leqslant t < 17$	1
$17 \leqslant t < 18$	3
$18 \leqslant t < 19$	3
$19 \leqslant t < 20$	3
$20 \leqslant t < 21$	1
$21 \leqslant t < 22$	1

2 Mean = 18.6 s, median = 18.4 s, modal class = $17 \leqslant t < 18$; $\leqslant 18t < 19$; $19 \leqslant t < 20$; (mode = 19.2 s)

3 For example:

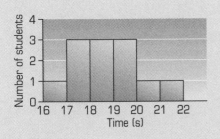

D3 Check out

1 a For example:

 Grouped frequency table with classes:

 $x < 50$, $50 \leqslant x < 60$, $60 \leqslant x < 70$,

 $70 \leqslant x < 80$, $80 \leqslant x < 90$, $90 \leqslant x < 100$

 or Bar chart for grouped data, above.

 or Stem and Leaf diagram.

 Because data is discrete, need to show low value of 32.

 c Range is large: 67. Most marks are in range 75–99. One mark is very low (32). Distribution is skewed.

2 b Time series for oak tree

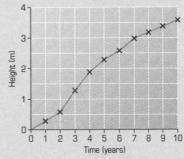

 After 7 years the tree grew more slowly.

1 a 3 equal sides, 3 equal angles, 3 lines of symmetry, rotational symmetry of order 3

b Opposite sides are equal and parallel, no lines of symmetry, rotational symmetry of order 2

c Adjacent sides are equal, one pair of opposite angles are equal, 1 line of symmetry, no rotational symmetry (order 1)

2 For example:

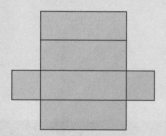

3 a 5 : 1

b 3 : 1

c 1 : 6000

d 3 : 16

1 a 380 cm²

b 33.8 cm

2 a Accurate drawing of triangle:

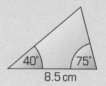

b 121 m

3 a

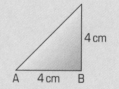

b

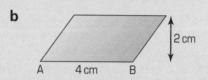

c

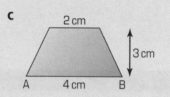

d

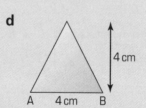

D4 Check in

1 a $\frac{1}{13}$

  b $\frac{1}{3}$

2 a 30

  b 21

  c 12

D4 Check out

1 a

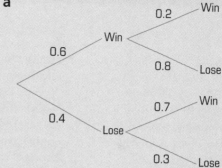

  b 0.76

  c 0.12

2 a $\frac{1}{16}$, $\frac{1}{8}$, $\frac{3}{16}$, $\frac{1}{4}$, $\frac{3}{16}$, $\frac{1}{8}$, $\frac{1}{16}$

  b $\frac{3}{50}$, $\frac{7}{50}$, $\frac{4}{25}$, $\frac{6}{25}$, $\frac{9}{50}$, $\frac{3}{20}$, $\frac{2}{25}$

  c When you convert the fractions to decimals the probabilities are similar. The dice seem to be fair.

B1 Check in

1 3

2 a 9 **b** 144 **c** 38.44 **d** 302.76

  e 9 **f** 14 **g** 17.1 **h** 6.8

3

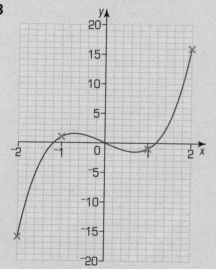

It is a cubic graph.

or: It is a smooth curve.

B1 Check out

1 a $6^2 + 7^2 = 85$ but $8^2 = 64$, so the triangle cannot be right-angled by Pythagoras' theorem.

  b 1.73 m

  c 26 units

2 a $x = 29.0°$

  b $y = 6.11$ km

  c $z = 8.89$ m

3 a $s^2 = 3^2 + 3^2 = 18$ by Pythagoras' theorem, so $s = \sqrt{18} = 4.242\ 640\ 687$ m

  b The answer should be rounded to 2 dp, giving $s = 4.24$ m.

Index